CONTENTS

ABOUT THIS BOOK

The objective of this guide is to give collectors the accurate market values of Great Britain stamps, as sold by most dealers, as opposed to the inflated prices quoted by some catalogues. The publisher of *British Stamp Market Values 2009* is not affiliated to any dealer.

Editor
Guy Thomas
Consultant Editor
Richard West
Art Director
Alexandra Bourdelon
Designers
Kathryn Slack, Sophie Harwin
Advertisement Manager
Jay Jones
Sales Executive
Uty Rohrs
Advertisement Production
Jessica Imms

Publisher
IPC Media, Leon House,
233 High Street, Croydon,
Surrey CR9 1HZ.
Tel: 020 8726 8241.
Copyright
IPC Media Ltd, 2008
ISBN 978 086 296 308 8
This guide is produced by
the team behind
Stamp Magazine, Britain's
longest-running
philatelic magazine.
www.stampmagazine.co.uk

Printing
Positive Images UK, 44 Wates
Way, Mitcham, Surrey.
News trade distribution
MarketForce, London.
Tel: 020 7633 3300.
Book trade distribution
BookSource, Glasgow.
Tel: 0845 370 0067.
ipc@booksource.net
Sales enquiries
Chris Lynn.
Tel: 020 3148 3498.
magazinesales@ipcmedia.com

Bonhams
Knightsbridge

Stamps, Postcards and Cigarette Cards
Bonhams Stamp Department is a major player in the philatelic world. The department's international presence, reputation and knowledge of the market attracts buyers and sellers worldwide.

The Stamp Department
The Stamp department is based at our Knightsbridge salerooms in London, where auctions are aimed principally at the collector's market.

Our Stamp specialists have the combined knowledge of many years of experience in the field of philately and our experts specialise in providing advice, guidance and practical help to philatelists around the world.

Our comprehensive auction schedule includes a diverse array of lots. We hold several major auctions each year, dealing with all levels of the stamp market, ranging from complete collections to individual rarities.

In addition to these sales we hold specialised auctions of 'Postcards and Cigarette Cards' where material ranges from general collections to individual sets.

Enquiries
+44 (0) 20 7393 3898
stamps@bonhams.com

Illustrated:
1935 Silver Jubilee 2½d. Prussian blue. Sold for £7,637.50 in a recent auction.

Bonhams
Montpelier Street
London SW7 1HH
+44 (0) 20 7393 3900
+44 (0) 20 7393 3905 fax
www.bonhams.com/stamps

London · New York · Paris · San Francisco · Los Angeles · Hong Kong · Melbourne · Dubai   www.bonhams.com

WHY STAMPS ARE WORTH MONEY

It isn't always immediately obvious why some stamps are worth more than others. But here are the key factors in the British market

ABOVE: The Prussian Blue shade of the 1935 Silver Jubilee 2½d went on sale by mistake, creating one of Britain's great rarities

Working out how stamps become valuable isn't rocket science. Their value is largely linked to their rarity and their condition, although there are other variables too.

LOW NUMBERS

Some stamps are valuable today because not many survive, although there are few really scarce British stamps other than errors. More often, they are rare because comparatively few people bought them when they were in use.

Some of the Victorian era stamps had very high original face values, and only a few people could afford them. Examples include the 10/- and £1 values from the 1867-83 series, when the average pay was under £1 a week.

Recent examples are much fewer, but they do exist. For instance, the Welsh-language version of the Princess Diana presentation pack of 1998 can be classed as a modern rarity.

ERRORS

One major difference between stamps and other collectables is that mistakes are valuable. Printing errors include missing colours, misperforations, inverted watermarks and double prints.

Although errors did occur prior to the reign of Elizabeth II, it was in the 1960s that their numbers exploded. More multicoloured stamps were being issued at the time, so there was more chance of something going wrong. Very rare or unique missing-colour errors from this period can now fetch over £20,000 at auction.

ABOVE: High-value Victorian stamps such as this 1867-83 £1 can be rare if only a few people could afford to use or save them at the time

ABOVE: If you have a 2006 Victoria Cross prestige stamp book with a pane missing the Queen's head, it could be worth over £8,000

In addition there have been a few occasions when limited numbers of stamps featuring design or colour shade errors have been sold in post offices by mistake, their rarity making them highly desirable.

Victorian stamps which command a premium include the so-called 'abnormals', printed from plates which were never put into regular use. There is also the Penny Red from plate 77, which at the time was regarded as a sub-standard printing but is now worth over £100,000.

Even very modern errors are in demand. In 2007, a 2006 Victoria Cross prestige stamp book with the first pane missing bronze and phosphor (and therefore without the Queen's head) sold at auction for over £8,000.

Most errors are beyond the scope of this guide. You can check on their value at www.errors.info

MARKET DEMAND
Naturally, stamps' values vary with the level of demand in the market.

In recent years the British philatelic market has gone through a boom period, with higher prices paid at auctions, due to new rarities emerging, investors identifying stamps as a way to make money, and a scramble among collectors to obtain the highest quality material they can afford

One of the key influences on this has been the online trading of stamps, both through dealers and through auction websites. Internet bidders have been forcing up the prices being paid for the most sought-after material. □

ABOVE: 1960s printing errors can be spectacular. This 1963 Red Cross 3d is missing red, so the cross itself fails to appear

WHERE TO BUY YOUR STAMPS

The traditional places where stamps are bought and sold still exist, but they've recently been joined by some new ones

The majority of new definitives and special issues can be purchased from most (but sadly no longer all) local post offices for some months after their day of their issue, or at least until stocks run out.

For booklets that are issued only in a certain area, regional or country stamps, presentation packs and stamp cards, you'll have to pay a visit one of the philatelic counters (Post Shops), which are located only in larger post offices.

Some items are hard to find even at these, in which case you will need to buy them through Royal Mail's Philatelic Bureau in Edinburgh.

You can save yourself a lot of hassle by signing up to one of the subscription services provided by the Bureau, whether you want to opt for definitives or special issues, singles or cylinder blocks, mint stamps or first day covers. You can also order specific items from its stock list.

For non-current stamp issues, there are many sources of material for collectors.

ABOVE: Bidding in person at a fast-moving public auction is an exciting way to try to fill holes in your collection

STARTING OFF

Many beginners start off their collections by buying or being given a mixed packet of stamps.

At one time most stationers and newsagents sold packets, ranging from 50 to 1,000 stamps all different, but sadly that method of retailing seems to have all but vanished. However, some dealers still specialise in the packet trade, and can offer packets of up to 100,000.

Once you become more experienced you might try a bag of kiloware, which is simply a mixture of unsorted, used stamps on cuttings from envelopes, sold by weight. These can bulk up a collection quickly, and might occasionally reveal some rarities, although you will need to soak them off the paper yourself.

SHOPS & FAIRS

There was a time when every British town had a stamp shop. Today, sadly, many of these have closed. There are still many stamp dealers, but most of them do business by mail order or at fairs and exhibitions.

There's a monthly fair within easy reach of most collectors, and these gatherings give you the chance to shop around. To find out about fairs taking place near you, and dealers who specialise in your particular interests, check out the What's On listings and the adverts that appear in the pages of *Stamp Magazine*.

There are five or six major stamp shows and exhibitions in the UK every year, the best known regulars being Stampex and Philatex in London. Many major dealers and auction houses will be present, to sell and buy stamps, and for many collectors it's an unmissable day out.

ABOVE: Many collectors find major shows such as Stampex in London great places to search for new material

AUCTIONS

Stamp auctions range from club sales, in which members can dispose of surplus material of low value, through regional sales, which can have an impressive amount of quality lots, to the great international sales, in which single lots sell for tens or hundreds of thousands of pounds.

Auctions offer the opportunity to acquire everything from whole collections to individual rarities, and may be the only realistic way to fill holes in really specialist collections.

You can simply peruse the sale catalogue and put in bids by post. Indeed, some auctions are conducted solely through postal bidding. But it is preferable to take advantage of a prior viewing of the material, so you can check its quality at

first hand. And it's more enjoyable to attend the sale itself in person, so you can see who you are bidding against.

If you haven't bought at an auction before, go along to a few and observe how they are conducted before you take part in bidding. You might be surprised at the pace at which lots go under the hammer.

When bidding, make up your mind in advance how much an item is worth to you. You can pick up terrific bargains at auction, but some buyers get carried away and end up paying more than a stamp is worth, or more than they can afford.

The advertisement pages and the monthly What's On listing in *Stamp Magazine* will tell you what auctions are coming up.

WEBSITES

The internet has made it easier than ever to buy philatelic material from around the world. Dealers and private collectors are increasingly using online auction sites such as eBay.

You don't get the chance to view a stamp in person. But often you do get the benefit of seeing a high-quality enlarged image on screen, and you can browse through lists at your leisure.

The well established sites offer good security for buyers. eBay's 'feedback' system gives you confidence that a seller is trustworthy, and its PayPal banking system makes transactions safe and easy. □

ABOVE: Auction websites such as eBay are now a well established and popular way of buying and selling stamps

A TO Z OF PHILATELIC TERMINOLOGY

Here's an easy-to-understand alphabetical guide to stamp collecting jargon, from simple concepts to complex printing processes

AEROGRAMME
A specially printed, ready stamped letter sheet on lightweight paper, which is intended for air mail use. It is also known as an air letter.

AIR MAIL
Any item of post that is sent to its destination by air.

ALBINO
A colourless impression that is usually produced in embossing.

ALPHABET LETTERS
The lettering printed in the corners of Queen Victoria stamps from 1840-1887 to make forgery difficult.

Each stamp in a sheet had a unique combination of letters, with those in the top row lettered AA, AB, AC, and so on, and those in the second row BA, BB, BC and so on, this pattern continuing throughout the sheet.

Originally these letters appeared in the lower corners only, but later they appeared in the top corners too, in reverse order.

FIRST DAY COVER: for the 2008 Houses of Lancaster & York set

ARROWS

The margins of many sheets of stamps feature arrows, intended to help post office clerks to divide the sheets into sections.

BACKSTAMP

A postmark on the back of an envelope, usually applied in transit or on arrival.

BANTAM

A stamp printed in a reduced size.

BISECT

A stamp cut in half (normally diagonally) to create two stamps, each of half the usual value. For example, 2d stamps may be bisected to meet a 1d postal rate, in times of shortage.

BLIND PERFORATION

Perforation in which the stamp paper is merely dented because the perforating machine has blunt teeth.

BLOCK

Four or more stamps still joined together.

BOOKLET

A small book containing one or more panes of stamps, either stitched in or stuck within a card cover. Today's GB booklets fall into two main types: definitive booklets, which usually contain standard 1st class or 2nd class stamps, and prestige stamp books, which are issued several times a year and include a mixture of definitives and commemoratives, along with historical or other background information.

CACHET

A postal mark, other than the cancellation, applied to cards and covers. This is often private or unofficial in nature, with a commemorative purpose.

CANCELLATION

The original term for the postmark applied to a stamp on an envelope or card, to prevent re-use.

CANCELLED TO ORDER (CTO)

Postmarked in bulk, usually for sale to collectors on first day covers rather than for actual use in the post.

OFFICIAL STAMP: with an 'IR Official' overprint

REGIONAL STAMP: a 2nd class value for Northern Ireland

MALTESE CROSS: on a Penny Black   WILDING: an early QEII definitive

CHALK-SURFACED PAPER
Paper with a security coating to prevent a cancellation being cleaned off so that a stamp can be re-used.

CHANGELING
A stamp whose colour has altered through immersion in water or excessive exposure to sunlight.

CHARITY STAMPS
Stamps issued to support a charity, usually sold with a surcharge above their postal face value.

COILS
Stamps issued in reels (usually for sale from vending machines), which can therefore be collected in strips. They may be imperforate on two opposite sides or have sideways watermarks.

COLOUR TRIALS
Proofs produced in various colours prior to the issue of a stamp, to determine the most suitable colour for it.

COMB PERFORATION
Perforation applied to three sides of a stamp at a single stroke, with the fourth side being perforated by the following stroke. This technique is aimed at providing perforations which meet perfectly at the corners.

COMPOUND PERFORATION
Perforation which has different gauges on different sides of a stamp.

CONTROL NUMBERS
Letters and numerals printed in the sheet margins of British stamps from 1881-1947 for accounting purposes. A letter indicates which part of the year the stamps were printed, and the number represents the last two digits of the year.

CORNER BLOCK
Four or more stamps still joined together from the corner of the sheet, with margins.

COVER
Envelope or wrapper with stamps affixed or pre-printed.

CYLINDER BLOCK
Four or more stamps still joined together, with the cylinder numbers showing in the margin.

CYLINDER NUMBERS
Tiny numerals printed in the sheet margin, for security reasons, denoting the cylinder from which it was printed. There is usually one number for each colour in which the stamp is printed, appearing in the respective colour.

DEFINITIVES
Stamps in general use over a period of years, as opposed to commemoratives or 'special stamps', which have a limited period on sale.

DIE
The piece of soft steel onto which the design of recess (intaglio) printed stamps has to be engraved.

DIE PROOF
A proof impression taken from the die to check that it is satisfactory.

DOCTOR BLADE
The blade used to wipe off excess ink from the cylinder in photogravure printing.

DOCTOR BLADE VARIETY
A streak of ink appearing across a printed sheet of stamps, after a build-up of dust forces the doctor blade away from the cylinder for a moment.

STAMP CARD: reproducing the enlarged image of a 1999 stamp in the Millennium series

DUMB CANCELLATION
Postmark with no inscription or identifying mark, for example applied to naval mail in wartime for security reasons.

DUTY PLATE
Plate used to print the 'duty' (value) on stamps in conjunction with the key plate. A different duty plate is used for each different denomination in stamps sharing a common design.

EMBOSSING
A portion of a stamp design that has a relief or raised impression. This is achieved by placing the paper between male (relief) and female (recess) dies during the printing process.

ERROR
Stamp deviating from the normal in some respect, for example with missing, shifted or inverted colours or perforations, caused by problems at the printing stage. Errors that are spotted during checks at the printers' should be destroyed, but some slip though the net and are sold at post offices.

ESSAY
Preliminary design for a stamp, which might or might not subsequently be issued.

FAKE
A genuine stamp that has been tampered with in some way in an attempt to make it more valuable, usually by forging an overprint or removing a cancellation.

FISCAL
Stamp originally intended for fiscal or revenue purposes, although possibly subsequently authorised for postal use.

FIRST DAY COVER (FDC)

Souvenir envelope bearing stamps postmarked on their first day of issue. In modern times, envelopes are designed specifically to match a set of stamps, and pictorial handstamps are available to suit the theme, both from Royal Mail and from private providers.

FLAW

A defect in printing, resulting in a constant blemish on the same stamp in every sheet.

FRANK

A mark or label that indicates that mail is transmitted free of postage. This is widely used by government departments and armed forces.

GRAPHITE LINES

Black lines incorporated into the back of some stamps between 1957 and 1959, which could be recognised by experimental electronic sorting machines.

GUM

The adhesive on the back of a stamp. On early issues this was a natural product, gum arabic, which has a shiny appearance. On later issues it was a synthetic product, polyvinyl alcohol (PVA), which is colourless but usually given a yellow tinge by printers; with dextrin added, this is known as PVAD, and has a bluish tinge.

GUTTER

The white central margin separating two panes of stamps on sheets printed by Harrison & Sons' Jumelle printing press. The machine was capable of printing in several colours and perforating in one operation, but this layout of sheets was necessary because the circumference of the printing and perforating cylinders differed.

GUTTER PAIR

Two stamps from adjoining panes, with a gutter in the middle.

IMPERFORATE

Stamps printed on sheets without perforations, and needing to be cut apart with scissors. Early

Victorian stamps were imperforate before the concept of perforating them became a practical reality. Stamps imperforate on one or more adjoining sides could be from booklets; those imperforate on opposite sides will be from coils.

IMPRIMATUR

The first sheet of stamps off the printing press, marked to indicate that it has been approved. All imprimatur sheets should have been retained by the Post Office (now Royal Mail), but some have 'escaped' into the hands of collectors.

IMPRINT

Inscription in a sheet margin giving the printer's name or logo, the date of printing and sometimes other details.

INTAGLIO PRINTING

A printing process, also known as 'recess', which requires the design of the stamp to be engraved into the printing cylinder. When the ink is applied, it fills the recesses and any excess ink is wiped away. On contact with the paper, the design is transferred as the ink leaves the recesses. Intaglio stamps can be identified from the way the ink parts of the design feel raised when you run a finger over them.

INVERT

A stamp with part of the design upside-down in relation to the rest.

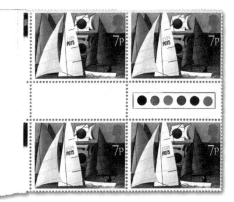

GUTTER BLOCK: of the 1975 Sailing set, with traffic lights

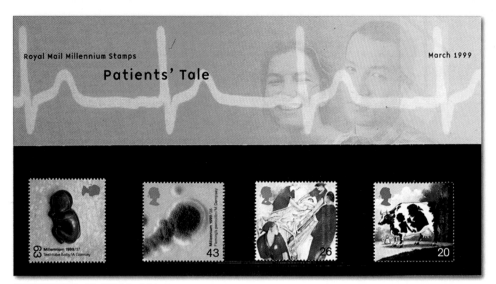

Royal Mail Millennium Stamps

Patients' Tale

March 1999

PRESENTATION PACK: of the 1999 Patient's Tale stamps

IVORY HEAD

An outline of the portrait of Queen Victoria which can be seen on the backs of certain stamps printed on blued paper.

JUBILEE LINE

A line of printer's rule reinforcing the edge of the printing plate, appearing as a bar of colour at the foot of the sheet. It is so-named because it first appeared on the 'Jubilee' issue of 1887.

KEY PLATE

A plate that provides the main part of a stamp design (usually the sovereign's head and border) where two separate printings are required, for example in a two-colour stamp. The key plate is used in conjunction with different duty plates, so the same basic design can be reproduced with different values.

KILOWARE

Any mixture of stamps sold by weight. Originally the term applied to those sold in sealed one-kilogramme bags of stamps on paper.

LINE PERFORATION

A form of perforation in which the horizontal and vertical perforations are applied by separate processes. This frequently results in ragged edges at the corners of stamps.

LITHOGRAPHIC PRINTING

A printing process in which the design appears as a number of dots, as in photogravure printing, but with the dots differing in size. The larger the dot, the deeper the colour. A lithographed stamp can be differentiated from a photogravure stamp by examining any lettering, which will appear solid.

LOCAL

A stamp (or more correctly a 'label') whose validity is restricted to a limited local area, and which cannot be used on national or international mail. For example, labels may be attached to items covering carriage from offshore islands to the mainland before entering the national postal system; onward postage must be paid by the requisite national or international stamps.

MACHIN

British definitive stamp design featuring a profile of Queen Elizabeth II's head, in use for all low-value issues since 1967. The name comes from the designer of the profile, Arnold Machin.

MALTESE CROSS
The cancellation used for the first British stamps, from 1840 to 1844. The name comes from its shape.

METER MARK
A mark applied by a meter to indicate pre-payment of postage. This usually consists of an indicium (country name and value), a date and a slogan advertising a firm or organisation.

MINIATURE SHEET
A small sheet containing a single stamp or a small group of stamps, often with broad decorative margins. Some modern stamps are issued only in a miniature sheet and in no other format.

MINT
Unused stamp with its full, original gum intact. Collectors will generally prefer 'unmounted mint', with the gum undisturbed by any mounting.

OBLITERATION
Original term for the postmarking of stamps to prevent their re-use.

OFFICIAL
A stamp produced solely for the use of government departments.

CONTROL NUMBER: on a George V 6d definitive, also showing a Jubilee line

ERROR: a strip of the 1964 Botanical Congress 1s 3d value on which some stamps are missing yellow

OVERPRINT
An additional printing applied to a stamp after the original printing, to convert it to some other purpose, denote a surcharge or commemorate a current event.

PANE
Originally this term meant a portion of a sheet divided by gutters, but it is now also applied to a block of stamps issued in a booklet.

PERFIN
An abbreviation for 'perforated initial'. Some stamps have been perforated with the initials of firms or government departments as a security measure, to prevent pilferage or improper use.

PERFORATION
Tiny circles of paper punched out by machine between stamps on a sheet, to make it easier to separate them. Different printings and varieties can sometimes be identified by a difference in the style or number of their perforations.

PHOSPHOR BANDS
Almost invisible stripes of phosphor coating applied to the face of modern stamps to facilitate electronic sorting.

PHOTOGRAVURE PRINTING
A printing process, also known as 'gravure', in which the printing cylinder consists of a large number of very small cells, each containing ink, with the depth of the cell determining how dark the colour will look. The printed stamp appears as a series of minute dots of equal size.

PLATE
Flat or curved piece of metal from which stamps are printed.

PLATE NUMBERS

The cylinder numbers of recess (intaglio) printed stamps are often referrred to as 'plate numbers'. With many Queen Victoria stamps, these were incorporated into the design of the stamp.

POSTAGE DUE

Label denoting the amount of postage to be recovered from the addressee, on unpaid or underpaid mail. Sometimes called a 'to pay' label.

POSTAGE PAID IMPRESSION (PPI)

Mark printed or handstruck on bulk postings denoting prepayment of postage.

POSTAL STATIONERY

Envelope or postcard that is sold ready-stamped to the required basic postal rate, usually as part of its design.

PRESENTATION PACK

A set of stamps mounted within a black card and contained in a folder which gives background details of the issue. The first proper example was made available with the Shakespeare Festival issue of 1964, although the 1960 prepackagings of certain definitives are now regarded as presentation packs by collectors.

PRESS SHEET

Printed sheet of miniature sheets, which is sold to collectors in its entirety rather than being cut up into separate items.

PROVISIONAL

A stamp temporarily overprinted or surcharged to meet a shortage of regular issues.

RE-ENTRY

Part of an intaglio printing plate which is re-engraved by the transfer roller. This can usually be detected by a slight doubling of the lines.

REGIONAL

Definitive issued in deference to a specific region of the UK, and depicting appropriate regional symbols, but valid for postage throughout the nation. More recent examples for England,

Wales, Scotland and Northern Ireland are known as 'country' definitives.

REPRINT

A stamp printed from the original plate, but long after the issue has ceased. This is usually distinguishable from the original by a difference on colour, paper or watermark.

RETOUCH

A repair to a letterpress (surface printing) plate or photogravure cylinder to correct a flaw.

ROULETTE

A form of separation effected using serrated instruments to produce cuts in the paper.

SELF-ADHESIVE

A stamp that is attached to a backing paper and, when peeled off, has sticky adhesive on the back that is sufficient to stick it to an envelope with no wetting agent required.

SE-TENANT

The term applied to two or more stamps of different designs printed side by side on a sheet.

SMARTSTAMPS

A modern service whereby small businesses can order their own special postal barcodes online, to save them going to post offices to buy stamps. Businesses can include their logo in the design.

SMILERS

A modern service whereby an individual can buy sheets of stamps with se-tenant customised labels bearing an image of his choice. Where these are supplied with labels chosen by Royal Mail, they are known as Smilers generic sheets.

SPECIAL STAMPS

Limited-lifespan stamps issued in addition to the standard definitives, often to commemorate a particular event or anniversary. In recent times Royal Mail has released 10 or 11 sets each year.

SPECIMEN

Overprint on a stamp printed for record or

MINIATURE SHEET, accompanying the 2004 Christmas issue

publicity purposes, signifying that it has no postal validity.

STAMP CARD
A postcard (also known as a PHQ card) issued by Royal Mail reproducing an enlarged image of a new stamp.

SURCHARGE
An overprint that alters the face value of a stamp, either upward or downward.

SURFACE PRINTING
A printing process, also known as 'typography' or 'letterpress', in which the design to be printed stands proud of the surface of the cylinder. The ink is applied only to the raised parts, so only the design is printed on contact with the paper.

TÊTE-BÊCHE
French term denoting se-tenant stamps which are upside-down in relation to each other.

TRAFFIC LIGHTS
The solid circles of colour which appear in the margins of many sheets of stamps, as a check to prove that all colours have been printed.

TRAINING LABEL
Stamp found with thick black bars on the front of it, which has probably been used at a Post Office training school. The bars render the stamp invalid for postage.

THEMATIC
A form of philately which involves collecting philatelic material surrounding a chosen theme.

UNDERPRINT

A motif printed on the gummed side of a stamp, usually from a booklet, to indicate that it has been sold at a discount off face value. Typically, this is the letter 'D' or a star pattern.

USED

A stamp that has performed its postal function and has had a cancellation applied. Collectors will prefer a neat and clear cancellation, which can easily be read and doesn't obscure too much of the stamp design.

VARIETY

Any stamp which varies from the norm, in shade, paper, perforation, watermark, and so on. A variety differs from an error in that it usually applies to small corrections that are made deliberately, and affect every sheet printed.

VENDING MACHINE LABEL

Stamp of 1984-85 (also widely known by collectors as a Frama label), whose denomination was printed by a machine on insertion of a suitable value in coins.

VIGNETTE

The central pictorial portion of a stamp design.

WATERMARK

A translucent impression used as a security device in stamp printing paper, usually visible only when held up to the light.

WILDING

British definitive stamp featuring a bust of Queen Elizabeth II, in use from 1952-1967. The name comes from that of the photographer, Dorothy Wilding. □

CYLINDER BLOCK: with cylinder numbers in the left margin, and traffic lights in the right

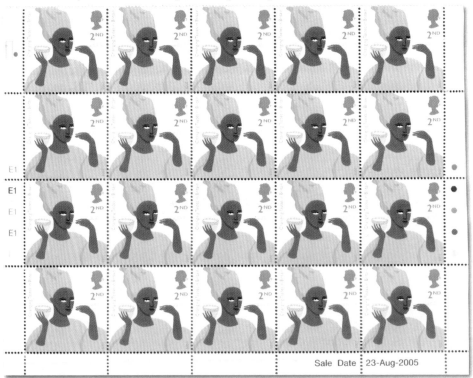

Sale Date 23-Aug-2005

GB AT SANDAFAYRE

WE OFFER **THOUSANDS OF ITEMS AND COLLECTIONS EVERY WEEK** IN OUR EXCITING **MAIL-SALE CATALOGUES** AND ON OUR WEBSITE.

There's something for everyone with lots priced from £15 to £15,000.

We've got it all, whatever your interest, including GB, Commonwealth, USA, Latin America, Old and 'New' Europe and the many lands of Asia. Whether it's single items, starter collections or medal winners, sorter cartons or entire estates you'll find it at Sandafayre.

Send the coupon today for your **FREE** introductory mail-sale catalogues or access our online sales at: **www.sandafayre.com**

SANDAFAYRE
THE WORLD'S MOST EXCITING STAMP SALES

SANDAFAYRE LTD, KNUTSFORD, WA16 8XN, UK Tel: +44 (0)1565 653214 Fax: +44 (0)1565 651637

PLEASE SEND ME MY **FREE** INTRODUCTORY **SANDAFAYRE** CATALOGUES

Name:

Address:

Postcode: E-mail:

My collecting interests are:

(BMV)

SANDAFAYRE'S • See lots that only match your interests • No unwanted catalogues
COLLECTORS REGISTER • **FREE** to register and use • Just email your details to stampregister@sandafayre.com

LOOKING AFTER YOUR COLLECTION

Stamps are easy to damage, so it's vitally important to look after your investment. Here are some top tips on how to care for your collection

Most collectors spend a great deal of time and money on compiling their collection, and are justifiably proud of it. However, a few are careless about protecting it, which will allow it to deteriorate.

Follow a few basic rules and you should ensure that your stamps are well kept and remain a stunning display and a good investment.

ABOVE: A choice of dedicated GB albums is available to help you house and organise your collection

HANDLING

Always handle any philatelic material with tweezers. But make sure you use proper stamp tweezers, with blunt prongs, not those intended for other purposes such as plucking eyebrows!

If you are removing used stamps from paper, do not be in too much of a hurry. Float them on water until they slide easily off the piece, without being forced, and then dry them with care.

If mounting them using hinges, buy good quality hinges and apply as little moisture as possible to the part of the hinge that affixes to the stamp. The hinge should be placed just below the perforations, never over them.

Remember that applying hinges could adversely affect the value of a stamp, especially an unused classic stamp.

If using protective mounts, again buy good quality ones. Be very careful as you cut the mount to fit the stamp.

Remember that it is beneficial for a stamp to be removed from its mount from time to time.

STORAGE

If you have stamps waiting to be arranged on exhibition sheets or mounted on album pages, the best way to keep them safe is in a stockbook, which may work as a long-term or short-term 'holding album'.

As always, look for quality when you buy a stockbook. Interleaving between the pages will protect the stamps against damage caused by contact with each other.

Keep stockbooks in an upright position, turning over the pages from time to time. Do not overfill them, as this may cause the pages to distort, and be careful as you insert or remove items;

it is surprisingly easy to fold over the corner perforations of a stamp as you slip it inside the holding strips.

Remember that the top edge of poor or distorted strips could cause damage to your stamps, leaving a mark on them, so check the strips carefully.

Most collectors use stamp albums as a permanent home for their stamps. A range of dedicated album and album pages is available for GB collections, with reserved spaces not only for each different issue but often for printing, watermark and shade varieties, and so on.

When buying a stamp album, check that it meets the requirements of your collection and opt for the highest quality you can afford.

ABOVE: Always use proper philatelic tweezers when handling stamps

Nothing looks worse than a bulging album caused by the leaves not being strong enough to hold the material.

Avoid over-filling albums and store them upright, turning over the leaves from time to time to give them some air.

Covers, miniature sheets, presentation packs, booklets and blocks do not always fit easily into albums. Many collectors store them in simple boxes such as shoe boxes.

Wherever your collection is kept, avoid extremes of heat, light and humidity. Take immediate action if you have even the remotest suspicion of dampness or discoloration. ☐

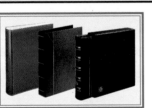

HOW TO USE THIS BOOK

The prices we quote and the abbreviations we use

This guide offers independent and accurate price information about all GB stamps issued between 1840 and 2008.

It quotes not the inflated prices that some dealers and catalogue publishers might hope to achieve, but accurate market prices to help you pinpoint the exact worth of your collection.

The publisher of *British Stamp Market Values* is not affiliated to any dealer.

ABBREVIATIONS

The following abbreviations are used:
Des: designer
Perf: perforation
Wmk: watermark

GENERAL NOTES

☐ Unused prices assume stamps are se-tenant where applicable, but used prices do not.

☐ Used prices quoted are for fine examples with full perforations or reasonable margins as applicable, and with either a light Duplex cancellation (pre-1880) or a clear steel datestamp (post-1880).

☐ When a dash (–) appears in a price column it means that the stamp doesn't exist in that particular state, or that it is impracticable to price it.

☐ Due to the proliferation of modern GB special stamps, the price for a full set may be given instead of individual prices.

THE EXPERTS WHO PROVIDED THE PRICING IN THIS GUIDE

RUSHSTAMPS
PO Box 1, Lyndhurst, Hampshire SO43 7PP
Rushstamps, run by Allan Grant, deals primarily in Great Britain and publishes a bulging catalogue offering a wide range of material. This is available upon request.

BB STAMPS
PO Box 6277, Overton, Basingstoke, Hampshire RG25 3RN
Run by Brian Bayford, BB Stamps deals in GB stamps from Queen Victoria to Wildings.

MARK BLOXHAM
PO Box 204, Morpeth NE61 9AA
Mark Bloxham is a specialist in classic British stamps at the top end of the market.

PACKS & CARDS
Oaklands House, Reading Road North, Fleet, Hampshire GU51 4AB
Packs & Cards specialises in presentation packs and PHQ cards, selling by mail order, from its website and via eBay. It also supplies unusual items such as Post Office posters.

DON STADDON
Stamp Magazine contributor
Don Staddon is one of the leading authorities on Machin definitives.

IAN HARVEY
Member of the RPSL Expert Committee
Ian Harvey is a leading specialist collector of booklets from Edward VII to Elizabeth II

GUIDE TO WATERMARKS

Identify the watermarks referred to in the price listings

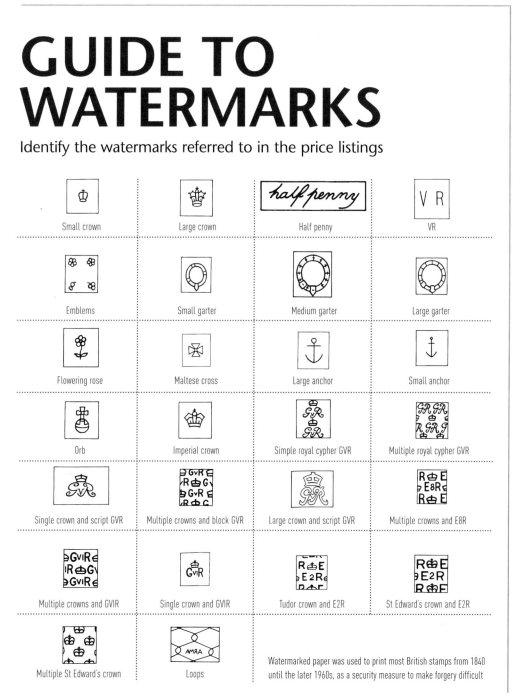

Small crown	Large crown	Half penny	VR
Emblems	Small garter	Medium garter	Large garter
Flowering rose	Maltese cross	Large anchor	Small anchor
Orb	Imperial crown	Simple royal cypher GVR	Multiple royal cypher GVR
Single crown and script GVR	Multiple crowns and block GVR	Large crown and script GVR	Multiple crowns and E8R
Multiple crowns and GVIR	Single crown and GVIR	Tudor crown and E2R	St Edward's crown and E2R
Multiple St Edward's crown	Loops		

Watermarked paper was used to print most British stamps from 1840 until the later 1960s, as a security measure to make forgery difficult

QUEEN VICTORIA

For this reign prices are given for lightly mounted unused (left) and fine used (right). The exception is for the 1840-1841 imperforate stamps, where fine used prices are subdivided into examples with four margins (centre) and three margins (right).

Take care when buying unmounted mint because there are known cases of regumming.

LINE-ENGRAVED ISSUES

1d black

■ 1840, May 6. Penny Black
Engraved by Charles and Frederick Heath. Printed in recess by Perkins, Bacon, Wmk: Small crowns, Imperforate. Letters in lower corners only.

1d black	£7,500	£200	78.00
1d intense black	£8,500	£225	90.00
1d grey black	£8,000	£250	90.00
Plate 1a	£12,000	£275	90.00
Plate 1b	£7,500	£200	80.00
Plate 2	£7,500	£200	80.00
Plate 3	£9,000	£225	85.00
Plate 4	£7,500	£200	80.00
Plate 5	£7,500	£200	80.00
Plate 6	£7,500	£200	80.00
Plate 7	£8,000	£240	90.00
Plate 8	£9,000	£275	95.00
Plate 9	£9,500	£325	£125
Plate 10	£24,000	£600	£175
Plate 11	£14,000	£3,500	£750
Wmk inverted	£25,000	£1,400	£295
Bleute paper	£12,500	£375	95.00
Red Maltese cross cancellation	-	£225	90.00
Black Maltese cross cancellation	-	£200	78.00
Blue Maltese cross cancellation	-	£8,000	£2,000
Magenta Maltese cross cancellation	-	£1,950	£400
Ruby Maltese cross cancellation	-	£750	£225
Violet Maltese cross cancellation	-	£12,000	£3,000
Number in cross (1-12)	-	£10,000	£3,000
Penny Post cancellation only	-	£2,600	£600
Town datestamp only	-	£2,750	£600
1844 cancellation	-	£1,000	£175

2d blue

■ 1840, May 8. Twopenny Blue
Engraved by Charles and Frederick Heath. Printed in recess by Perkins, Bacon, Wmk: Small crowns, Imperforate. Letters in lower corners only.

2d blue	£18,000	£500	£140
2d deep full blue	£22,000	£600	£170
2d pale blue	£17,000	£550	£150
Plate 1	£18,000	£500	£140
Plate 2	£24,000	£600	£170
Wmk Inverted	£50,000	£2,500	£850
Red Maltese cross cancel (Plate 1)	-	£550	£150
Red Maltese cross cancel (Plate 2)	-	£1,000	£225
Black Maltese cross cancellation	-	£500	£140
Blue Maltese cross cancellations	-	£6,000	£1,250
Magenta Maltese cross cancellation	-	£4,000	£850
Ruby Maltese cross cancellation	-	£2,000	£500
Number in cross (1-12)	-	£9,000	£3,000
Penny Post cancellation only	-	£5,000	£1,200
Town datestamp only	-	£3,750	£800
1844 cancellation	-	£1,250	£250

1d red

■ 1841, February 10. Penny Red
Engraved by Charles and Frederick Heath. Printed in recess by Perkins, Bacon, Wmk: Small crowns, Imperforate. Letters in lower corners only.

1d red brown	£275	9.00	3.00
1d deep red brown	£550	15.00	4.00
1d orange brown	£1,200	£120	12.00
1d lake red	£3,500	£550	£100
Plate 1b	£18,000	£225	40.00
Plate 2	£18,000	£175	25.00
Plate 5	£5,000	£150	20.00
Plate 8	£8,000	90.00	20.00
Plate 9	£4,000	90.00	20.00
Plate 10	£2,000	90.00	20.00
Plate 11	£4,000	75.00	15.00
Wmk inverted	£4,000	£250	75.00
Lavender Paper	£1,000	£150	40.00
Red Maltese cross cancellation	-	£3,850	£875
Black Maltese cross cancellation	-	40.00	6.00
Blue Maltese cross cancellation	-	£375	75.00
Green Maltese cross cancellation	-	£8,000	£1,000
Violet Maltese cross cancellation	-	£9,000	£1,500
Number in cross (1-12)	-	95.00	22.50
Penny Post cancellation only	-	£700	£125
Black town datestamp only	-	£300	95.00
Blue town datestamp only	-	£1,200	£275
Green town datestamp only	-	£2,750	£650
Black 1844 cancellation	-	9.00	3.00
Blue 1844 cancellation	-	£100	25.00
Green 1844 cancellation	-	£1,250	£250
Red 1844 cancellation	-	£12,000	£3,000
Violet 1844 cancellation	-	£2,500	£600
B blank error	-	£40,000	£18,000

2d blue

■ 1841, March 13. Twopenny Blue

Engraved by Charles and Frederick Heath. Printed in recess by Perkins, Bacon, Wmk: Small crowns, Imperforate. Letters in lower corners only. White lines added to design.

2d blue	£3,000	50.00	12.00
2d pale blue	£3,200	55.00	12.00
2d deep full blue	£4,000	70.00	15.00
2d violet (lavender paper)	£18,000	£950	£175
Plate 3	£3,000	60.00	12.00
Plate 4	£3,500	50.00	12.00
Wmk inverted	£7,500	£400	£125
Black Maltese cross cancellation	-	£150	22.50
Blue Maltese cross cancellation	-	£3,000	£400
Number in cross (1-12)	-	£250	60.00

Black town datestamp only	-	£1,000	£275
Blue town datestamp only	-	£4,000	£700
Black 1844 cancellation	-	50.00	12.00
Blue 1844 cancellation	-	£475	£100
Green 1844 cancellation	-	£2,750	£750
Red 1844 cancellation	-	£17,500	£3,500

■ 1854

As above but perf: 16

1d red-brown (February 1854)	£195	12.00
2d blue (March 1, 1854)	£2,100	60.00

■ 1855

As above but perf: 14.

1d red-brown (January 1855)	£450	45.00
2d blue (March 4, 1855)	£7,000	£160

■ 1855

As above but wmk. Large crown and perf: 16

1d red-brown (May 15, 1855)	£700	65.00
2d blue (July 20, 1855)	£9,000	£230

■ 1855

As above but perf: 14

1d red-brown (August 18, 1855)	£160	8.00
2d blue (July 20, 1855)	£1,600	30.00

■ 1858-1870

As above with wmk: 'half penny' extending over three stamps (½d) or Large Crowns (1d, 1½d, 2d). Perf: 14 but letters in all four corners. These plates have the number included in the design of the stamps.

½d rose-red (October 1, 1870)	75.00	10.00

½d rose-red

Plate 1	£180	50.00
Plate 3	£120	25.00
Plate 4	£100	18.00
Plate 5	75.00	10.00
Plate 6	80.00	10.00
Plate 8	£225	60.00
Plate 9	£5,000	£550
Plate 10	85.00	10.00
Plate 11	80.00	10.00
Plate 12	80.00	10.00
Plate 13	80.00	10.00
Plate 14	80.00	10.00
Plate 15	£115	24.00
Plate 19	£140	28.00
Plate 20	£200	50.00

1d rose-red

1d rose-red (April 1, 1864)	12.00	1.50
Plate 71	22.00	2.00
Plate 72	27.00	2.50
Plate 73	24.00	2.00
Plate 74	25.00	1.50
Plate 76	25.00	1.50
Plate 77	-	-
Plate 78	45.00	1.50
Plate 79	22.00	1.50
Plate 80	30.00	1.50
Plate 81	35.00	1.50
Plate 82	85.00	2.75
Plate 83	£110	6.00
Plate 84	40.00	1.60
Plate 85	27.00	1.60
Plate 86	35.00	2.75
Plate 87	22.00	1.50
Plate 88	£150	7.00
Plate 89	25.00	1.50
Plate 90	25.00	1.50
Plate 91	35.00	4.50
Plate 92	21.00	1.50
Plate 93	30.00	1.50
Plate 94	28.00	4.00
Plate 95	25.00	1.50
Plate 96	28.00	1.50
Plate 97	25.00	2.50
Plate 98	30.00	4.50
Plate 99	35.00	4.00
Plate 100	40.00	1.50
Plate 101	40.00	7.50
Plate 102	28.00	1.50
Plate 103	30.00	2.75
Plate 104	60.00	4.00
Plate 105	55.00	5.50
Plate 106	35.00	1.50
Plate 107	40.00	5.00
Plate 108	60.00	1.75
Plate 109	65.00	2.50
Plate 110	40.00	7.50
Plate 111	36.00	1.75
Plate 112	50.00	1.70
Plate 113	30.00	9.00
Plate 114	£240	9.00
Plate 115	85.00	1.75
Plate 116	60.00	7.50
Plate 117	28.00	1.50
Plate 118	30.00	1.50
Plate 119	28.00	1.50
Plate 120	12.00	1.50
Plate 121	25.00	8.00

Plate 122	12.00	1.50
Plate 123	25.00	1.50
Plate 124	22.00	1.50
Plate 125	25.00	1.50
Plate 127	35.00	1.75
Plate 129	25.00	6.50
Plate 130	35.00	1.75
Plate 131	45.00	12.00
Plate 132	£125	18.00
Plate 133	£105	7.50
Plate 134	12.00	1.50
Plate 135	70.00	22.00
Plate 136	65.00	17.00
Plate 137	22.00	1.75
Plate 138	14.00	1.50
Plate 139	40.00	12.50
Plate 140	14.00	1.50
Plate 141	£100	7.00
Plate 142	50.00	22.00
Plate 143	40.00	12.00
Plate 144	75.00	16.00
Plate 145	23.00	1.75
Plate 146	25.00	4.50
Plate 147	30.00	2.00
Plate 148	25.00	2.00
Plate 149	25.00	4.50
Plate 150	12.00	1.50
Plate 151	40.00	7.50
Plate 152	40.00	4.00
Plate 153	90.00	7.00
Plate 154	30.00	1.50
Plate 155	30.00	1.75
Plate 156	35.00	1.50
Plate 157	30.00	1.50
Plate 158	23.00	
Plate 159	23.00	
Plate 160	23.00	
Plate 161	40.0	
Plate 162	30	
Plate 163	3	
Plate 164	3	
Plate 165	3	
Plate 166	3	
Plate 167		
Plate 168		
Plate 169		
Plate 170		
Plate 171	12.00	
Plate 172	23.00	
Plate 173	48.00	6.50
Plate 174	23.00	1.50
Plate 175	40.00	2.50
Plate 176	40.00	1.75
Plate 177	32.00	1.50
Plate 178	40.00	2.50
Plate 179	30.00	1.75
Plate 180	40.00	4.00
Plate 181	36.00	1.50
Plate 182	75.00	4.00
Plate 183	35.00	2.00

Plate 184	23.00	1.75
Plate 185	30.00	2.00
Plate 186	35.00	1.75
Plate 187	30.00	1.50
Plate 188	50.00	7.50
Plate 189	50.00	5.50
Plate 190	30.00	4.50
Plate 191	23.00	5.50
Plate 192	30.00	1.50
Plate 193	23.00	1.50
Plate 194	30.00	6.50
Plate 195	30.00	6.50
Plate 196	30.00	4.00
Plate 197	35.00	7.00
Plate 198	32.00	4.50
Plate 199	35.00	4.50
Plate 200	40.00	2.00
Plate 201	23.00	4.00
Plate 202	40.00	6.50
Plate 203	23.00	13.00
Plate 204	35.00	1.75
Plate 205	35.00	2.25
Plate 206	35.00	7.00
Plate 207	40.00	7.00
Plate 208	35.00	12.50
Plate 209	30.00	8.00
Plate 210	45.00	10.00
Plate 211	50.00	18.00
Plate 212	40.00	10.00
Plate 213	40.00	10.00
Plate 214	45.00	15.00
Plate 215	45.00	15.00
Plate 216	50.00	15.00
Plate 217	50.00	6.00
Plate 218	45.00	7.00
Plate 219	80.00	58.00
Plate 220	32.00	6.00
Plate 221	50.00	15.00
Plate 222	60.00	30.00
Plate 223	75.00	50.00
Plate 224	£110	45.00
Plate 225	£2,400	£550

1½d rose-red

1½d rose-red (October 1, 1870)	£250	25.00
Plate 1*	£450	48.00
Plate 3	£275	32.00
(* plate 1 does not appear in the stamp design)		

2d blue (July 1858)	£250	8.00
Plate 7	£925	40.00
Plate 8	£850	25.00
Plate 9	£250	8.00
Plate 12	£1,500	£100
Plate 13	£260	15.00
Plate 14	£340	16.00
Plate 15	£320	16.00

EMBOSSED ISSUES

10d brown

■ 1847-1854
Die engraved at the Royal Mint by William Wyon. Printed using the embossed process at Somerset House. Wmk: VR (6d), unwatermarked (10d, 1/-). Imperforate.

6d lilac (March 1, 1854)	£10,000	£525
10d brown (November 6, 1848)	£8,000	£775
1/- green (September 11, 1847)	£12,000	£550

(* The above are priced cut square; examples cut to shape are worth considerably less.)

SURFACE-PRINTED ISSUES

4d carmine

■ 1855-1857
Surface-printed by De La Rue. Perf: 14.

4d carmine (Wmk: Small Garter) (July 31, 1855)	£6,500	£275
4d carmine (Wmk: Medium Garter) (February 25, 1856)	£5,000	£325
4d carmine (Wmk: Large Garter) (January 1857)	£1,050	55.00

Great Britain 1839–1951

A selection of exceptional items sold in recent years

Free Quarterly and Specialised Lists featuring all aspects of British Philately from 1839 to 1951 are available on request.

We are keen to help you find the items you are looking for and supply fine quality material, with emphasis on the unusual. Our stock includes issued stamps, proofs, essays, imprimaturs, specialised shades, covers.

We are also interested in **buying** fine single items and specialised collections and are happy to provide valuations and estate advice.

Andrew G Lajer
The Old Post Office, Davis Way, Hurst
Berkshire RG10 0TR, United Kingdom
T: +44 (0)1189 344151 F: +44 (0)1189 344947
E: andrew.lajer@btinternet.com
www.andrewglajer.co.uk

Andrew Claridge
PO Box 1999, White Notley, Witham
Essex CM8 1XN, United Kingdom
T: +44 (0)1376 584412 F: +44 (0)1376 585388
E: andrew.claridge@btinternet.com

6d lilac

■ 1865-1867

Designs as above, but with large corner letters (all values). The designs of the 3d and 4d values are as the 1862 issue. Wmk: Larger Garter (4d), Emblems (3d, 6d, 9d, 10d, 1/-).

3d carmine (March 1, 1865) (plate 4)	£1000	£125
4d vermilion (July 4, 1865)	£400	40.00
Plate 7	£440	65.00
Plate 8	£400	40.00
Plate 9	£400	40.00
Plate 10	£475	85.00
Plate 11	£400	40.00
Plate 12	£400	40.00
Plate 13	£400	40.00
Plate 14	£440	60.00
6d lilac (April 1, 1865)	£650	55.00
Plate 5	£650	55.00
Plate 6	£1,800	£100
9d bistre (December 1, 1865) (plate 4*)	£2,000	£360
10d brown (November 11, 1867) (plate 1)	-	£35,000
1/- green (February 1, 1865) (plate 4)	£1,100	£125

(* Copies of the 9d from an Imprimatur sheet of plate 5 are known to exist.)

■ 1856

As above but wmk: Emblems.

6d lilac (October 21, 1856)	£775	68.00
1/- green (November 1, 1856)	£1,200	£160

9d bistre

2/- blue

■ 1862-1864

As above but wmk: Large Garter (4d), Emblems (3d, 6d, 9d, 1/-).

3d carmine (May 1, 1862)	£1,200	£225
4d red (January 15, 1862)	£875	55.00
6d lilac (December 1, 1862)	£1,050	50.00
9d bistre (January 15, 1862)	£2,750	£280
1/- green (December 1, 1862)	£1,700	£150

(* The 1/- exists with either a number 1 or a number 2 in the border)

■ 1867-1880

Wmk: Flowering rose.

3d red (July 12, 1867)	£375	35.00
Plate 4	£675	£125
Plate 5	£375	35.00
Plate 6	£400	35.00
Plate 7	£500	35.00
Plate 8	£400	35.00
Plate 9	£400	35.00
Plate 10	£550	75.00
6d lilac (June 21, 1867)	£400	55.00
Plate 8	£400	55.00
Plate 9	£400	55.00
Plate 10	-	£29,000
9d bistre (October 3, 1867) (plate 4)	£1,300	£200
10d brown (July 1, 1867)	£1,900	£225
Plate 1	£1,900	£200
Plate 2	£30,000	£10,000
1/- green (July 13, 1867)	£480	25.00
Plate 4	£675	40.00
Plate 5	£500	25.00
Plate 6	£700	25.00
Plate 7	£750	45.00
2/- blue (July 1, 1867) (plate 1)	£2,100	£140
2/- brown (February 27, 1880) (plate 1)	£15,000	£2,250

4d vermilion

6d grey

■ 1872-1873
Wmk: Flowering Rose.

6d brown (April 12, 1872)	£450	35.00
Plate 11	£450	35.00
Plate 12	£1,700	£160
6d grey (April 24, 1873) (plate 12)	£1100	£130

£1 brown

■ 1867-1868
Wmk: Maltese Cross. Perf: 15 x 15.
5/- red (July 1, 1867)

Plate 1	£3,850	£450
Plate 2	£5,000	£550
10/- grey-green (September 26, 1878)		
Plate 1	£50,000	£1,900
£1 brown (September 26, 1878)		
Plate 1	£65,000	£3,000

£5 orange

■ 1882-1883
Wmk: Large Anchor. Perf: 14.
5/- red (November 25, 1882)

Plate 4	£24,000	£1,950
10/- grey-green (February 1883)		
Plate 1	£100,000	£3,000
£1 brown (December 1882)		
Plate 1	£120,000	£6,000
£5 orange (March 21, 1882)		
Plate 1	£10,000	£4,500

2½d mauve

■ 1873-1880
A) Wmk: Small Anchor
2½d mauve (July 1, 1875)

Plate 1	£385	55.00
Plate 2	£385	55.00
Plate 3	£600	80.00

B) Wmk: Orb
2½d mauve (May 16, 1876)

Plate 3	£750	75.00
Plate 4	£350	35.00
Plate 5	£350	35.00
Plate 6	£350	35.00
Plate 7	£350	35.00
Plate 8	£350	35.00
Plate 9	£350	35.00
Plate 10	£375	40.00
Plate 11	£350	35.00
Plate 12	£350	35.00
Plate 13	£350	35.00
Plate 14	£350	35.00
Plate 15	£350	35.00
Plate 16	£350	35.00
Plate 17	£1050	£190
2½d blue (February 5, 1880)		
Plate 17	£325	40.00
Plate 18	£350	22.50
Plate 19	£325	22.50
Plate 20	£350	22.50

C) Wmk: Flowering Rose.
3d red (July 5, 1873)

Plate 11	£300	30.00
Plate 112	£325	30.00
Plate 114	£375	30.00
Plate 115	£300	30.00

Selling your stamp collection?

Warwick and Warwick have an expanding requirement for world collections, single country collections, single items, covers, proof material and specialised collections, with G.B. material being particularly in demand. Our customer base is increasing dramatically and we need an ever-larger supply of quality material to keep pace with demand. The market has never been stronger and if you are considering the sale of your collection, now is the time to act.

FREE VALUATIONS
We will provide a free, professional valuation of your collection, without obligation on your part to proceed. Either we will make you a fair, binding private treaty offer, or we will recommend inclusion of your property in our next public auction.

FREE TRANSPORTATION
We can arrange insured transportation of your collection to our Warwick offices completely free of charge. If you decline our offer, we ask you to cover the return carriage costs only.

FREE VISITS
Visits by our valuers are possible anywhere in the country or abroad, usually within 48 hours, in order to value larger collections. Please phone for details.

VALUATION DAYS
We are staging a series of valuation days across the country. Please visit our website or telephone for further details.

EXCELLENT PRICES
Because of the strength of our customer base we are in a position to offer prices that we feel sure will exceed your expectations.

ACT NOW
Telephone or email Ian Hunter today with details of your property.

Get the experts on your side!

Warwick & Warwick
AUCTIONEERS AND VALUERS
www.warwickandwarwick.com

Warwick & Warwick Ltd.
Chalon House, Scar Bank, Millers Road
Warwick CV34 5DB England
Tel: (01926) 499031 • Fax: (01926) 491906
Email: ian.hunter@warwickandwarwick.com

Plate 116	£300	30.00
Plate 117	£325	30.00
Plate 118	£325	30.00
Plate 119	£300	30.00
Plate 120	£300	55.00
6d buff (March 15, 1873)		
Plate 13	-	£17,000
6d grey (March 31, 1874)		
Plate 113	£300	40.00
Plate 114	£300	40.00
Plate 115	£300	40.00
Plate 116	£300	40.00
Plate 117	£525	90.00
1/- green (September 1, 1873)		
Plate 18	£500	80.00
Plate 19	£500	80.00
Plate 110	£500	90.00
Plate 111	£500	80.00
Plate 112	£475	65.00
Plate 113	£475	65.00
Plate 114	-	£24,000
1/- brown (October 14, 1880)		
Plate 13	£2,400	£400
D) Wmk: Large Garter.		
4d vermilion (March 1, 1867)		
Plate 15	£1,400	£300
Plate 16	-	£24,000
4d green (March 12, 1877)		
Plate 15	£825	£180
Plate 16	£775	£170
Plate 17	-	£14,000
4d brown (August 15, 1880)		
Plate 17	£1,250	£325
8d orange (September 11, 1876)		
Plate 1	£900	£175

Plate 21	£380	55.00
3d (in red) on 3d lilac (January 1, 1883)		
Plate 21	£400	80.00
4d brown (December 9, 1880)	£300	38.00
Plate 17	£300	38.00
Plate 18	£300	38.00
6d grey (January 1, 1881)	£310	45.00
Plate 17	£350	45.00
Plate 18	£310	45.00
6d (in red) on 6d lilac (January 1, 1883)		
Plate 18	£425	80.00
1/- brown (May 29, 1881)	£425	90.00
Plate 13	£525	90.00
Plate 14	£425	90.00

5d indigo

■ 1880-1881
Wmk: Imperial Crown.

½d green (October 14, 1880)	35.00	6.00
1d brown (January 1, 1880)	18.00	3.00
1½d red-brown (October 14, 1880)	£140	30.00
2d red (December 8, 1880)	£180	60.00
5d indigo (March 15, 1881)	£550	65.00

3d (red) on 3d lilac

■ 1880-1883
Wmk: Imperial Crown.

2½d blue (March 23, 1881)	£325	14.00
Plate 21	£350	18.00
Plate 22	£325	18.00
Plate 23	£325	14.00
3d red (February 1881)	£380	55.00
Plate 20	£500	90.00

1d lilac

■ 1881
Wmk: Imperial Crown.
A) 14 white dots in each corner

1d lilac (July 12, 1881)	£150	15.00

B) 16 white dots in each corner

1d lilac (December 12, 1881)	1.75	0.75

5/- red

■ 1883-1884
Wmk: Large Anchor.

2/6 lilac (July 2, 1883)	£350	70.00
5/- red (April 1, 1884)	£700	£110
10/- blue (April 1, 1884)	£1,800	£275

£1 green, 1891

■ 1884-1891
A) Wmk: Imperial Crowns.

£1 brown (April 1, 1884)	£26,000	£1,850
£1 green (January 27, 1891)	£6,000	£550

B) Wmk: Orbs.

£1 brown (February 1, 1888)	£60,000	£2,800

6d green

■ 1883-84, 'Lilac & Green issue'
Wmk: Imperial Crown (sideways on 2d, 2½d, 6d, 9d)

½d blue (April 1, 1884)	14.00	3.50
1½d lilac (April 1, 1884)	80.00	23.00
2d lilac (April 1, 1884)	£140	40.00

2½d lilac (April 1, 1884)	57.50	5.00
3d lilac (April 1, 1884)	£135	38.00
4d green (April 1, 1884)	£325	£100
5d green (April 1, 1884)	£325	£100
6d green (April 1, 1884)	£300	£110
9d green (August 1, 1883)	£725	£300
1/- green (April 1, 1884)	£775	£150

9d violet, blue

■ 1887, January 1. 'Jubilee issue'
Wmk: Imperial Crown.
A) Wmk upright.

½d orange	1.20	0.50
½d green (April 17, 1900)	1.40	0.60
1½d purple, green	10.00	2.00
2d green, red	18.00	8.00
2½d purple (blue paper)	14.00	0.75
3d purple (yellow paper)	18.00	1.50
4d green, brown	22.00	7.00
4½d green, red	7.00	25.00
5d purple, blue	26.00	5.00
6d purple (red paper)	20.00	5.00
9d violet, blue	45.00	25.00
10d purple, red	40.00	24.00
1/- green	£150	40.00
1/- green, red (July 11, 1900)	45.00	70.00
Set	£400	£200

B) Wmk inverted

½d orange	25.00	20.00
½d green	25.00	25.00
1½d purple, green	£600	£250
2d purple, red	£525	£325
2½d purple (blue)	£850	£550
4d green, brown	£500	£275
5d purple	£9,500	£525
6d purple (red)	£1,700	£600
9d violet, blue	£1,800	£675
10d purple, red	£2,600	£650
1/- green	£700	£350
1/- green, red	£750	£675

 **Great Britain** 1839–1951

Only the best.

Andrew G Lajer
The Old Post Office, Davis Way, Hurst
Berkshire RG10 0TR, United Kingdom
T: +44 (0)1189 344151 F: +44 (0)1189 344947
E: andrew.lajer@btinternet.co
www.andrewglajer.co.uk

Andrew Claridge
PO Box 1999, White Notley, Witham
Essex CM8 1XN, United Kingdom
T: +44 (0)1376 584412 F: +44 (0)1376 585388
E: andrew.claridge@btinternet.com

KING EDWARD VII

For this reign most stamps are priced in three columns: unmounted mint (left), mounted mint (centre) and fine used (right). The exception is booklet panes, priced at mounted mint only.

To help you distinguish the work of the three printers, note that the De La Rue printings are generally cleaner, with good centering and clean perforations, whereas the Harrison & Sons and Somerset House printings are coarser, with poor centering and ragged perforations.

A vast range of shades exists on all printings. Full details of these are beyond the scope of this publication.

½d yellow-green   5/- red

■ **1902, January 1**
Designs as Queen Victoria 1887 issues and 1883-84 high values.

A) Surface printed by De La Rue. Wmk. Imperial Crown (½d to 1/-), Large Anchor (2/6, 5/-, 10/-), Three Imperial Crowns (£1). Perf: 14.

½d blue-green	2.00	1.00	0.70
½d yellow-green	2.00	1.00	0.70
Wmk inverted	20.00	12.00	12.00
1d scarlet	1.75	1.00	0.50
Wmk inverted	7.00	5.00	6.00
1½d purple, green	60.00	30.00	10.00
on chalky paper	60.00	30.00	10.00
2d green, red (Mar 25, 1902)	70.00	30.00	10.00
on chalky paper	60.00	28.00	12.00
2½d blue	25.00	12.00	3.00
3d purple (yellow paper)	70.00	30.00	7.00
on chalky paper	60.00	30.00	10.00
4d green, brown	95.00	40.00	18.00
on chalky paper	65.00	30.00	15.00
4d orange (Nov 1, 1909)	32.00	15.00	10.00
5d purple blue (May 14, 1902)	90.00	40.00	15.00
on chalky paper	85.00	45.00	15.00
Wmk inverted	£5,500	£4,000	£3,000
6d purple	60.00	28.00	14.00
on chalky paper	60.00	30.00	14.00
7d grey	10.00	7.00	16.00
9d purple, blue	£170	70.00	40.00
on chalky paper	£155	60.00	40.00
10d purple, red (Jul 3, 1902)	£210	60.00	40.00
on chalky paper	£175	55.00	40.00
1/- green, red (Mar 24, 1902)	£165	60.00	20.00
on chalky paper	£165	60.00	24.00
2/6 lilac (Apr 5, 1902)	£450	£200	75.00
on chalky paper	£450	£300	90.00
Wmk inverted	£6,500	£4,000	£2,500
5/- red (Apr 5, 1902)	£600	£280	£120
10/- blue (Apr 5, 1902)	£1,800	£525	£350
£1 green (Jun 16, 1902)	£2,200	£1,200	£600

Booklet panes	*Wmk Upright*	*Inverted*
Pane of five se-tenant with label showing St Andrew's Cross	£400	£400
Pane of six ½d	55.00	90.00
Pane of six 1d	40.00	70.00

B) As above but printed by Harrison.

½d yellow-green (May 3, 1911)	3.50	2.00	1.30
Wmk inverted	30.00	15.00	12.00
1d red (May 3, 1911)	10.00	6.00	8.00
Wmk inverted	30.00	15.00	10.00
2½d blue (Jul 10, 1911)	£100	45.00	18.00
Wmk inverted	£1,500	£750	£750
3d purple (Sep 12, 1911) yellow paper	£140	80.00	£140
4d orange (Jul 13, 1911)	£130	60.00	45.00

Booklet panes	*Wmk Upright*	*Inverted*
Pane of five ½d se-tenant with label showing St Andrew's Cross	£900	£900
Pane of six ½d	80.00	£110
Pane of six 1d	70.00	90.00

C) As above but printed by Somerset House.

1½d purple, green (Jul 13, 1911)	50.00	25.00	12.00
2d green, red (Mar 11, 1912)	46.00	24.00	11.00
5d purple, blue (Aug 7, 1911)	50.00	28.00	11.00
6d purple (Oct 31, 1911)	50.00	26.00	14.00
chalky paper	50.00	28.00	60.00
7d grey (Aug 1, 1912)	20.00	12.00	15.00
9d purple, blue (Jul 24, 1911)	£105	65.00	40.00
10d purple, red (Oct 9, 1911)	£140	75.00	45.00
1/- green, red (Jul 17, 1911)	£115	58.00	25.00
Wmk inverted	£250	£150	-
2/6 purple (Sep 27, 1911)	£450	£190	85.00
5/- red (Feb 29, 1912)	£600	£280	£120
10/- (Jan 14, 1912)	£1,800	£600	£400
£1 green (Sep 3, 1911)	£2,100	£1,200	£700

D) As above, but printed by Harrison with perf: 15x14.

½d green (Oct 30, 1911)	50.00	30.00	30.00
1d red (Oct 5, 1911)	32.00	16.00	8.50
2½d blue (Oct 14, 1911)	45.00	21.00	7.00
3d purple (Sep 22, 1911) yellow paper	55.00	30.00	13.00
4d orange (Nov 22, 1911)	48.00	26.00	10.00

■ **1910**
A 2d value with a new design printed in Tyrian plum was prepared for use but the death of the King prevented its release. Copies are known unused and one example used.

KING GEORGE V

For this reign the stamps are priced in three columns: unmounted mint (left), mounted unused (centre) and fine used (right).

Many stamps are found in a wide variety of shades. Full details of these are beyond the scope of this guide.

½d green

1911-1912
Des: Bertram Mackennal and G. W. Eve. Portrait based on photograph by Downey. Die engraved by J. A. C. Harrison. Printed in typography by Harrison. Perf: 15x14.

A) Wmk: Imperial Crown.

½d green (Jun 22, 1911)	7.50	3.50	2.00
Wmk inverted	15.00	7.50	3.50
1d red (Jun 22, 1911)	6.50	3.00	1.50
Wmk inverted	12.50	7.00	3.00

(* These stamps also exist with Wmk sideways and printed in error with perf: 14.)

Booklet panes	Wmk Upright	Inverted
Pane of six ½d	80.00	£120
Pane of six 1d	75.00	£110

B) Wmk: Simple Royal Cypher. Issued August 1912 in booklets.

½d green	70.00	30.00	28.00
Wmk inverted	70.00	30.00	28.00
1d green	35.00	16.00	18.00
Wmk inverted	35.00	16.00	18.00

Booklet panes	Wmk Upright	Inverted
Pane of six ½d	£500	£500
Pane of six 1d	£250	£240

1912
As above except that the King's hair is lighter on the ½d and the lion is shaded on the 1d.

A) Wmk: Imperial Crown

½d green (Jan 1, 1912)	8.50	4.50	1.00
Wmk inverted	£1,100	£800	£450
1d red (Jan 1, 1912)	5.00	2.00	0.80
Wmk inverted	£450	£350	£250

B) Wmk: Simple Royal Cypher.

½d green (Aug 1912)	8.00	4.00	1.25
Wmk inverted	£225	£140	60.00
1d red (Aug 1912)	7.00	3.50	1.00
Wmk inverted	22.00	14.00	12.00

C) Wmk: Multiple Royal Cypher.

½d green (Oct 1912)	12.00	7.00	9.00
Wmk inverted	15.00	12.00	12.50
Wmk sideways	-	-	£3,250
1d red (Oct 1912)	15.00	9.00	4.50
Wmk inverted	20.00	15.00	16.00
Wmk sideways	£220	£150	£160

1d red

1912-1913
Designed and engraved as before. Printed in typography by Harrison (all values except 6d) and at Somerset House (½d, 1d, 1½d, 2d, 2½d, 3d, 4d, 5d, 6d, 7d, 8d, 9d, 10d, 1/-)

A) Wmk: Simple Royal Cypher.
i) Wmk upright

½d green (Jan 1913)	1.00	0.40	0.40
Wmk inverted	4.00	2.25	1.10
1d red (Oct 1919)	1.00	0.40	0.40
Wmk inverted	4.00	2.25	0.90
1½d brown (Oct 1912)	3.50	2.00	0.80
Wmk inverted	8.00	4.00	1.60
2d orange (Aug 1912)	3.50	1.75	0.60
Wmk inverted	20.00	10.00	8.50
2½d blue (Oct 1912)	16.00	8.00	2.25
Wmk inverted	90.00	45.00	45.00
3d violet (Oct 1912)	8.00	3.75	1.00
Wmk inverted	£120	65.00	65.00
4d green (Jan 1913)	16.00	7.00	1.50
Wmk inverted	40.00	25.00	25.00
5d brown (Jun 1913)	20.00	8.00	4.00
Wmk inverted	£700	£400	£400
6d purple (Aug 1913)			
chalky paper	18.00	8.00	2.00
Wmk inverted	65.00	35.00	35.00
7d green (Aug 1913)	28.00	11.00	7.50
Wmk inverted	65.00	40.00	40.00
8d black (Aug 1913)			
yellow paper	42.00	20.00	11.00
Wmk inverted	£180	110.00	110.00
9d black (Jun 1913)	20.00	10.00	3.75
Wmk inverted	£160	100.00	100.00
9d green (Sep 1922)	£200	75.00	24.00

Wmk inverted	£1,000	£700	£625
10d blue (Aug 1913)	32.00	15.00	18.00
Wmk inverted	£3,500	£2,500	£1,400
1/- brown (Aug 1913)	28.00	13.00	1.80
Wmk inverted	£240	£150	£140

Booklet panes		*Wmk Upright*	*Inverted*
Pane of six ½**d**		35.00	45.00
Pane of six **1d**		35.00	45.00
Pane of six 1½**d**		60.00	75.00
Pane of four 1½**d** with two advert labels		£750	£750
Pane of six **2d**		80.00	£130

B) Wmk: Multiple Royal Cypher.

½**d** green (Aug 1913)	£160	£100	95.00
Wmk inverted	£500	£350	£350
1d red (Aug 1913)	£350	£225	£180
Wmk inverted	£800	£600	£600

■ **1924-1926**

As above, but printed by typography by Waterlow (all values except 6d), Harrison (all values) or Somerset House (1½d, 6d), Wmk: Multiple Crown and block GVR.

½**d** green (Feb 1924)	0.60	0.30	0.20
Wmk inverted	5.00	2.50	1.00
Wmk sideways	11.00	5.50	4.50
1d red (Feb 1924)	0.85	0.35	0.20
Wmk inverted	5.00	2.50	1.25
Wmk sideways	26.00	15.00	16.00
1½**d** brown (Feb 1924)	0.90	0.40	0.20
Wmk inverted	2.50	1.25	1.00
Wmk sideways	14.00	7.00	4.50
2d orange (Sept 1924)	2.00	0.85	0.70
Wmk inverted	40.00	25.0	18.00
Wmk sideways	£175	60.00	65.00
2½**d** blue (Oct 1924)	7.50	4.00	1.10
Wmk inverted	65.00	45.00	30.00
3d violet (Oct 1924)	11.00	5.00	1.00
Wmk inverted	65.00	45.00	30.00
4d green (Nov 1924)	18.00	7.00	1.40
Wmk inverted	£160	85.00	60.00
5d brown (Nov 1924)	30.00	12.00	2.00
Wmk inverted	£110	70.00	55.00
6d purple (Sep 1924)	3.80	1.50	0.50
chalky paper	15.00	9.00	1.75
ordinary paper, Wmk inverted	65.00	48.00	35.00
chalky paper, Wmk inverted	70.00	50.00	40.00
9d green (Dec 1924)	20.00	7.00	2.50
Wmk inverted	£105	75.00	70.00
10d blue (Nov 1923)	65.00	28.00	22.00
Wmk inverted	£3,500	£2,200	£1,600
1/- brown (Oct 1924)	35.00	16.00	1.40
Wmk inverted	£550	£400	£260

Booklet panes		*Wmk Upright*	*Inverted*
Pane of six ½**d**		35.00	45.00
Pane of six **1d**		35.00	45.00
Pane of six 1½**d**		60.00	75.00
Pane of four 1½**d** with two advert labels		£125	£125
(* A wide range of advertising labels exists)			

1/- brown

■ **1934-1936**

As above but printed in photogravure by Harrison. Designs differ in the shading behind the portrait. Wmk: Multiple Crown and block GVR, Perf: 15 x 14.

½**d** green (Nov 19, 1934)	0.25	0.10	0.15
Wmk inverted	15.00	7.00	3.00
Wmk sideways	9.00	6.00	3.00
1d red (Sep 24, 1934)	0.25	0.20	0.15
Wmk inverted	15.00	7.00	2.50
Wmk sideways	22.00	11.00	14.00
1½**d** brown (Aug 20, 1934)	0.20	0.15	0.10
Wmk inverted	2.50	1.25	0.60
Wmk sideways	10.00	6.00	2.50
2d orange (Jan 21, 1935)	0.60	0.35	0.40
Wmk sideways	£175	70.00	65.00
2½**d** blue (Mar 18, 1935)	1.40	0.90	0.75
3d violet (Mar 18, 1935)	1.80	1.00	0.75
4d green (Dec 2, 1935)	2.50	1.40	0.75
5d brown (Feb 17, 1936)	9.00	5.00	2.50
9d deep green (Dec 2, 1935)	16.00	7.00	2.25
10d blue (Feb 24, 1936)	25.00	11.00	9.00
1/- brown (Feb 24, 1936)	32.00	12.00	0.75

Booklet panes		*Wmk Upright*	*Inverted*
Pane of six ½**d**		60.00	£100
Pane of six **1d**		60.00	£150
Pane of six 1½**d**		20.00	25.00
Pane of four 1½**d** with two advert labels		75.00	75.00

2/6 brown

■ **1913-1934. High values. 'Seahorses'**
Des: Bertram Mackennal. Dies engraved by J.A.C. Harrison. Wmk: Simple Royal Cypher. Perf: 11x12

A) Printed in recess by Waterlow. Released in July 1913.

2/6 brown	£500	£175	£100

5/- red	£1,000	£325	£175
10/- blue	£1,900	£700	£300
£1 green	£4,000	£2,250	£110

B) Printed in recess by De La Rue. Released in December 1915.

2/6 brown	£450	£200	£100
5/- red	£900	£280	£190
10/- blue	£3,000	£2,000	£600

C) Printed in recess by Bradbury, Wilkinson. Released in December 1918.

2/6 brown	£225	75.00	32.00
5/- red	£325	£150	45.00
10/- blue	£600	£300	£100

(* To distinguish between the above, note that the De La Rue printings have a yellow gum, while the Waterlow design is about 22mm high and that of Bradbury, Wilkinson 23mm high.)

D) Printed in recess by Waterlow by die re-engraved so that the background to the portrait consists of horizontal and diagonal lines. Released in October 1934.

2/6 brown	£130	60.00	12.00
5/- red	£350	£120	45.00
10/- blue	£500	£300	50.00

1d, 1½d
(inscribed '1924'
and later '1925')

1924-1925. British Empire Exhibition

Des: H. Nelson. Printed in recess by Waterlow. Wmk: Multiple Crown and block GVR. Perf: 14.

Set	18.00	8.00	8.00
Inscribed '1925'	45.00	30.00	30.00
First Day Cover	-	-	£375
Inscribed '1925'	46.00	-	£1,500

£1

1929, May 10. Postal Union Congress

Des: J. Farleigh (½d, 2½d), E. Linzell (1d, 1½d), H. Nelson (£1). Printed in typography by Waterlow (½d to 2½d) or in recess by Bradbury, Wilkinson (£1). Wmk: Multiple Crown and block GRV (½d to 2½d), Large Crown and script GVR (£1). Perf: 15x14 (½d to 2½d), 12 (£1).

½d green	1.50	0.50	0.45
Wmk inverted	20.00	11.00	8.00
Wmk sideways	70.00	25.00	25.00
1d red	2.50	1.50	1.00
Wmk inverted	25.00	13.00	14.00
Wmk sideways	90.00	60.00	60.00
1½d brown	2.00	1.25	0.80
Wmk inverted	12.00	6.00	4.50
Wmk sideways	65.00	20.00	20.00
2½d blue	16.00	7.00	5.00
Wmk inverted	£3,500	£2,000	£900
Set	20.00	9.00	6.75
First Day Cover	-	-	£450
£1 black	£900	£480	£480
First Day Cover	-	-	£6,500

Booklet panes		Wmk Upright	Inverted
Pane of six ½d		40.00	£120
Pane of six 1d		45.00	£200
Pane of six 1½d		30.00	90.00
Pane of four 1½d with two advert labels		£250	£280

2½d

1935, May 7. Silver Jubilee

Des: B. Freedman. Printed in photogravure by Harrison Wmk: Multiple Crown and block GVR. Perf: 15x14

½d green	0.80	0.40	0.30
Wmk inverted	11.00	6.00	6.00
1d red	1.40	0.70	0.70
Wmk inverted	11.00	6.00	6.00
1½d brown	1.25	0.50	0.40
Wmk inverted	2.00	1.00	0.90
2½d blue	3.00	2.00	4.00
2½d Prussian blue	£12,000	£9,000	£9,000
Set (excluding Prussian blue)	6.00	3.25	4.75
First Day Cover	-	-	80.00
Pictorial cover	-	-	£800

Booklet panes		Wmk Upright	Inverted
Pane of four ½d		30.00	60.00
Pane of four 1d		30.00	60.00
Pane of four 1½d		15.00	20.00

KING EDWARD VIII

For this reign stamps are priced in two columns: unmounted mint (left) and fine used (right). The exception is booklet panes, which are priced only for unmounted mint with good perforations.

Mounted unused stamps can normally be obtained for about 50% of the quoted unmounted prices.

½d green

■ **1936**

Printed by Photogravure by Harrison. Wmk: Multiple Crown and E8R. Perf: 15x14.

½d green (September, 1, 1936)	0.10	0.10
Wmk inverted	6.00	2.50
1d red (September 14, 1936)	0.20	0.20
Wmk inverted	5.00	2.25
1½d brown (September 1, 1936)	0.20	0.10
Wmk inverted	0.75	0.80
2½d blue (September 1, 1936)	0.20	0.30
Set	0.50	0.50

Booklet panes	Wmk Upright	Inverted
Pane of six ½d	15.00	42.00
Pane of six 1d	15.00	42.00
Pane of two 1½d	10.00	10.00
Pane of four 1½d with two advert labels	55.00	55.00
Pane of six 1½d	8.00	14.00

KING GEORGE VI

For this reign, prices are priced in two columns: unmounted mint (left) and fine used (right). The exception is booklet panes, which are priced only for unmounted mint with good perforations.

1½d

■ 1937, May 13. Coronation

Des: E. Dulac. Printed in photogravure by Harrison. Wmk: Multiple Crown and GVIR. Perf: 15x14

1½d	0.25	0.15
First Day Cover		3.00
Pictorial cover		20.00

½d, 1d, 1½d, 2d, 2½d, 3d

4d, 5d, 6d

7d, 8d, 9d, 10d, 11d, 1/-

■ 1937-47 Definitives

Des: E. Dulac and E. Gill (½d to 6d), E. Dulac (7d to 1/-). Printed in photogravure by Harrison. Wmk: Multiple Crown and GVIR. Perf: 15x14

A) Original colours

½d green (May 10, 1937)	0.15	0.10
Wmk inverted	7.00	0.50
Wmk sideways	0.25	0.30
1d red (May10, 1937)	0.15	0.10
Wmk inverted	30.00	2.50
Wmk sideways	15.00	5.00
1½d red-brown (July 30, 1937)	0.15	0.15
Wmk inverted	9.00	1.00
Wmk sideways	1.00	0.50
2d orange (January 31, 1938)	0.50	0.35
Wmk inverted	36.00	2.50
Wmk sideways	36.00	20.00
2½d blue (May 10, 1937)	0.25	1.00
Wmk inverted	32.00	3.00
Wmk sideways	50.00	25.00
3d violet (January 31, 1938)	1.50	0.60
4d green (November 21, 1938)	1.75	0.20
5d brown (November 21, 1938)	2.00	0.30
6d purple (January 30, 1939)	1.00	0.15
7d emerald (February 27, 1939)	3.50	0.50
8d carmine (February 27, 1939)	5.00	0.50
9d deep green (May 1, 1939)	4.00	0.50
10d blue (May 1, 1939)	3.00	0.50
11d brown-purple (December 29, 1947)	1.75	1.00
1/- brown (May 1, 1939)	4.00	0.15
Set	24.00	4.00

Booklet panes	Wmk Upright	Inverted
Pane of two ½d	10.00	10.00
Pane of six ½d	15.00	25.00
Pane of two 1d	10.00	50.00
Pane of six 1d	15.00	£150
Pane of two 1½d	5.00	10.00
Pane of four 1½d with two advert labels (*)	£110	£110
Pane of six 1½d	20.00	25.00
Pane of six 2d	50.00	£200
Pane of six 2½d	50.00	£195
		Wmk Sideways
Pane of four ½d		45.00
Pane of four 1d		70.00

(* 15 different combinations of advertising labels exist. Prices quoted are for the cheapest; scarcer panes can fetch up to twice as much)

B) As above, but with paler colours

½d pale green (September 1, 1941)	0.15	0.10
Wmk inverted	3.00	0.40
1d pale red (August 11, 1941)	0.20	0.10
Wmk sideways	3.00	3.00
1½d pale red-brown (September 28, 1942)	0.50	0.35
2d pale orange (October 6, 1941)	0.50	0.25
Wmk inverted	3.00	0.40
Wmk sideways	10.00	8.00
2½d pale blue (July 21, 1941)	0.15	0.10

Wmk inverted	1.00	0.50
Wmk sideways	7.00	6.00
3d pale violet (November 3, 1941)	1.00	0.25
Set	1.50	1.00

Booklet panes	Wmk Upright	Inverted
Pane of two ½**d**	9.00	-
Pane of six ½**d**	10.00	25.00
Pane of two 1**d**	9.00	-
Pane of two 1½**d**	9.00	-
Pane of six **2d**	7.50	30.00
Pane of six 2½**d** pale blue	4.00	15.00

C) As above, but with colours changed

½**d** orange (May 3, 1951)	0.10	0.20
Wmk inverted	0.20	0.30
1**d** blue (May 3, 1951)	0.10	0.10
Wmk inverted	2.25	1.00
Wmk sideways	0.20	0.40
1½**d** green (May 3, 1951)	0.25	0.20
Wmk inverted	2.75	2.00
Wmk sideways	1.25	1.50
2d red-brown (May 3, 1951)	0.25	0.25
Wmk inverted	4.00	3.50
Wmk sideways	0.75	0.75
2½**d** red (May 3, 1951)	0.15	0.15
Wmk inverted	1.00	0.50
Wmk sideways	0.60	0.85
4d blue (October 2, 1950)	1.00	0.65
Set	1.50	1.10

Booklet panes	Wmk Upright	Inverted
Pane of two ½**d**	9.00	-
Pane of four ½**d**	7.00	9.00
Pane of six ½**d**	5.00	6.00
Pane of two 1**d**	9.00	-
Pane of three 1**d** with three labels reading 'MINIMUM INLAND PRINTED PAPER RATE 1½**d**'	25.00	25.00
Pane of three 1**d** with three labels reading 'SHORTHAND IN ONE WEEK'	35.00	35.00
Pane of four 1**d**	6.00	7.00
Pane of six 1**d**	5.00	20.00
Pane of two 1½**d**	5.00	-
Pane of four 1½**d**	6.00	14.00
Pane of six 1½**d**	8.50	22.00
Pane of six **2d**	17.00	60.00
Pane of six 2½**d**	3.50	6.50

2/6, 5/-

10/-, £1

■ 1939-1948. High Values

Des: E. Dulac (2/6, 5/-), G. R. Bellew (10/-, £1). Printed in recess by Waterlow. Wmk: Single Crown and GVIR. Perf: 14

2/6 brown (September 4, 1939)	45.00	5.00
2/6 green (March 9, 1942)	9.00	0.50
5/- red (August 21, 1939)	18.00	1.25
10/- dark blue (October 30, 1939)	£220	17.00
10/- ultramarine (November 30, 1942)	30.00	3.50
£1 brown (October 1, 1948)	18.00	12.00
Set	£280	40.00

½d green, 1d red,
1½d brown,
2d orange, 2½d blue,
3d violet

■ 1940, May 6. Centenary of First Adhesive Postage Stamp

Des: H. L. Palmer. Printed in photogravure by Harrison. Wmk: Multiple Crown and GVIR. Perf: 14½ x 14

Set	4.00	3.50
First Day Cover		7.50
Pictorial cover		35.00

2½d blue,
3d violet

■ 1946, June 11. Victory

Des: H. L. Palmer (2½d), Reynolds Stone (3d). Printed in photogravure by Harrison. Wmk: Multiple Crown and GVIR. Perf: 15x14

Set	0.20	0.25
First Day Cover		9.00
Pictorial cover		45.00

2½d

£1

■ **1948, April 26. Royal Silver Wedding**
Des: G.T. Knipe and Joan Hassall (from photographs by Dorothy Wilding Studios). Printed in photogravure by Harrison. Wmk: Multiple Crown and GVIR. Perf: 15x14 (2½d), 14 x 15 (£1).

Set	27.00	25.00
First Day Cover		50.00
Pictorial cover		£400

■ **1948, May 10. Liberation of the Channel Islands**
Although this set was placed on sale at eight post offices in Great Britain, it is listed under Regional Issues

Globe surrounded by a Laurel Wreath (2½d)
Globe with Olympic Rings (3d)
Olympic Rings (6d)
Victory and Olympic Rings (1/-)

■ **1948, July 29. Olympic Games**
Des: P. Metcalfe, A. Games, S. Scott and E. Dulac. Printed in photogravure by Harrison. Wmk: Multiple Crown and GVIR. Perf: 15x14

Set	2.50	1.20
First Day Cover		8.00
Pictorial cover		35.00

Two Hemispheres (2½d)
UPU Monument (3d)
Globe and Compass (6d)
Globe and Posthorn (1/-)

■ **1949, October 10. 75th Anniversary of the Universal Postal Union**
Des: Mary Adshed (2½d), P. Metcalfe (3d). H. Fleury (6d), G. R. Bellew (1/-). Printed in photogravure by Harrison. Wmk: Multiple Crown and GVIR. Perf: 15x14.

Set	1.50	1.25
First Day Cover		9.50
Pictorial cover		47.00

H.M.S. Victory (2/6)
White Cliffs of Dover (5/-)
St. George and the Dragon (10/-)
Royal Coat of Arms (£1)

■ **1951, May 3. High Values**
Des: Mary Adshead (2/6, 5/-), P. Metcalfe (10/-, £1). Printed in recess by Waterlow. Wmk: Single Crown and GVIR. Perf: 11x12.

Set	50.00	15.00

2½d red,
4d blue

■ **1951, May 3. Festival of Britain**
Des: E. Dulac (2½d), A. Games (4d). Printed in photogravure by Harrison. Wmk: Multiple Crown and GVIR. Perf: 15x14.

Set	0.35	0.40
First Day Cover		3.00
Pictorial cover		17.00

QUEEN ELIZABETH II PRE-DECIMALS

In this section, prices are priced in two columns: unmounted mint (left) and fine used (right). The exception is booklet panes, which are priced only for unmounted mint with good perforations.

Except where otherwise stated, all the stamps have the same technical details: Printed in photogravure by Harrison. Perf: 15x14 (definitives), 15x14 (special issues with a horizontal design) or 14x15 (special issues with a vertical design).

½d, 1d, 1½d, 2d

2½d, 3d

4d, 4½d

5d, 6d, 7d

8d, 9d, 10d, 11d

1/-, 1/6

1/3

■ 1952-1968. Wilding Definitives
Des: Miss E. Mark (½d, 1d, 1½d, 2d). M.C. Farrar-Bell (2½d, 3d, 4d, 4½d), G. Knipe (5d, 6d, 7d), Miss M. Adshead (8d, 9d, 10d, 11d), E. Dulac (1/-, 1/3, 1/6): portrait by Dorothy Wilding Studios.
On the 2½d value the top line of the diadem was initially broken (Type I), but this was later corrected (Type II).

A) Wmk: Multiple Tudor Crown and E2R.

½d orange (August 31, 1953)	0.10	0.10
Wmk inverted	0.15	0.40
1d blue (August 31, 1953)	0.15	0.10
Wmk inverted	4.50	2.50
1½d green (December 5, 1952)	0.10	0.10
Wmk inverted	0.35	0.30
Wmk sideways	0.35	0.30
2d deep brown (August 31, 1953)	0.20	0.15
Wmk inverted	20.00	12.00
Wmk sideways	0.75	0.50
2½d carmine (type 1) (December 5, 1952)	0.15	0.10
Wmk inverted (type 2)	0.40	0.30
Wmk sideways (type 1)	3.50	4.00
3d violet (January 18, 1954)	1.00	0.20
4d blue (November 2, 1953)	1.00	0.70
5d brown (July 6, 1953)	4.00	2.50
6d purple (January 18, 1954)	3.00	0.75
7d pale green (January 18, 1954)	8.00	2.00
8d magenta (July 6, 1953)	5.00	0.75
9d myrtle-green (February 8, 1954)	14.00	1.50
10d blue (February 8, 1954)	12.00	1.50
11d brown-red (February 8, 1954)	30.00	10.00
1/- bistre (July 6, 1953)	1.00	0.50
1/3 deep-green (November 2, 1953)	3.00	1.50
1/6 grey-blue (November 2, 1953)	12.00	1.25
Set	60.00	20.00
Wmk inverted	18.00	14.00
Wmk sideways	4.50	4.50
First Day Cover		£140
Pictorial cover		£600

Booklet panes	Wmk Upright	Inverted
Pane of two ½d	2.00	-
Pane of four ½d	4.00	4.00
Pane of six ½d	2.00	4.00
Pane of two 1d	2.00	
Pane of four 1d	3.00	25.00
Pane of three 1d with three labels reading: MINIMUM INLAND PRINTED PAPER RATE 1½d	£300	£300
Pane of three 1d with three labels reading: PLEASE POST EARLY IN THE DAY	40.00	40.00
Pane of three 1d with three labels reading: PACK YOUR PARCELS SECURELY/ ADDRESS YOUR LETTERS CORRECTLY/ POST EARLY IN THE DAY	40.00	40.00
Pane of six 1d	8.00	30.00
Pane of two 1½d	2.00	-
Pane of four 1½d	4.00	4.00
Pane of six 1½d	2.00	4.00
Pane of six 2d	27.00	£160
Pane of six 2½d	3.50	3.50

B) As before but Wmk: St. Edward's Crown and E2R.

½d (August 1955)	0.15	0.10
Wmk inverted	0.20	0.20
1d (September 19, 1955)	0.20	0.10
Wmk inverted	0.50	0.50

1½d (August 1955)	0.15	0.10
Wmk inverted	0.30	0.20
Wmk sideways	0.20	0.25
2d deep brown (September 6, 1955)	0.25	0.30
Wmk inverted	7.00	5.00
Wmk sideways	0.50	0.50
2d brown (October 17, 1956)	0.25	0.10
Wmk inverted	5.00	4.00
Wmk sideways	5.00	3.00
2½d (type 1) (September 28, 1955)	0.25	0.15
Wmk inverted	0.75	1.00
Wmk sideways	0.75	1.00
2½d (type 2) (September 1955)	0.30	0.60
Wmk inverted	0.30	0.30
3d (July 17, 1956)	0.25	0.20
Wmk inverted	1.75	1.50
Wmk sideways	12.00	7.50
4d (November 14, 1955)	1.50	2.00
5d (September 21, 1955)	5.00	3.00
6d purple (December 20, 1955)	3.50	1.00
6d deep purple (May 8, 1958)	3.00	1.00
7d (April 23, 1956)	30.00	7.00
8d (December 21, 1955)	4.00	1.25
9d (December 15, 1955)	12.00	2.00
10d (September 22, 1955)	10.00	2.00
11d (October 28, 1955)	0.50	1.25
1/- (November 3, 1955)	6.50	0.50
1/3 (March 27, 1956)	14.00	1.00
1/6 (March 27, 1956)	20.00	0.75
Set	100.00	25.00
Wmk inverted	14.00	7.00
Wmk sideways	14.00	9.00

Booklet panes	Wmk Upright	Inverted
Pane of two ½d	3.00	-
Pane of four ½d	4.00	4.00
Pane of six ½d	2.00	3.50
Pane of two 1d	3.50	-
Pane of three 1d with three labels reading:		
PACK YOUR PARCELS SECURELY/		
ADDRESS YOUR LETTERS CORRECTLY/		
POST EARLY IN THE DAY	30.00	35.00
Pane of four 1d	4.00	4.00
Pane of six 1d	2.50	3.00
Pane of two 1½d	3.50	-
Pane of four 1½d	4.00	4.00
Pane of six 1½d	2.00	2.00
Pane of six 2d deep brown	13.00	65.00
Pane of six 2d brown	8.00	22.50
Pane of six 2½d	3.00	3.00
Pane of four 3d	10.00	15.00
Pane of six 3d	6.00	20.00

C) As before but Wmk: Multiple St. Edward's Crown.

½d (November 25, 1958)	0.10	0.10
chalky paper (July 15, 1963)	2.00	2.50
Wmk inverted	0.30	0.10
chalky paper and Wmk inverted	1.50	2.00
Wmk sideways	0.25	0.15

1d (November 1958)	0.10	0.10
Wmk inverted	0.20	0.20
Wmk sideways	0.60	0.35
1½d (December 1958)	0.15	0.15
Wmk inverted	1.00	0.40
Wmk sideways	4.50	3.50
2d brown (December 4, 1958)	0.10	0.10
Wmk inverted	75.00	40.00
Wmk sideways	0.50	0.40
2½d (type 1) (October 4, 1961)	0.10	0.40
Wmk sideways	0.20	0.25
2½d (type 2) (November 1958)	0.35	0.20
chalky paper (July 15, 1963)	0.30	0.25
Wmk inverted	3.50	0.90
chalky paper & Wmk inverted	0.30	0.25
Wmk sideways	0.40	0.50
3d (November 1958)	0.15	0.10
Wmk inverted	0.25	0.20
Wmk sideways	0.25	0.15
4d blue (October 29, 1958)	0.50	0.25
4d deep blue (April 28, 1965)	0.20	0.12
Wmk inverted	0.35	0.20
Wmk sideways	0.35	0.15
4½d red-brown (February 9, 1959)	0.12	0.12
5d (November 10, 1958)	0.20	0.10
6d deep purple (December 23, 1958)	0.25	0.10
7d (November 26, 1958)	0.50	0.20
8d (February 24, 1960)	0.35	0.10
9d (March 24, 1959)	0.35	0.20
10d (November 18, 1958)	0.75	0.25
1/- (October 30, 1958)	0.35	0.25
1/3 (June 17, 1959)	0.35	0.15
1/6 (December 16, 1958)	3.00	0.15
Set	5.00	1.50
Wmk inverted	80.00	42.00
Wmk sideways	5.50	4.00

Booklet panes	Wmk Upright	Inverted
Pane of three ½d and one 2½d (chalky paper)	8.00	8.00
Pane of four ½d	2.50	2.50
Pane of six ½d	1.25	2.00
Pane of four 1d	2.50	2.50
Pane of six 1d	1.50	2.50
Pane of four 1½d	2.50	2.50
Pane of six 1½d	5.00	6.00
Pane of six 2d	40.00	£500
Pane of four 2½d (chalky paper)	1.00	1.00
Pane of six 2½d	3.00	15.00
Pane of four 3d	2.00	2.00
Pane of six 3d	1.50	1.50
Pane of six 4d deep blue	1.50	1.50
		Wmk Sideways
Pane of two ½d se-tenant with two 2½d (type 2)		1.00
Pane of four ½d		2.00
Pane of two 1d se-tenant with two 3d to left		5.00
Pane of two 1d se-tenant with two 3d to right		5.00
Pane of four 1d		3.00
Pane of four 1½d		25.00
Pane of four 3d		2.00
Pane of four 4d		2.00

■ Graphite Lined Issues

As before but each stamp has two black lines on the back, except for the 2d which has just one line on the right as viewed from the back.

A) Wmk: St. Edward's Crown E2R upright. Released on November 19, 1957.

½d	0.20	0.20
1d	0.20	0.20
1½d	1.25	0.50
2d brown	1.00	1.25
2½d (type 2)	4.50	3.50
3d	0.75	0.50
Set	6.75	5.50
First Day Cover		75.00

B) Wmk: Multiple St. Edward's Crown.

½d (June 15, 1959)	5.00	5.00
Wmk inverted	1.00	1.25
1d (December 18, 1958)	1.00	1.00
Wmk inverted	1.00	0.75
1½d (August 4, 1959)	60.00	50.00
Wmk inverted	20.00	20.00
2d (December 4, 1958)	4.75	2.50
2½d (type 2) (June 9, 1959)	6.00	6.00
Wmk inverted	35.00	30.00
3d (November 24, 1958)	0.60	0.45
Wmk inverted	0.55	0.40
4d (April 29, 1959)	3.25	3.25
4½d (June 3, 1959)	3.50	2.25
Set	70.00	55.00
Wmk inverted	60.00	50.00

Booklet panes	Wmk Upright	Inverted
Pane of six ½d	20.00	12.00
Pane of six 1d	7.50	7.00
Pane of six 1½d	£500	£125
Pane of six 2½d	30.00	£300
Pane of six 3d	4.00	4.00

■ Phosphor Graphite Issue

As before but in addition to the graphite lines on the back, each stamp has two bands of phosphor on the front, except for the 2d which has just one band to the left.

A) Wmk: Multiple St. Edward's Crown and E2R. Released on November 18, 1959.

½d	3.00	3.00
1d	9.00	9.00
1½d	2.50	3.00
2d brown	95.00	90.00

ii) Wmk: Multiple St. Edwards Crown.

2d brown	4.00	3.00
2½d (type2)	10.00	10.00
3d	14.00	7.50
4d blue	8.00	5.00
4½d	25.00	20.00
Set	50.00	40.00
First Day Cover		75.00

■ Phosphor Issue

As before but without graphite lines. Each stamp has two bands of phosphor on the front except where stated. Released on June 22, 1960 except where stated. Wmk: Multiple St. Edward's Crown.

½d	0.15	0.15
Wmk inverted	1.00	1.00
Wmk sideways	5.00	7.50
1d	0.10	0.10
Wmk inverted	0.35	0.30
Wmk sideways	0.40	0.50
1½d	0.12	0.20
Wmk inverted	5.00	5.00
Wmk sideways	5.00	7.50
2d brown (one band)	14.00	12.00
2d brown (October 4, 1961)	0.20	0.10
Wmk sideways	0.30	0.25
2½d (type 2)	0.20	0.20
Wmk inverted	£135	£120
2½d (type 2 – one band)	1.50	0.50
Wmk inverted	24.00	17.00
2½d (type 1 – one band)	30.00	25.00
3d	0.50	0.35
Wmk inverted	0.80	0.50
Wmk sideways	1.25	0.55
3d (April 29, 1965) (one band at left)	0.30	0.40
Wmk inverted	40.00	42.00
Wmk sideways	4.00	4.00
3d (one band at right)	0.30	0.40
Wmk inverted	6.00	6.50
Wmk sideways	4.00	4.00
Se-tenant pair	0.60	1.50
Se-tenant pair with Wmk inverted	47.00	49.00
Se-tenant pair with Wmk sideways	8.00	10.00
3d (December 8, 1966) (one band in centre)	0.25	0.25
Wmk inverted	3.00	3.50
Wmk sideways	0.40	0.50
4d blue	2.75	3.25
4d deep blue (April 28, 1965)	0.15	0.25
Wmk inverted	0.25	0.20
Wmk sideways	0.35	0.25
4½d (September 13, 1961)	0.15	0.25
5d (June 9, 1967)	0.20	0.25
6d deep purple (June 27, 1960)	0.20	-
7d (February 15, 1967)	0.20	0.25
8d (June 28, 1967)	0.20	0.25
9d (December 29, 1966)	0.50	0.25
10d (December 30, 1966)	0.50	0.40
1/- (June 28, 1967)	0.40	0.20
1/3	1.00	1.00
1/6 (December 12, 1966)	2.00	2.00

Set (one of each value)	4.50	5.00
Wmk inverted	£180	£170
Wmk sideways	15.00	18.00

Booklet panes	Wmk Upright	Inverted
Pane of six ½d	3.00	4.00
Pane of six 1d	2.00	2.00
Pane of six 1½d	8.00	30.00
Pane of six 2½d (type 2 with two bands)	80.00	£1,100
Pane of six 2½d (type 2 with one band)	22.00	£140
Pane of six 3d (two bands)	5.00	5.00
Pane of six 3d (one band at left or right)	20.00	90.00
Pane of six 3d (one centre band)	4.00	15.00
Pane of six 4d	2.00	3.00
		Wmk sideways
Pane of four ½d		35.00
Pane of two 1d se-tenant with two 3d (two bands)		3.00
Pane of two 1d se-tenant with two 3d (one band, left)		11.00
Pane of two 1d se-tenant with two 3d (one band, right)		11.00
Pane of four 1d		5.00
Pane of four 1½d		35.00
Pane of four 3d (two bands)		5.00
Pane of four 4d		1.00

Carrickfergus Castle (2/6)
Caernarvon Castle (5/-)
Edinburgh Castle (10/-)
Windsor Castle (£1)

■ 1955-1968. Castle High Values
Printed in recess. Perf: 11x12

A) Wmk: St. Edward's Crown and E2R upright.
i) Printed by Waterlow.

2/6 brown (September 23, 1955)	14.00	2.00
5/- carmine (September 23, 1955)	30.00	3.00
10/- blue (September 1, 1955)	60.00	10.00
£1 black (September 1, 1955)	85.00	20.00
Set	£160	30.00
First Day Cover		£300
Pictorial cover		£850

ii) Printed by De La Rue.

2/6 (July 17, 1958)	25.00	3.50
5/- (April 30, 1958)	50.00	8.00
10/- (April 25, 1958)	£150	14.00
£1 (April 28, 1958)	£200	30.00
Set	£375	47.00

(* The top perforation tooth of each side of the stamps from the De La Rue printing is narrower than that found on the Waterlow printing.)

B) Wmk: St. Edward's Crown and E2R upright.
i) Printed by De La Rue.

2/6 (July 22, 1958)	12.00	0.50
5/- (June 15, 1959)	50.00	1.00
10/- (July 21, 1959)	40.00	2.75
£1 (June 23, 1959)	80.00	12.00
Set	£150	15.00

ii) Printed by Bradbury, Wilkinson.

2/6 (July 1, 1963)	0.50	0.15
5/- (September 3, 1963)	2.00	0.40
10/- (October 16, 1963)	3.50	2.50
£1 (November 14, 1963)	9.50	3.00
Set	13.50	7.00

iii) Printed by Bradbury, Wilkinson on chalky paper.

2/6 (May 30, 1968)	0.50	0.75

(* The Queen's diadem is more detailed on the Bradbury, Wilkinson printing than on the De La Rue printing.)

C) No Wmk. Printed by Bradbury, Wilkinson.

2/6 (July 1, 1968)	0.30	0.40
5/- (April 10, 1968)	1.50	0.75
10/- (April 10, 1968)	6.00	4.00
£1 (December 4, 1967)	7.00	4.50
Set	10.50	10.50

Four different designs (2½d, 4d, 1/3, 1/6)

■ 1953, June 3. Coronation
Des: E.G. Fuller (2½d), M. Goaman (4d), E. Dulac (1/3), M.C. Farrar-Bell (1/6). Wmk: Multiple Tudor Crown E2R.

Set	8.00	4.00
First Day Cover		27.00

Scout Badge (2½d)
Flying Birds (4d)
Globe within compass (1/3)

■ 1957, August 1. World Scout Jubilee Jamboree
Des: Mary Adshead (2½d), Pat Keely (4d), W. H. Brown (1/3). Wmk: St Edward's Crown and E2R.

Set	3.50	2.75
First Day Cover		15.00

(* These stamps were issued in coils as well as normal sheets.)

4d

■ **1957, September 12. Inter-Parliamentary Union Conference**
Wmk: Multiple St. Edward's Crown and E2R.

4d	0.50	0.50
First Day Cover		75.00

Welsh Dragon (3d)
Games emblem (6d)
Welsh Dragon (1/3)

■ **1958, July 18. British Empire & Commonwealth Games**
Des: Reynolds Stone (3d), W.H. Brown (6d), Pat Keely (1/3).
Wmk: Multiple St. Edward's Crown and E2R.

Set	1.25	1.00
First Day Cover		60.00

1660 Postboy (3d)
1660 Posthorn (1/3)

■ **1960, July 7. Anniversary of General Letter Office**
Des: Reynolds Stone (3d), Faith Jacques (1/3). Wmk: Multiple St. Edward's Crown.

Set	1.75	1.75
First Day Cover		35.00

Europa emblem (6d, 1/6)

■ **1960, September 19. Europa (First Anniversary)**
Des: P. Rahikainen and Reynolds Stone. Wmk: Multiple St. Edward's Crown.

Set	6.00	3.00
First Day Cover		22.00

Thrift plant (2½d)
Squirrel and stylised tree (3d)
Thrift plant (1/6)

■ **1961, August 28. Post Office Savings Bank Centenary**
Des: P. Gauld (2½d), M. Goaman (3d, 1/6). Wmk: Multiple St. Edward's Crown.
A) Printed on a Timson machine.

Set	1.25	1.00
First Day Cover		35.00

B) Printed on a Thrissell machine: 2½d, 3d only

Pair	1.50	1.50

(* The portrait on the 2½d is greyer from the Thrissell machine, and that on the 3d is much clearer on the Timson printing.)

CEPT emblem (2d)
Doves and emblem (4d)
Doves and emblem (10d)

■ **1961, September 18. CEPT Conference**
Des: M. Goaman and T. Kurperschoek. Wmk: Multiple St. Edward's Crown.

Set	0.25	0.25
First Day Cover		2.75

Roof of Westminster Hall (6d)
Palace of Westminster (1/3)

■ 1961, September 23. Commonwealth Parliamentary Conference
Des: Faith Jacques. Wmk: Multiple St. Edward's Crown.

Set	1.25	1.25
First Day Cover		18.00

Boxes bearing arrows (2½d)
Arrows over the British Isles (3d)
Joining arrows (1/3)

■ 1962, November 14. National Productivity Year
Des: D. Gentleman. Wmk: Multiple St. Edward's Crown, inverted on 2½d and 3d values.

A) Non-phosphor issue: 2½d, 3d, 1/3

Set	1.25	1.00
First Day Cover		20.00

B) Phosphor issue: 2½d (one band); 3d, 1/3 (three bands.)

Set	14.00	10.00
First Day Cover		90.00

Ears of Wheat (2½d)
Three Children (1/3)

■ 1963, March 21. Freedom from Hunger.
Des: M. Goaman. Wmk: Multiple St. Edward's Crown, inverted on both values.

Ai) Non-phosphor issue: 2½d, 1/3.

Set	1.25	1.25
First Day Cover		17.00

B) Phosphor issue: 2½d (one band), 1/3 (three bands).

Set	13.00	10.00
First Day Cover		24.00

1863 Paris Postal Conference Centenary (6d)

■ 1963, May 7. Paris Postal Conference Centenary
Des: Reynolds Stone. Wmk: Multiple St. Edward's Crown, inverted.

A) Non-phosphor issue.

6d	30	25
First Day Cover		10.00

B) Phosphor issue (three bands).

6d	3.50	3.00
First Day Cover		19.00

Bee on flowers (3d)
Selection of wildlife (4½d)

■ 1963, May 16. National Nature Week
Des: S. Scott (3d), M. Goaman (4½d). Wmk: Multiple St. Edward's Crown.

A) Non-phosphor issue.

Set	0.15	0.20
First Day Cover		12.00

B) Phosphor issue (three bands).

Set	1.75	1.75
First Day Cover		21.00

Helicopter over boat (2½d)
Lifeboat (4d)
Lifeboatmen (1/6)

■ 1963, May 31. International Lifeboat Conference
Des: D. Gentlemen. Wmk: Multiple St. Edward's Crown.

A) Non-phosphor issue.

Set	1.50	1.50
First Day Cover		20.00

B) Phosphor issue: 2½d (one band), 4d, 1/6 (three bands).

Set	25.00	15.00
First Day Cover		35.00

Red Cross (3d, 1/3, 1/6 with different borders)

■ 1963, August 15. Red Cross Centenary Congress
Des: H. Bartram. Wmk: Multiple St. Edward's Crown.
A) Non-phosphor issue.

Set	3.00	3.00
First Day Cover		22.00

B) Phosphor issue (three bands).

Set	35.00	25.00
First Day Cover		50.00

Cable over globe (1/6)

■ 1963, December 3. Opening of COMPAC Cable
Des: P. Gauld. Wmk: Multiple St. Edward's Crown.
A) Non-phosphor issue.

1/6	1.50	1.25
First Day Cover		17.00

B) Phosphor issue (three bands).

1/6	7.50	6.50
First Day Cover		20.00

Puck and Bottom (3d)
Feste (6d)
Romeo and Juliet (1/3)
Henry V (1/6)
Hamlet (2/6)

■ 1964, April 23. Shakespeare Festival
Des: D. Gentleman (3d to 1/6); C. and R. Ironside (2/6). Printed
in recess by Bradbury, Wilkinson (2/6). Perf: 11x12 (2/6). Wmk:
Multiple St. Edward's Crown.
A) Non-phosphor issue: 3d, 6d, 1/3, 1/6, 2/6

Set	2.50	2.50
First Day Cover		5.00

B) Phosphor issue (three bands): 3d, 6d, 1/3, 1/6

Set	6.50	6.00
First Day Cover		8.00

Flats, Richmond Park (2½d)
Shipbuilding, Belfast (4d)
Forest Park, Snowdonia (8d)
Nuclear Reactor, Dounreay (1/6)

■ 1964, July 1. International Geographical Congress
Des: D. Bailey. Wmk: Multiple St. Edward's Crown.
A) Non-phosphor issue: 2½d, 4d, 8d, 1/6

Set	2.25	2.25
First Day Cover		12.00

B) Phosphor issue: 2½d (one band), 4d, 8d, 1/6 (three bands).

Set	15.00	11.00
First Day Cover		19.00

Spring Gentian (3d)
Dog Rose (6d)
Honeysuckle (9d)
Fringed Water Lily (1/3)

■ 1964, August 5. International Botanical Congress
Des: Michael and Sylvia Goaman. Wmk: Multiple St. Edward's
Crown.
A) Non-phosphor issue.

Set	2.50	2.50
First Day Cover		12.00

B) Phosphor issue (three bands).

Set	15.00	11.00
First Day Cover		19.00

Forth Road Bridge (3d)
Forth Road and Railway Bridges (6d)

■ 1964, September 4. Opening of the Forth Road Bridge
Des: A. Restall. Wmk: Multiple St. Edward's Crown.
A) Non-phosphor issue.

Set	0.25	0.30
First Day Cover		3.50

B) Phosphor issue (three bands).

Set	2.50	2.75
First Day Cover		8.00

Sir Winston Churchill (4d, 1/3 with slightly different designs)

■ 1965, July 8. Churchill Commemoration
Des: D. Gentleman and Rosaline Dease. Wmk: Multiple St.
Edward's Crown.
A) Non-phosphor issue.

Set	0.30	0.30
First Day Cover		2.00

B) Phosphor issue (three bands).

Set	1.50	1.50
First Day Cover		3.00

C) Printed on a Timson machine

4d	0.10	0.10

(* The Timson printing shows far more details on the portrait
of Churchill.

Seal of Simon de Montfort (6d)
Parliament Buildings (2/6)

**■ 1965, July 19. 700th Anniversary of Simon de
Montfort's Parliament**
Des: S.R. Black (6d), Professor R. Guyatt (2/6). Wmk: Multiple St.
Edward's Crown.
A) Non-phosphor issue: 6d, 2/6

Set	0.65	0.65
First Day Cover		8.00

B) Phosphor issue (three bands): 6d only

6d	0.50	0.60
First Day Cover		15.00

Salvation Army Band (3d)
Three Salvation Army members (1/6)

■ 1965, August 9. Centenary of Salvation Army
Des: M.C. Farrar-Bell (3d), G. Trenaman (1/6). Wmk: Multiple St.
Edward's Crown.
A) Non-phosphor issue.

Set	0.55	0.60
First Day Cover		11.00

B) Phosphor issue: 3d (one band), 1/6 (three bands).

Set	1.35	1.25
First Day Cover		14.00

Carbolic Spray (4d)
Joseph Lister (1/-)

**■ 1965, September 1. Centenary of Joseph Lister's
Discovery of Antiseptic Surgery**
Des: P. Gauld (4d), F. Ariss (1/-). Wmk: Multiple St. Edward's
Crown.
A) Non-phosphor issue.

Set	0.50	0.60
First Day Cover		7.00

B) Phosphor issue (three bands).

Set	1.50	1.50
First Day Cover		9.00

Trinidad Carnival Dancers (6d)
Canadian Folk Dancers (1/6)

**■ 1965, September 1. Commonwealth Arts
Festival**
Des: D. Gentleman and Rosalind Dease. Wmk: Multiple St.
Edward's Crown.
A) Non-phosphor issue.

Set	0.60	0.60
First Day Cover		8.50

B) Phosphor issue (three bands).

Set	1.70	1.75
First Day Cover		10.00

Spitfires (4d)
Pilot in hurricane (4d)
Overlapping wings (4d)
Spitfires attacking Heinkel bomber (4d)
Spitfire attacking Stuka bomber (4d)
Tail wing of Dornier bomber (4d)
Anti-aircraft Artillery (9d)
St Paul's Cathedral (1/3)

■ 1965, September 13. 25th Anniversary of the Battle of Britain
Des: D. Gentleman and Rosalind Dease (4d, 1/3), A. Restall (9d).
Wmk: Multiple St. Edward's Crown. Six 4d values se-tenant.
A) Non-phosphor issue.

Set	4.50	5.00
First Day Cover		12.00

B) Phosphor issue (three bands).

Set	8.00	8.50
First Day Cover		13.00

Post Office Tower (3d)
Post Office Tower and Nash Terrace (1/3)

■ 1965, October 8. Opening of the Post Office Tower
Des: C. Abbott. Wmk: Multiple St. Edward's Crown.
A) Non-phosphor issue.

Set	0.25	0.30
First Day Cover		3.00

B) Phosphor issue: 3d (one band), 1/3 (three bands).

Set	0.40	0.50
First Day Cover		5.00

UN emblem (3d)
ICY emblem (1/6)

■ 1965, October 25. 20th Anniversary of United Nations and International Co-operation Year
Des: J. Matthews. Wmk: Multiple St. Edward's Crown.
A) Non-phosphor issue.

Set	0.50	0.60
First Day Cover		7.00

B) Phosphor issue: 3d (one band), 1/6 (three bands).

Set	1.50	1.60
First Day Cover		8.00

Telecommunications (9d)
Radio Waves (1/6)

■ 1965, November 15. International Telecommunication Union Centenary
Des: A. Restall. Wmk: Multiple St. Edward's Crown.
A) Non-phosphor issue.

Set	0.75	0.60
First Day Cover		8.50

B) Phosphor issue (three bands).

Set	2.75	2.75
First Day Cover		11.00

Robert Burns (4d)
Robert Burns (portrait by Nasmyth) (1/3)

■ 1966, January 25. Robert Burns
Des: G.F. Huntly. Wmk: Multiple St. Edward's Crown.
A) Non-phosphor issue.

Set	0.30	0.40
First Day Cover		1.50

B) Phosphor issue (three bands).

Set	1.00	1.00
First Day Cover		2.75

Westminster Abbey (3d)
Roof of Westminster Abbey (2/6)

■ 1966, February 28. 900th Anniversary of Westminster Abbey
Des: Sheila Robinson (3d), Bradbury Wilkinson (2/6). Printed in recess by Bradbury Wilkinson (2/6). Wmk: Multiple St. Edward's Crown. Perf: 11 x 12 (2/6)
A) Non-phosphor issue: 3d, 2/6

Set	0.50	0.50
First Day Cover		3.00

B) Phosphor issue: 3d only (one band).

3d	0.15	0.20
First Day Cover		8.00

Sussex Downs (4d)
Antrim, Northern Ireland (6d)
Harlech Castle (1/3)
The Cairngorms (1/6)

■ 1966, May 2. Landscapes
Des: L. Rosoman. Wmk: Multiple St. Edward's Crown.
A) Non-phosphor issue.

Set	0.50	0.60
First Day Cover		3.50

B) Phosphor issue (three bands).

Set	0.50	0.70
First Day Cover		4.00

Two footballers (4d)
Four footballers (6d)
Saving the ball (1/3)

■ 1966, June 1. World Cup
Des: D. Gentleman (4d), W. Kempster (6d), D. Caplan (1/3).
Wmk: Multiple St. Edward's Crown.
A) Non-phosphor issue: 4d, 6d, 1/3

Set	0.40	0.40
First Day Cover		9.00

B) Phosphor issue: 4d (two bands), 6d, 1/3 (three bands).

Set	0.30	0.40
First Day Cover		10.00

Black-headed Gull (4d)
Blue Tit (4d)
Robin (4d)
Blackbird (4d)

■ 1966, August 8. British Birds
Des: J. Norris Wood. Wmk: Multiple St. Edward's Crown. All four values in se-tenant blocks.
A) Non-phosphor issue.

Se-tenant block of four	0.40	0.50
First Day Cover		4.00

B) Phosphor issue (three bands).

Se-tenant block of four	0.40	0.50
First Day Cover		4.00

Two footballers and legend 'ENGLAND WINNERS' (4d)

■ 1966, August 18. England's World Cup Victory
As June 1 issue, but with inscription 'ENGLAND WINNERS'. Non-phosphor only.

4d	0.20	0.25
First Day Cover		7.50

Jodrell Bank Radio Telescope (4d)
Jaguar 'E' type and Mini cars (6d)
Hovercraft (1/3)
Windscale Nuclear Reactor (1/6)

■ 1966, September 19. British Technology
Des: D. and A. Gillespie (4d, 6d), A. Restall (1/3, 1/6). Wmk:
Multiple St. Edward's Crown.
A) Non-phosphor issue.

Set	0.40	0.45
First Day Cover		1.75
B) Phosphor issue (three bands).		
Set	0.45	0.50
First Day Cover		2.00

Scenes from the Bayeux Tapestry (4d, six different designs)
Norman Ship (6d)
Norman horseman attacking Harold's troops (1/3)

■ 1966, October 14. 900th Anniversary of the Battle of Hastings
Des: D. Gentleman. Wmk: Multiple St. Edward's Crown,
sideways on 1/3 value. Six 4d values se-tenant.
A) Non-phosphor issue.

Set	1.00	1.25
First Day Cover		2.50
B) Phosphor issue: 4d, 6d (three bands), 1/3 (four bands).		
Set	1.00	1.25
First Day Cover		3.00

King of the Orient (3d)
Snowman (1/6)

■ 1966, December 1. Christmas
Des: Miss T. Shemza (3d), J. Berry (1/6), both aged six. Wmk:
Multiple St. Edward's Crown, upright on both values.
A) Non-phosphor issue.

Set	0.15	0.20
First Day Cover		1.00
B) Phosphor issue: 3d (one band), 1/6 (two bands).		
Set	0.15	0.20
First Day Cover		1.00

(* Phosphor 3d can be found with band at left or right).

Loading freight on a ship (9d)
Loading freight on an aeroplane (1/6)

■ 1967, February 20. European Free Trade Association
Des: C. Abbott. Wmk: Multiple St. Edward's Crown.
A) Non-phosphor issue.

Set	0.15	0.20
First Day Cover		0.75
B) Phosphor issue (three bands).		
Set	0.15	0.20
First Day Cover		0.80

Hawthorn and Bramble (4d)
Bindweed and Viper's Bugloos (4d)
Daisy, Buttercup and Coltsfoot (4d)
Bluebell, Anemone and Red Campion (4d)
Dog Violet (9d)
Primrose (1/9)

■ 1967, April 24. British Flowers
Des: Keeble Martin (4d), Mary Grierson (9d, 1/9). Wmk:
Multiple St. Edward's Crown. Four 4d values se-tenant.
A) Non-phosphor issue.

Set	0.60	0.75
First Day Cover		1.50
B) Phosphor issue (three bands).		
Set	0.35	0.50
First Day Cover		1.50

'Master Lambton' by Lawrence (4d)
'Mares and Foals in a Landscape' by Stubbs (9d)
'Children coming Out of School' by Lowry (1/6)

■ **1967, July 10. British Paintings**
No Wmk.

Set	0.20	0.20
First Day Cover		1.50

Gipsy Moth IV (1/9)

■ **1967, July 24. Sir Francis Chichester's Single-Handed Voyage Around the World**
Des: Michael and Sylvia Goaman. No Wmk. Three phosphor bands.

1/9 •	0.10	0.10
First Day Cover		0.50

Radar screen (4d)
Penicillin Mould (1/-)
Jet Engine (1/6)
Television Equipment (1/9)

■ **1967, September 19. British Discoveries**
Des: C. Abbott (4d, 1/-), Negus and Sharland (1/6,1/9). Wmk: Multiple St. Edward's Crown. Three phosphor bands on the 4d.

Set	0.25	0.30
First Day Cover		0.75

'The Adoration of the Shepherds' by the School of Seville (3d)
'Madonna and Child' by Murillo (4d)
'The Adoration of the Shepherds' by Louis Le Nan (1/6)

■ **1967. Christmas**
No Wmk. 3d has one central phosphor band.
3d released on November 27, 4d on October 18, 1/6 on November 27.

Set	0.15	0.20
First Day Cover		0.75

Tarr Steps (4d)
Aberfeldy Bridge (9d)
Menai Bridge (1/6)
M4 Viaduct (1/9)

■ **1968, April 29. British Bridges**
Des: J. Matthews (4d, 1/9), A. Restall (9d), L. Rosoman (1/6). No Wmk.

Set	0.25	0.30
First Day Cover		0.75

Trades Union Congress (**4d**)
Votes for Women (9d)
Royal Air Force: Sopwith Camel (1/-)
James Cook Signature and 'Endeavour' (1/9)

■ **1968, May 29. Anniversaries**
Des: D. Gentleman (4d), C. Abbott (others). No Wmk.

Set	0.25	0.30
First Day Cover		2.25

'Queen Elizabeth I' by an unknown artist (4d)
'Pinkie' by Lawrence (I/-)
'Ruins of St Mary le Port' by Piper (1/6)
'The Hay Wain' by Constable (1/9)

■ 1968, August 12. British Paintings.
No Wmk.

Set	0.25	0.30
First Day Cover		0.60

Boy and Girl and Rocking Horse (4d)
Girl and Doll's House (9d)
Boy and Train Set (1/6)

■ 1968, November 25. Christmas
Des: Rosalind Dease. No Wmk.
A) Printed on a Rembrandt machine: 4d, 9d, 1/6

Set	0.20	0.20
First Day Cover		0.50

B) Printed on a Thrissell machine: 4d only.

4d	0.15	0.20

(*The Thrissell printing can be distinguished by the boy's
pullover having a more mottled appearance.)

RMS Queen Elizabeth 2

'Queen Elizabeth 2' (5d)
Elizabethan Galleon (9d)
East Indiaman (9d)
'Cutty Sark' (9d)
SS 'Great Britain' (1/-)
RMS 'Mauretania' (1/-)

■ 1969, January 15. British Ships
Des: D. Gentleman. No Wmk. Three 9d ivalues in se-tenant strip.
Two 1/- values in se-tenant pair.

Set	0.75	1.20
First Day Cover		1.75

Concorde over Great Britain and France (4d)
Silhouettes of Concorde (9d)
Nose and Tail of Concorde (1/6)

■ 1969, March 3. Flight of Concorde
Des: Michael and Sylvia Goaman (4d), D. Gentleman (9d, 1/6).
No Wmk.

Set	0.75	0.50
First Day Cover		1.75

First Transatlantic Flight: Vickers 'Vimy', Alcock & Brown (5d)
Europa/CEPT (9d)
International Labour Organisation: hand holding wrench (1/-)
NATO: Flags (1/6)
First England-Australia Flight: Vickers 'Vimy', route on globe (1/9)

■ 1969, April 2. Anniversaries
Des: P. Sharland (5d, 1/-, 1/6), Michael and Sylvia Goaman (9d, 1/9).
No Wmk.

Set	0.50	0.60
First Day Cover		1.10

Durham Cathedral (5d)
York Minster (5d)
St Giles' Cathedral, Edinburgh (5d)
Canterbury Cathedral (5d)
St Paul's Cathedral (9d)
Liverpool Metropolitan Cathedral (1/6)

■ **1969, May 28. British Cathedrals**
Des: P. Gauld. No Wmk. Four 5d values se-tenant.
Set 0.60 0.75
First Day Cover 1.20

The King's Gate, Caernarvon Castle (5d)
The Eagle Tower, Caernarvon Castle (5d)
Queen Eleanor's Gate, Caernarvon Castle (5d)
Celtic Cross, Margam Abbey (9d)
Prince of Wales (1/-)

■ **1969, July 1. Investiture of the Prince of Wales**
Des: D. Gentleman. No Wmk. Three 5d values se-tenant.
Set 0.30 0.50
First Day Cover 0.90

Gandhi and Flag of India (1/6)

■ **1969, August 13. Gandhi Centenary Year**
Des: Biman Mullick.
1/6 0.15 0.15
First Day Cover 0.50

National Giro symbol (5d)
Telephone Dials (9d)
Pulse Code Modulation (1/-)
Automatic Sorting (1/6)

■ **1969, October 1. Post Office Technology**
Des: D. Gentleman. Printed in litho by De La Rue. No Wmk.
Perf: 13½x14.
Set 0.30 0.40
First Day Cover 0.60

The Herald Angel (4d)
The Three Shepherds (5d)
The Three Kings (1/6)

■ **1969, November 26. Christmas**
Des: F. Wegner. No Wmk.
Set 0.15 0.20
First Day Cover 0.50

Fife Harling (5d)
Cotswold Limestone (9d)
Welsh Stucco (1/-)
Ulster Thatch (1/6)

■ **1970, February 11. Rural Architecture**
Des: D. Gentleman (5d, 9d), Sheila Robinson (1/-, 1/6). No Wmk.
Set 0.30 0.40
First Day Cover 0.65

Signing the Declaration of Arbroath (5d)
Florence Nightingale and Patients (9d)
Signing the International Co-operative Alliance (1/-)
Sailing of the 'Mayflower' (1/6)
Royal Astronomical Society: Sir William and Sir John Herschel
with Francis Bailey (1/9)

■ **1970, April 1. Anniversaries**
Des: F. Wegner (5d, 9d, 1/6), Marjorie Seynor (1/-, 1/9).
No Wmk.

Set	0.35	0.40
First Day Cover		1.00

Mr Pickwick and Sam (5d)
Mr and Mrs Micawber (5d)
David Copperfield and Betsey Trotwood (5d)
Oliver Twist asking for more (5d)
Grasmere (1/6)

■ **1970, June 3. Literary Anniversaries**
Des: Rosalind Dease. No Wmk. Four 5d vaues se-tenant.

Set	0.75	0.80
First Day Cover		1.00

Runners (5d)
Swimmers (1/6)
Cyclists (1/9)

■ **1970, July 15. British Commonwealth Games**
Des: A. Restall. Printed in litho by De La Rue. No Wmk. Perf:
13½x14.

Set	0.60	0.70
First Day Cover		0.60

Penny Black (line engraved) (5d)
1/- Green (embossed) (9d)
4d Carmine (surface printed) (1/6)

■ **1970, September 18. Philympia 1970 International
Stamp Exhibition**
Des: D. Gentleman. No Wmk.

Set	0.30	0.40
First Day Cover		0.75

The Angel appearing to the Shepherds (4d)
Mary, Joseph and Jesus (5d)
The Wise Men bringing gifts (1/6)

■ **1970, November 25. Christmas**
Des: Sally Stiff (based on the De Lisle Psalter). No Wmk.

Set	0.25	0.25
First Day Cover		0.50

PRE-DECIMAL MACHIN DEFINITIVES

In this section, prices are given for **unmounted mint** (left) and **fine used** (right). Exceptions are made where used prices are not applicable, for example booklet panes and gum varieties.

The Machin head of Queen Elizabeth II is so-called because it is from a sculpture by Arnold Machin. All designs in the series are similar, but small differences can be found in the head itself and in its setting in the design.

There are also varieties in the number and positioning of phosphor bands.

4d sepia

■ 1967-1969. Definitives
Des: A. Machin. Printed in photogravure by Harrisons. No wmk.
Head 1 with two phosphor bands except where stated

A) Gum Arabic.

3d violet (August 8, 1967) (one band)	0.30	-
4d sepia (June 5, 1967)	0.50	-
head 2	£2,000	-
4d red (one band)	20.00	-
9d green (August 8, 1967)	0.45	-
1/- pale violet (June 5, 1967)	0.40	-
1/- deep violet	1.50	-
1/6 green, deep blue (August 8, 1967)	0.70	-
1/9 orange, black (June 5, 1967)	1.10	-
First Day Cover (4d, 1/-, 1/9)		1.25
First Day Cover (3d, 9d, 1/6)		1.25

Se-tenant coil stamps.
Released on August 27, 1969

1d olive (head 2, one band)	0.50	-
2d brown (head 2, one band)	0.35	0.30
3d violet (head 2, one band)	0.50	-
4d red (head 2, one band)	0.50	-
Se-tenant coil of two 2d, one 1d, one 3d and one 4d	1.00	1.25

Booklet panes

Pane of six **4d** sepia (head 1)	17.50	-
Pane of six **4d** red (head 1)	£120	-

B) PVA gum.

½**d** orange (February 5, 1968)	0.20	0.10
1d olive (February 5, 1968)	0.20	0.10
head 2	0.25	0.10
head 2 (one centre band)	0.40	0.50
2d brown (February 5, 1968)	0.25	0.10
setting 2	0.25	0.20
3d violet (one centre band)	0.25	0.10
head 2 (one centre band)	5.00	0.10
3d violet	0.35	0.10
head 2	0.50	0.10
4d sepia (shades)	0.35	0.10
head 2	0.35	0.10
4d sepia (one centre band)	0.20	0.10
head 2 (one centre band)	0.20	0.10
4d red (January 6, 1969) (one centre band)	0.20	0.10
head 2 (one centre band)	0.20	0.10
head 2 (one band at left)	1.00	1.25
head 2 (one band at right)	2.25	2.00
5d blue (July 1, 1968)	0.40	0.30
head 2	0.25	0.15
head 2 (two bands on 'all over' phosphor)	£275	-
6d purple (February 5, 1968)	0.30	0.15
head 2	10.00	4.00
7d green (July 1, 1968) (head 2)	0.50	0.30
8d red (July 1, 1968)	0.40	0.25
8d light-blue (January 6, 1969) (head 2)	0.75	0.40
9d green	0.45	0.20
10d brown (July 1, 1968)	0.75	0.40
1/- deep violet	0.50	0.20
1/6 green, deep blue	0.50	0.20
'all-over' phosphor	1.00	0.45
1/9 orange, black	1.10	0.30
Set (one of each value)	3.00	3.00
First Day Cover (½d, 1d, 2d, 6d)		1.00
First Day Cover (5d, 7d, 8d, 10d)		1.25
First Day Cover (4d red, 8d light blue)		1.00

Booklet panes of four

Four **4d** sepia (head 2, two bands)	1.00	-
Four **4d** sepia (head 2, one centre band)	2.00	-
Four **4d** red (head 2, one centre band)	1.00	-
Two **1d** left of two **3d** (head 2, two bands)	2.50	-
Two **1d** right of two **3d** (head 2, two bands)	2.50	-
Two **4d** sepia (head 2, one centre band) with two labels reading '£4,315 FOR YOU AT AGE 55' and 'SEE OTHER PAGES'	2.50	-
Two **4d** red (head 2, one centre band) with two labels reading '£4,315 FOR YOU AT AGE 55' and 'SEE OTHER PAGES'	1.50	-

Booklet panes of six

Six **1d** olive (head 2, two bands)	1.25	-
Six **3d** violet (head one, centre band)	15.00	-
Six **4d** sepia (head 1, two bands)	1.00	-
Six **4d** sepia (head 1, one centre band)	1.50	-

Six **4d** red (head 1, one centre band)	3.00	-
Six 4d red (head 2, one centre band)	1.25	-
Six **5d** blue (head 2, two bands)	1.00	-
Four **1d** olive (one centre band) with two **4d** sepia (head 2, one centre band)	3.50	-
Four **1d** olive (two bands) with two **4d** red (head 2, one left band)	3.50	-

Booklet panes of 15 (all head 2)

Six 1d olive (two bands) with three **4d** red **(one** band at left), three **4d** (one band at right) and three **5d** blue, attached to recipe label	10.00	
Fifteen 4d red (one centre band) attached **to** a label headed 'Stuffed Cucumber'	3.00	
Fifteen 4d red (one centre band) attached **to** a label headed 'Method'	3.00	
Fifteen 5d blue (two bands) attached **to** a recipe label	3.00	

(*These panes come from the £1 Stamps For Cooks booklet and can be found with just four holes in the binding margin, where stapled together, or with a larger number of equally spaced holes, where stitched.)

5/- brown-red

■ 1969, March 5. High values
Des: A. Machin. Printed in recess by Bradbury, Wilkinson. Perf: 12.

2/6 brown	0.40	0.20
5/- brown-red	1.00	0.40
10/- deep blue	3.00	1.50
£1 black	3.50	2.00
Set	6.00	3.50
First Day Cover		7.00

DECIMAL MACHIN DEFINITIVES

In this section, prices are given for unmounted mint (left) and fine used (right). Exceptions are made where used prices are not applicable, for example in the case of booklet panes and gum varieties.

All stamps have fluorescent coated paper unless otherwise stated

Gum

These stamps can be found with three different gums:

Gum Arabic is either colourless or yellow in appearance and is very shiny.

Polyvinyl alcohol gum (PVA) is likewise colourless but has a matt appearance.

Polyvinyl alcohol with dextrin gum (PVAD) is also matt, but has a blueish or greenish tinge.

In recent years self-adhesive definitives have become more common.

Phosphor

As with the earlier non-decimal definitives and special issues, the phosphor at first was applied in the form of 'bands'.

When you hold a stamp up to the light and look along the surface, the paper itself appears shiny while the bands have a dull appearance.

Most stamps have two phosphor bands, on the two vertical edges; others have just one, which can be central or down the left or right vertical edge.

The width of the phosphor bands can vary, as can the size of the printing screen used to apply them, but these differences are beyond the scope of this publication.

In recent times, booklet panes, where stamps of the second-class rate (requiring a single phosphor band) have been printed adjacent to other stamps (needing two phosphor bands), have been found with the phosphor printed as bars rather than bands. Whereas bands extend across the perforations to the next stamp, these bars stop at the edge of the stamp design.

The term *all over phosphor* means that the phosphor was printed over the entire surface of the stamp, rather than in the form of bands. In some cases it was printed onto the paper before the stamp design was printed; in other cases it was printed above the stamp design. You can positively identify all-over phosphor from certain marginal stamps, where the phosphor will be seen to end in the sheet margin.

The term *no phosphor* is usually applied to stamps discovered with the phosphor omitted in error; such errors are outside the scope of this publication. However, two values have been printed without phosphor in the normal course of events: the 50p and 75p, both with PVAD gum.

Paper

At first these stamps were printed on what is now known as *original coated paper,* which gives a dull violet reaction when the front of the stamp is viewed ultra-violet light.

This was replaced by *fluorescent coated paper*, which gives a bright reaction under ultra-violet light, and then by *phosphor-coated paper*, which adds the after-glow of phosphor.

With phosphor coated paper, the phosphor is included with the coating of the surface of the paper. This makes the stamp appear uniformly shiny. Note that most stamps intended to have phosphor bands have been found with the phosphor omitted, which also produces a uniformly shiny surface, so those with phosphor coated paper can only be positively identified by their reaction under ultra-violet light.

The appearance of stamps with phosphor coated paper can vary considerably, due to variations in their drying time after printing. The differences range from dull to very shiny. A dull appearance is listed in this guide as *Phosphor Coated Paper I* (PCPI), and a highly glazed appearance as *Phosphor Coated Paper II* (PCPII).

Some stamps have been found with the fluorescent brightener omitted (with phosphor coated paper). These still give the phosphor afterglow, but the paper gives a dull violet reaction similar to that found with original coated paper.

Attempts to standardise the paper have produced what is known as *Advanced Coated Paper* (ACP), which has been used for a number of National and Country definitives. The visual difference between ACP and PCPI is slight, but the former gives a brighter reaction under ultra-violet light.

Printers and processes

Many of the Machin decimal definitives have been printed in photogravure by Harrisons. But some of the work has been undertaken by John Waddington, House of Questa, Walsall, Enschedé and De La Rue. Initially lithography was used, but Royal Mail then decided that it preferred the photogravure process

In 1979 the 10p definitive was printed on a Chambon press at Harrisons which produced sheets of 200 stamps, comprising two panes of 100 stamps separated by a horizontal gutter. Stamps from this printing have either two phosphor bands on top of phosphor coated paper or two phosphor bands on top of fluorescent coated paper.

Value position and portrait types

Changes can be noted in the position of the value in relation to the Queen's portrait, and the position of the portrait in relation to the base of the stamp.

Booklet panes

At first booklets were held together by stitching, so that a number of small holes can be found in the binding margin on the left hand side of panes. Later, the panes were stuck into booklet covers by the binding margins; in many such cases, panes can be found with the binding margin to the left or to the right.

In the case of stitched booklets, the booklet panes are recorded separately. Where the panes are stuck into the covers, most collectors prefer these as complete booklets, so the separate panes are not recorded.

Many of the early decimal booklet panes included labels se-tenant with the stamps in the pane, adjacent to the binding margin. At first these panes were perforated between the labels and the margin, but later they were not.

In 1987, as an experiment to counter complaints about the poor guillotining of panes, two booklet panes were produced with imperforate sides. These produce stamps with either the left or right-hand edge imperforate.

MACHINS

A further experiment of 1987 was to introduce booklets with 'bar codes' on the back cover, and with a window in the front cover, so that the stamp content could be ascertained. The panes in these booklets have a margin surrounding the stamps, and as such are listed separately.

Coils
There are two different types of coils from which stamps may be found.
Some coils contain just one value, with the stamps joined either horizontally or vertically. Today, these usually comprise the basic 1st or 2nd class letter rate stamps, and are prepared for use by businesses. They are not separately listed, but where the source of a particular stamp is given as 'coils', this refers to the single value version.

Other coils contain a mixture of values joined as a se-tenant strip. These have been produced for sale through vending machines, although two cases are known of coils specially produced for a commercial mailing shot. These are referred to here as 'se-tenant coils', and they are also separately listed.

Cartons
In an experiment staged in Scotland in 1976-78, 1st and 2nd-class definitives (including Country stamps) were sold in cartons from vending machines. Sold at 30p or 60p, they contained either 6½p and 8½p, or 7p and 9p stamps.

LOW VALUES WITH NON-ELLIPTICAL PERFORATIONS, 1971-93

Designed by Arnold Machin. Printed in photogravure by Harrisons, no Wmk, Perf: 15x14, except where stated.

■ **½p turquoise, February 15, 1971**
A) gum Arabic, two phos bands

i. original coated paper	0.30	-	se-tenant coils
ii. original coated paper with silicone	40.00	-	se-tenant coils
iii. fluorescent coated paper	0.20	-	sheets
iv. fluorescent coated paper with silicone	0.40	-	se-tenant coils
B) PVA gum, two phos bands			
i. original coated paper	0.20	-	sheets, se-tenant coils, booklets
ii. fluorescent coated paper	0.40	-	sheets, booklets
C) PVA gum, one band at left	45.00	22.00	£1 Wedgwood booklet
D) PVAD gum, two phos bands	0.20	0.15	sheets, se-tenant coils, booklets
E) PVAD gum, one centre band	0.20	0.15	se-tenant coils, booklets
F) PVAD gum, phos-coated paper			
i. PCPI	0.20	0.15	sheets, se-tenant coils
ii. PCPII	0.25	0.30	sheets
iii. fluorescent brightener omitted (poor gum)	50.00	17.50	se-tenant coils
iv. fluorescent brightener omitted (good perfs and gum)	£950	-	se-tenant coils

■ **1p purple, February 15, 1971**
A) gum Arabic, two phos bands

i. original coated paper	0.30	-	se-tenant coils
ii. original coated paper with silicone	40.00	-	se-tenant coils
iii. fluorescent coated paper	0.60	-	coils

iv. fluorescent coated paper with silicone	0.40	-	se-tenant coils
B) PVA gum, two phos bands			
i. original coated paper	0.20	-	sheets
ii. fluorescent coated paper	1.10	-	sheets, booklets
C) PVAD gum, two phos bands			
i. value low	0.20	0.20	10p booklets
ii. value in intermediate position	0.50	0.35	10p se-tenant coils, 50p booklets,
iii. value high	0.50	0.30	sheets, 5p se-tenant coils
D) PVAD gum, one centre phos band			
i. portrait above bottom margin	0.20	0.15	se-tenant coils
ii. portrait closer to bottom margin	0.50	0.30	se-tenant coils, 10p, 50p booklets,
E) PVAD gum, all over phos	0.25	0.15	sheets
F) PVAD gum, phos-coated paper			
i. PCPI, portrait above bottom margin	0.20	0.15	sheets
ii. PCPI, portrait closer to bottom margin	0.20	0.15	sheets, se-tenant coils
iii. PCPII	0.40	0.25	sheets
iv. ACP	0.30	0.25	sheets
G) PVAD gum, one phos band at left	1.00	0.80	50p booklet
H) PVAD gum, one phos band at right	2.50	2.25	£5 P&O booklet

■ 1½p black, February 15, 1971

A) PVA gum, two phos bands			
i. original coated paper	0.25	0.15	sheets, booklets
ii. fluorescent coated paper	0.90	0.70	sheets, booklets
B) PVAD gum, two phos bands	0.20	0.20	sheets, booklets

■ 2p green, February 15, 1971

A) gum Arabic, two phos bands			
i. original coated paper	1.25	-	se-tenant coils
ii. original coated paper with silicone	150.00	-	se-tenant coils
iii. fluorescent coated paper with silicone	2.00	-	se-tenant coils
B) PVA gum, two phos bands			
i. original coated paper	0.20	-	sheets, booklets
ii. fluorescent coated paper	1.75	-	sheets, booklets
C) PVAD gum, two phos bands			
i. portrait above bottom margin	0.20	0.15	sheets, se-tenant coils, booklets
ii. portrait close to bottom margin	1.00	0.80	booklets
D) PVAD gum, all over phos	0.30	0.15	sheets
E) PVAD gum, phos-coated paper			
i. PCPI	0.20	0.15	sheets
ii. PCPII	0.25	0.15	sheets
F) PVAD gum, phos-coated paper, litho by Questa, perf 13½x14	0.25	0.15	sheets
G) PVAD gum, phos-coated paper, litho by Questa, perf 15x14	0.20	0.15	sheets
H) PVAD, phos-coated paper, ACP, litho by Questa, perf 15x14	0.40	0.35	sheets

■ 2p deep green, February 23, 1988

A) PVAD gum, phos paper	0.35	0.20	sheets, booklets
B) PVAD gum phos paper, litho by Walsall	0.70	0.60	booklets

■ 2½p pink, February 15, 1971

A) gum arabic, one centre phos band	0.30	-	sheets, coils
B) PVA gum, one centre phos band			
i. original coated paper	0.20	0.15	sheets, coils, booklets,
ii. fluorescent coated paper	0.60	0.25	sheets, booklets
C) PVA gum, one phos band at left			
i. original coated paper	5.25	1.50	50p booklets,
ii. fluorescent coated paper	2.50	1.20	50p, £1 Wedgwood booklets
D) PVA gum, one phos band at right	2.50	1.50	£1 Wedgwood booklet
E) PVAD gum, two phos bands	0.30	0.20	sheets
F) PVAD gum, one centre phos band	0.20	0.15	sheets

■ 2½p rose, January 14, 1981

A) PVAD gum, phos-coated paper			
i. PCPI	0.50	0.20	sheets, se-tenant coils
ii. PCPII	0.70	0.60	sheets,
iii. fluorescent brightener omitted	30.00	30.00	se-tenant coils
B) PVAD gum, two phos bands	0.30	0.30	50p booklets

■ 3p blue, February 15, 1971

A) gum Arabic, two phos bands			
i. original coated paper	45.00	-	coils
ii. fluorescent coated paper	2.50	-	sheets, coils
B) gum arabic, one centre phos band	1.20	-	sheets
C) PVA gum, two phos bands			
i. original coated paper	0.30	0.20	sheets, coils, booklets
ii. fluorescent coated paper	0.60	0.25	sheets, booklets
iii. phos-coated paper	£1,200	-	only two examples known
D) PVA gum, one centre phos band	0.60	-	sheets, booklets
E) PVAD gum, one centre phos band	0.20	0.15	sheets, coils, booklets

■ 3p pink, October 22, 1980

A) PVAD gum, phos-coated paper			
i. PCPI	0.30	0.20	sheets, se-tenant coils
ii. PCPII	0.30	0.20	
iii. fluorescent brightener omitted	5.00	4.00	se-tenant coils
iv. ACP	0.30	0.20	sheets, £4 Royal Mint booklet
B) PVAD gum, two phos bands	0.30	0.20	50p, £4 SG booklets

■ 3½p olive green, February 15, 1971

A) PVA gum, two phos bands			
i. original coated paper	0.30	0.20	sheets
ii. fluorescent coated paper	1.75	-	sheets, 35p booklets
B) PVAD gum, two phos bands			
i. original coated paper	£175	50.00	sheets
ii. fluorescent coated paper	0.40	0.15	sheets, coils, 35p, 50p booklets
C) PVAD gum, one centre phos band	0.35	0.20	sheets, coils, 35p, 85p booklets

■ 3½p light red-brown, March 30, 1983

A) PVA gum, two phos bands			
i. PCPI	0.40	0.20	sheets,
ii. ACP	1.00	0.60	sheets, £4 Royal Mint booklet
B) PVAD gum, one centre phos band	0.90	0.60	50p booklets

■ 4p bistre, February 15, 1971

A) gum arabic, two phos bands	0.30	-	sheets
B) PVA gum, two phos bands			
i. original coated paper	0.30	0.20	sheets
ii. fluorescent coated paper	2.50	-	sheets
C) PVAD gum, two phos bands	0.30	0.20	sheets

■ 4p blue, January 30, 1980

A) PVA gum, two phos bands, litho by Waddingtons	0.20	0.15	sheets
B) PVAD gum, phos-coated paper, litho by Waddingtons	0.30	0.15	sheets
C) PVAD gum, phos-coated paper, litho by Questa, perf 15x14	0.50	0.45	sheets
D) PVAD gum, two phos bands	1.00	0.65	50p booklets
E) PVAD gum, phos-coated paper			
i. PCPI	0.35	0.25	se-tenant coils
ii. fluorescent brightener omitted (perfect gum)	£370	35.00	se-tenant coils
iii. PCPI, value high	0.35	0.20	se-tenant coils
F) PVAD gum, one centre phos band	0.75	0.70	50p booklets
G) PVAD gum, one phos band at left	1.20	1.00	£5 booklet

H) PVAD gum, one phos band at right   1.20   1.00   £5 booklet

■ 4p bright blue, July 26, 1988

A) PVAD gum, phos paper, litho by Questa	0.45	0.50	sheets
A) PVAD gum, phos paper			
	0.30	0.25	sheets and coils

■ 4½p grey-blue, October 24, 1973

A) PVAD gum, two phos bands	0.70	0.40	sheets, coils, 45p, 85p booklets
B) PVAD gum, two phos bands on all-over phos	0.65	-	sheets

■ 5p violet, February 15, 1971

A) PVA gum, two phos bands			
i. original coated paper	0.30	0.20	sheets
ii. fluorescent coated paper	4.00	-	sheets
B) PVAD gum, two phos bands	0.30	0.20	sheets
C) PVAD gum, phos-coated paper			
i. PCPI	0.35	0.20	sheets
ii. PCPI, value high	0.50	0.35	sheets
D) PVAD gum, phos-coated paper, litho by Questa	0.25	0.20	sheets
E) PVA gum, phos-coated paper, litho by Questa	0.40	0.30	sheets

■ 5p red-brown, January 27. 1982

A) PVAD gum, phos-coated paper, litho by Questa, perf 13½x14	0.40	'0.30	sheets
B) PVAD gum, phos-coated paper, litho by Questa, perf 15x14	0.40	0.30	sheets
C) PVAD gum, ACP, litho by Questa, perf 15x14	0.45	0.40	sheets
D) PVAD gum, one centre phos band	1.80	1.20	50p booklet

■ 5½p deep purple, October 24, 1973

A) PVAD gum, two phos bands	0.40	0.30	sheets
B) PVAD gum, one centre phos band	0.40	0.30	sheets

■ 6p light green, February 15, 1971

A) gum arabic, two phos bands	1.50	-	sheets
B) PVA gum, two phos bands			
i. original coated paper	0.30	-	sheets, se-tenant coils
ii. fluorescent coated paper	20.00	-	sheets
C) PVAD gum, two phos bands	0.30	0.20	sheets, se-tenant coils, 10p booklet

■ 6p olive, September 10, 1991

A) PVAD gum, phos paper	0.30	0.20	sheets

■ 6½p green-blue, September 7, 1974

A) PVA gum, two phos bands	25.00	-	sheets
B) PVAD gum, two phos bands	0.40	0.30	sheets
C) PVAD gum, one centre phos band			
i. portrait above bottom margin	0.40	0.30	sheets
ii. portrait close to bottom margin	0.30	0.25	sheets, coils, 65p booklets
D) PVAD gum, one phos band at left	0.40	0.30	50p booklets
E) PVAD gum, one phos band at right	0.60	0.30	50p booklets

■ 7p red-brown, January 15, 1975

A) PVAD gum, two phos bands	0.40	0.25	sheets
B) PVAD gum, one centre phos band			
i. portrait above bottom margin	0.40	0.25	sheets, coils
ii. portrait close to bottom margin	0.50	0.30	sheets, coils, se-tenants coils, booklets
C) PVAD gum, one phos band at left	0.60	0.45	50p booklets
D) PVAD gum, one phos band at right	0.60	0.50	50p booklets

■ 7p brick-red, October 29, 1985

A) PVAD gum, phos-coated paper	1.50	1.30	sheets

■ 7½p brown, February 15, 1971
A) PVA gum, two phos bands

i. original coated paper	0.30	0.20	sheets
ii. fluorescent coated paper	3.00	-	sheets
B) PVAD gum, two phos bands	0.50	0.25	sheets

■ 8p red, October 24, 1973
A) PVAD gum, two phos bands

A) PVAD gum, two phos bands	0.30	0.20	sheets
B) PVAD gum, one centre phos band, printed by Harrisons			
i. portrait high, value low	0.35	0.25	sheets
ii. portrait low, value high	0.50	0.30	sheets, coils, booklets
C) PVAD gum, one centre phos band, printed by Enschedé	0.35	0.25	sheets
D) PVAD gum, one phos band at left	0.40	0.30	50p booklets
E) PVAD gum, one phos band at right	0.40	0.30	50p booklets

■ 8½p lime green, September 24, 1975
A) PVAD gum, two phos bands

i. value high	0.40	0.25	sheets, coils, 85p booklets
ii. value low	0.45	0.35	50p booklets
B) PVAD gum, phos-coated paper	0.50	0.40	sheets

■ 9p orange and black, February 15, 1971
A) PVA gum, two phos bands

i. original coated paper	1.50	1.00	sheets
ii. fluorescent coated paper	2.75	-	sheets
B) PVAD gum, two phos bands	0.90	0.70	sheets

■ 9p violet, February 25, 1976

A) PVAD gum, two phos bands	0.50	0.25	sheets, coils, 50p, 90p, £1.60 booklets

■ 9½p purple, February 25, 1976

A) PVAD gum, two phos bands	0.35	0.30	sheets

■ 10p yellow and orange, August 11, 1971

A) PVA gum, two phos bands	0.50	-	sheets
B) PVAD gum, two phos bands	0.50	0.25	sheets

■ 10p orange, February 25, 1976
A) PVAD gum, two phos bands

i. base of value above edge of bust	0.40	0.20	sheets, £1.80 booklets
ii. base of value at edge of bust	0.40	0.25	50p booklets
iii. re-drawn (narrower) value	12.00	10.00	£4 Heritage booklet
B) PVAD gum, all-over phos	0.60	0.30	sheets, £1 booklets
C) PVAD gum, phosphor coated paper, PCPI	0.50	0.25	sheets
D) PVAD gum, ACP	0.40	0.25	sheets
E) PVAD gum, one centre phos band	0.35	0.20	sheets, £1, £2.20, £3 booklets
F) PVAD gum, one phos band at left	0.60	0.50	50p, £3 booklets
G) PVAD gum, one phos band at right	0.60	0.50	50p booklets
H) PVAD gum, two phos bands, PCPI, Chambon press	0.50	-	sheets
gutter pair	1.25	-	sheets
I) PVAD gum, two phos bands, fluoresc-coated paper, Chambon	0.45	0.35	sheets
gutter pair	1.00	1.50	sheets
J) PVAD gum, one centre phos band, PCPI	0.85	-	sheets

■ 10½p yellow, February 25, 1976

A) PVAD gum, two phos bands	0.40	0.35	sheets

■ 10½p blue, Aril 26, 1978

A) PVAD gum, two phos bands	0.40	0.30	sheets

■ 11p orange-pink, February 25, 1976
A) PVAD gum, two phos bands	0.40	0.30	sheets
B) PVAD gum, phos-coated paper			
PCPI	0.50	0.50	sheets

■ 11½p sepia, August 15, 1979
A) PVAD gum, phos-coated paper			
PCPI	0.60	0.30	sheets

■ 11½p mushroom, January 14, 1981
A) PVAD gum, one phos band	0.60	0.30	sheets, coils, £1.15, £2.55 booklets
B) PVAD gum, one phos band at left	0.50	0.30	50p, £1.30 booklets
C) PVAD gum, one phos band at right	0.50	0.30	50p, £1.30 booklets

■ 12p yellow-green, January 30, 1980
A) PVAD gum, phos-coated paper			
i. PCPI	0.50	0.25	sheets, coils, £1.20 booklet
ii. PCPII	1.50	0.40	sheets
B) PVAD gum, two phos bands	0.50	0.35	50p, £2.20, £3 booklets

■ 12p emerald-green, October 29, 1985
A) PVAD gum, one centre phos band	0.40	0.25	sheets, 50p, £1.20, £5 booklets
B) PVAD gum, one centre phos band, blue star on gummed side	0.50	-	sheets
C) PVAD gum, one centre phos band in ACP-type phos	0.40	0.30	sheets
D) PVAD gum, one phos band at left	0.75	0.50	£1.50, £5 booklets
E) PVAD gum, one phos band at right	0.75	0.50	£1.50, £5 booklets

■ 12½p light green, January 27, 1982
A) PVAD gum, one centre phos band	0.35	0.25	sheets, coils, 50p, £1.25, £4 SG booklets
B) PVAD gum, one centre phos band, PCPI	5.00	-	sheets
C) PVAD gum, one phos band at left	0.60	0.50	50p, £1.43, £1.46, £4 booklets
D) PVAD gum, one phos band at right	0.60	0.50	50p, £1.43, £1.46, £4 booklets
E) PVAD gum, one centre phos band, blue star on gummed side	0.60	0.50	£2.50 booklet
F) PVAD gum, one centre band, simple blue star on gummed side	0.60	0.40	£2.20 booklet

■ 13p olive, August 15, 1979
A) PVAD gum, phos-coated paper, PCPI	0.45	0.30	sheets

■ 13p light brown, August 28, 1984
A) PVAD gum, one centre phos band	0.40	0.25	sheets, 50p, £1.30, £5 booklets
B) PVAD gum, one centre phos band, blue star on gummed side	0.60	-	£1.20 booklet
C) PVAD gum, one centre phos band in ACP-type phos	0.60	0.30	sheets
D) PVAD gum, one phos band at left	0.65	0.35	50p, £1.54, £4 Heritage, £5 booklets
E) PVAD gum, one phos band at right	0.65	0.35	£1, £1.54, £4 Heritage, £5 booklets
F) PVAD gum, one centre phos band, litho by Questa	0.60	0.40	booklets
G) PVAD gum, one phos band at left, litho by Questa	0.60	0.40	booklets
H) PVAD gum, one phos band at right, litho by Questa	0.60	0.40	booklets

■ 13½p red-brown, January 30, 1980
A) PVAD gum, phosphor coated paper, PCPI	0.50	0.35	sheets

■ 14p grey-blue, January 14, 1981
A) PVAD gum, phos-coated paper			
i. PCPI	0.45	0.30	sheets, coils, £1.40 booklets
ii. PCPII	0.60	0.30	sheets, coils £1.40 booklets
iii. fluorescent brightener omitted	2.50	-	£1.40 booklets
B) PVAD gum, two phos bands	0.60	0.40	50p, £1.30, £2.55 booklets

■ 14p deep blue, August 23, 1988
A) PVAD gum, one centre phos band	0.50	0.25	sheets, booklets

B) PVAD gum, one phos band at right   1.40   1.00   booklets
C) PVAD gum, one centre phos band, litho by Questa   1.50   0.70   booklets
D) PVAD gum, one phos band at right, litho by Walsall   1.00   1.00   booklets

■ 15p blue, August 15, 1979
A) PVAD gum, phos-coated paper
i. PCPI   0.50   0.30   sheets
ii. PCPII   0.55   0.55   sheets

■ 15½p pale purple, January 14, 1981
A) PVAD gum, phosphor coated paper
i. PCPI   0.50   0.25   sheets, coils, £1.55 booklets
ii. PCPI   0.50   0.25   sheets
iii. fluorescent brightener omitted   15.00   -   sheets
iv. advanced coated paper   3.00   1.50   £1.55 booklets
B) PVAD gum, two phos bands   0.60   0.40   £1.43, £4 SG booklets
C) PVAD gum, two phos bands, blue star on gummed side   0.60   0.45   £2.50 booklets

■ 16p light mushroom, March 30, 1983
A) PVAD gum, phos-coated paper, PCPI   0.50   0.35   sheets, £1.60, £4 Royal Mint booklets
B) PVAD gum, PCPI and D on gummed side   0.60   0.30   £1.45 booklet
C) PVAD gum, ACP   0.50   0.30   sheets
D) PVAD gum, two phos bands   1.10   0.90   £1.46 booklet

■ 16½p light brown, January 27 1982
A) PVAD gum, phos-coated paper
i. PCPI   0.65   0.50   sheets
ii. PCPII   3.50   2.00   sheets

■ 17p sage green, January 30, 1980
A) PVAD gum, phos-coated paper
i. PCPI   0.60   0.30   sheets
ii. PCPII   3.00   2.00   sheets
iii. fluorescent brightener omitted   1.50   -   sheets

■ 17p steel blue, March 30, 1983
A) PVAD gum, PCPI   0.60   0.30   sheets, £1.70, £4 Heritage booklets
B) PVAD gum, PCPI, D on gummed side   0.70   -   £1.55 booklet
C) PVAD gum, ACP   0.60   0.40   sheets, £1.70, £5 booklets
D) PVAD gum, two phos bands   0.70   0.30   50p, £1.50, £1.54, £4 Heritage, £5 booklets
E) PVAD gum, two phos bands, stars on gummed side   0.60   -   50p booklet

■ 17p deep blue, September 4, 1990
A) PVAD gum, one centre phos band   0.65   0.35   sheets
B) PVAD gum, one phos band at left   0.65   0.65   booklets
C) PVAD gum, one phos band at right   1.20   1.20   booklets
D) PVAD gum, one centre phos band, litho by Questa   0.70   0.65   booklets

■ 17½p light brown, January 30, 1979
A) PVAD gum, phos-coated paper
i. PCPI   0.65   0.40   sheets
ii. PCPII   1.75   1.75   sheets

■ 18p violet, January 14, 1981
A) PVAD gum, phos-coated paper
i. PCPI   0.65   0.40   sheets
ii. PCPII   0.70   0.40   sheets

■ 18p grey-green, August 28, 1984
A) PVAD gum, ACP   0.65   0.30   sheets

B) PVAD gum, two phos bands	1.00	0.50	50p, £1 booklets
C) PVAD gum, phos-coated paper	0.70	0.60	£1.80 booklet
D) PVAD gum, phos paper, litho by Questa	0.80	0.75	booklets
E) PVAD gum, two phos bands, litho by Questa	3.75	4.00	booklets

■ 18p bright green, September 10, 1991

A) PVAD gum, one centre phos band	0.50	0.30	sheets
B) PVAD gum, one centre phos band, litho by Questa	0.75	0.40	booklets
C) PVAD gum, one phos band at left, litho by Questa	1.50	1.35	booklets
D) PVAD gum, one phos band at right, litho by Questa	1.00	0.70	booklets

■ 19p orange-red, August 23, 1988

A) PVAD gum, phos paper	0.50	0.30	sheets, booklets
B) PVAD gum, phos paper, litho by Questa	1.20	1.00	booklets
C) PVAD gum, two phos bands, litho by Walsall	1.50	1.50	booklets

■ 19½p, January 27, 1982

A) PVAD gum, phosphor coated paper, PCPI	1.75	1.25	sheets

■ 20p dull purple, February 25, 1976

A) PVA gum, two phos bands, litho by Waddingtons	0.85	0.50	sheets
B) PVAD gum, phos-coated paper, litho by Waddingtons	1.00	0.70	sheets
dull purple and sepia	4.50	3.00	sheets
C) PVAD gum, phos-coated paper, litho by Questa, perf 15x14	1.00	0.50	sheets
D) PVAD gum, two phos bands	0.70	0.30	sheets
E) PVAD gum, phos-coated paper			
i. PCPI	0.70	0.50	sheets
ii. PCPII	0.70	0.60	sheets

■ 20p turquoise, August 23, 1988

A) PVAD gum, phos paper	0.50	0.35	sheets

■ 20p brownish-black, September 26, 1989

A) PVAD gum, phos paper	0.45	0.35	sheets, booklets
B) PVAD gum, two phos bands	1.20	1.20	sheets

■ 20½p bright blue, March 30, 1983

A) PVAD gum, phos-coated paper, PCPI	1.20	0.70	sheets

■ 22p deep blue, October 22, 1980

A) PVAD gum, phos-coated paper			
i. PCPI	0.70	0.50	sheets
ii. PCPII	0.70	0.50	sheets
B) PVAD gum, experimental coated paper	1.50	1.50	sheets

■ 22p yellow-green, August 28, 1984

A) PVAD gum, ACP	0.60	0.45	sheets
B) PVAD gum, two phos bands, litho by Questa	4.50	4.50	booklets

■ 22p orange-red, September 4, 1990

A) PVAD gum, two phos bands	0.80	0.90	sheets
B) PVAD gum, phos paper	0.60	0.40	sheets
C) PVAD gum, phos paper, litho by Questa	0.70	0.50	booklets

■ 23p rose, March 30, 1983

A) PVAD gum, phos-coated paper, PCPI	1.20	0.70	sheets

■ 23p bright green, August 23, 1988

A) PVAD gum, phos paper	0.75	0.50	sheets

■ 24p light purple, August 28, 1984

A) PVAD gum, ACP	1.50	0.80	sheets

■ 24p red, September 26, 1989

A) PVAD gum, phos paper	0.30	0.65	sheets

■ 24p chestnut, September 10, 1991

A) PVAD gum, phos paper	2.00	0.90	sheets
B) PVAD gum, phos paper, litho by Questa	0.70	0.40	booklets
C) PVAD gum, two phos bands, litho by Questa	1.10	1.10	booklets
D) PVAD gum, phos paper, litho by Walsall	0.80	0.50	booklets

■ 25p purple, January 14, 1981

A) PVAD gum, phos-coated paper

i. PCPI	1.70	1.65	sheets
ii. PCPII	1.50	0.75	sheets

■ 26p red, January 27, 1982

A) PVAD gum, phos-coated paper, PCPI	0.75	0.50	sheets
B) PVAD gum, ACP	0.75	0.50	sheets
C) PVAD gum, two phos bands	6.00	5.50	£5 P&O booklet
D) PVAD gum, two phos bands, narrow value	3.50	3.00	£1.04 booklet

■ 26p drab, September 4, 1990

A) PVAD gum, phos paper	0.80	0.50	sheets

■ 27p chestnut, August 23, 1988

A) PVAD gum, phos paper	1.00	0.70	sheets, booklets

■ 27p violet, September 4, 1990

A) PVAD gum, phos paper	0.75	0.50	sheets

■ 28p blue, March 30, 1983

A) PVAD gum, phos-coated paper, PCPI	0.90	0.90	sheets
B) PVAD gum, ACP	1.00	0.90	sheets

■ 28p ochre, August 23, 1988

A) PVAD gum, phos paper	0.80	0.70	sheets

■ 28p blue-grey, September 10, 1991

A) PVAD gum , phos paper	0.70	0.60	sheets

■ 29p sepia, January 27, 1982

A) PVAD gum, phos-coated paper

i. PCPI	2.50	1.00	sheets
ii. PCPII	5.00	3.50	sheets

■ 29p mauve, September 26, 1989

A) PVAD gum, phos paper	1.50	1.00	sheets
B) PVAD gum, two phos bands, litho by Walsall	2.00	2.50	booklets
C) PVAD gum, phos paper, litho by Walsall	3.00	2.75	booklets

■ 30p olive, September 26, 1989

A) PVAD gum, phos paper	2.25	0.80	sheets

■ 31p purple, March 30, 1983

A) PVAD gum, phos-coated paper, PCPI	1.20	0.90	sheets
B) PVAD gum, ACP	1.00	0.75	sheets
C) PVAD gum, two phos bands	6.50	6.50	£5 British Rail Booklet

■ 31p ultramarine, September 4, 1990

A) PVAD gum, phos paper	1.10	0.90	sheets
B) PVAD gum, phosphor paper, litho by Walsall	1.20	1.00	booklets

■ 32p green-blue, August 23, 1988

A) PVAD gum, phos paper	1.00	0.90	sheets

■ 33p emerald, September 4, 1990

A) PVAD gum, phos paper	0.90	0.45	sheets
B) PVAD gum, phos paper, litho by Questa	1.30	1.10	booklets
C) PVAD gum, two phos bands, litho by Questa	1.20	1.00	booklets
D) PVAD gum, phos paper, litho by Walsall	1.00	1.00	booklets

■ 34p sepia, August 28, 1984

A) PVAD gum, phos-coated paper	1.10	1.00	sheets
B) PVAD gum, two phos bands	6.00	5.00	£5 Times booklet
C) PVAD gum, ACP	1.25	1.25	sheets
D) PVAD gum, two phos bands, litho by Questa	4.00	4.00	booklets

■ 34p blue-grey, September 26, 1989

A) PVAD gum, phos paper	1.00	0.90	sheets

■ 34p mauve, September 10, 1991

A) PVAD gum, phos paper	0.80	0.80	sheets

■ 35p sepia, August 23, 1988

A) PVAD gum, phos paper	9.00	5.00	sheets

■ 35p yellow, September 10, 1991

A) PVAD gum, phos paper	0.95	0.95	sheets

■ 37p rosine, September 26, 1989

A) PVAD gum, phos paper	1.40	1.00	sheets

■ 39p mauve, September 10, 1991

A) PVAD gum, phos paper	1.15	0.70	sheets
B) PVAD gum, two phos bands, litho by Questa	1.50	1.50	booklets
C) PVAD gum, phos paper, litho by Walsall	1.10	1.00	booklets

■ 50p dull brown, February 2, 1977

A) PVAD gum, two phos bands	1.40	0.50	sheets
B) PVAD gum, no phos	1.40	0.70	sheets

■ 50p ochre, March 13, 1990

A) PVAD gum, phos paper	1.40	1.10	sheets
B) PVAD gum, two phos bands	1.50	1.10	sheets

■ 75p deep grey, January 30, 1980

A) PVAD gum, no phos, litho by Questa, perf 13½x14	3.00	1.50	sheets
B) PVA gum, no phos, litho by Questa, perf 15x14	2.50	1.50	sheets
C) PVAD gum, no phos, litho by Questa, perf 15x14	3.00	2.00	sheets
D) PVA gum, no phos, litho by Questa: perf 15x14 on paper supplied by Coated Paper Ltd	3.00	-	sheets

■ 75p grey and black, February 23, 1988

A) PVAD gum, litho by Questa	8.00	5.00	sheets

■ 75p grey and black, July 26, 1988

A) PVAD gum, no phosphor	1.50	1.25	sheets

BOOKLET PANES WITH NON-ELLIPTICAL PERFORATIONS, 1971-93

From stitched booklets (see also prestige stamp books).

PVA gum panes of four
Two **2p** with two ½**p**
vertically se-tenant	5.00
horizontally se-tenant, original coated paper	9.00
horizontally se-tenant, fluorescent coated paper	4.00

Two **1p** with two 1½**p**
vertically se-tenant	4.00
horizontally se-tenant, original coated paper	5.00
horizontally se-tenant, fluorescent coated paper	1.00

PVA gum panes of six
Five ½**p** with label 'B ALAN LTD for GB STAMPS'	
perforated label	4.00
imperforate label	7.00
Five ½**p** with label 'LICK battery failure'	
perforated label	4.00
imperforate label	10.00
Five ½**p** with label 'MAKE YOUR LUCKY FIND PAY'	
imperforate label only	2.00
Four 2½**p** (one centre band) with labels	
'UNIFLO STAMPS' and 'STICK FIRMLY'	
perforated label	4.00
imperforate label	7.00
Five 2½**p** (one centre band) with label 'STICK FIRMLY'	
perforated label	4.50
imperforate label	9.00
Five 2½**p** (one centre band) with label 'TEAR OFF to ESSO'	
perforated label	4.00
imperforate label	6.00
Five 2½**p** (one centre band) with label 'STAMP COLLECTIONS'	
imperforate label only	3.25
Four 2½**p** (one centre band) with labels 'DO YOU	
COLLECT GB STAMPS' and 'BUYING or SELLING'	
imperforate label only	3.50
Five 2½**p** (one centre band) with label 'B ALAN'	
imperforate label only	3.50
Five **3p** (two bands) with label '£4,315 FOR YOU'	
perforated label	2.50
imperforate label, OCP	7.00
imperforate label, FCP	3.00
Four **3p** (two bands) with two 2½**p** (one band at left)	
OCP	5.00
FCP	5.00
Six **3p** (two bands)	
OCP	4.50
FCP	2.50
Five **3p** (one centre band) with blank imperforate label	8.00
Five 3½**p** (two bands) with blank imperforate label	12.00

PVAD gum panes of four
Two **2p** horizontally se-tenant with two ½**p**	1.00
Two **1p** horizontally se-tenant with two 1½**p**	1.00

PVAD gum panes of six
Five **3p** (one centre band) with blank imperforate label	5.00

Five 3½**p** (two bands) with blank imperforate label	2.50
Five 3½**p** (one centre band) with blank imperforate label	2.50
Five 4½**p** (two bands) with blank imperforate label	3.00

NON-VALUE INDICATORS WITH NON-ELLIPTICAL PERFORATIONS, 1989-93

From retail stamp books (at least one edge may be imperforate) or, marked *, from prestige stamp books.

■ **2nd class bright blue (first issued August 22, 1989)**
Printed in gravure by Harrison
With one centre phosphor band	0.70	1.55
With one phosphor band at right*	3.00	1.85

Printed in litho by Walsall
With one centre phosphor band	0.45	0.50

Printed in litho by Questa
With one centre phosphor band	0.60	0.50
With one phosphor band at left*	1.00	1.05
With one phosphor band at right*	1.20	1.00

■ **2nd class deep blue (first issued August 7, 1990)**
Printed in gravure by Harrison
With one centre phosphor band	0.70	0.55

Printed in litho by Walsall
With one centre phosphor band	0.55	0.55

Printed in litho by Questa
With one centre phosphor band	0.80	0.90
With one phosphor band at left*	1.25	1.30

■ **1st class brownish black (first issued August 22, 1989)**
Printed in gravure by Harrison
On phosphor paper	0.80	0.70
Two phosphor bands*	2.50	2.00

Printed in litho by Walsall
With two phosphor bands	1.30	1.35

Printed in litho by Questa
On phosphor paper	1.30	1.10

■ **1st class orange red (first issued August 7, 1990)**
Printed in gravure by Harrison
On phosphor paper	0.60	0.65

Printed in litho by Walsall
On phosphor paper. Perf: 14	0.60	0.65
On phosphor paper. Perf: 13	1.75	1.70

Printed in litho by Questa
On phosphor paper	0.80	0.85
With two phosphor bands*	1.30	1.00
With two phosphor bands*	1.10	1.00

LOW VALUES WITH ELLIPTICAL PERFORATIONS, 1993-date

With an elliptical perforation on each vertical side.

■ 1993-2005

Printed in gravure by Enschedé. Issued in sheets. Two phosphor bands, except where stated.

1p crimson (June 8, 1993)	0.30	0.30
2p deep green (April 11, 1995)	0.30	0.30
4p new blue (December 14, 1993)	0.35	0.35
5p claret (June 8, 1993)	0.35	0.35
6p lime green (April 27, 1993)	0.35	0.35
10p orange (June 8, 1993)	0.40	0.40
20p sea green (December 14, 1993) 0.50	0.50	
25p salmon pink (October 10, 1995)	0.85	0.80
29p light grey (October 26, 1993)	0.70	0.70
30p grey-green (July 27, 1993)	0.70	0.70
31p deep purple (June 25, 1996)	0.75	0.75
35p deep yellow (August 17, 1993)	0.75	0.75
35p lime-green (Apr 5, 2005) (phos band)	0.85	0.85
36p ultramarine (October 26, 1993) 0.80	0.80	
37p amethyst (June 25, 1996)	0.85	0.85
38p rosine (October 26, 1993)	1.00	0.85
39p magenta (June 25, 1996)	0.90	0.95
41p stone (October 26, 1993)	0.85	0.85
43p chocolate-brown (June 25, 1996)	1.10	1.10
50p ochre (December 14, 1993)	1.20	1.20
63p emerald (June 25, 1996)	1.40	1.30
£1 bluish-violet (August 22, 1995)	2.50	2.50
Stamp card (£1 stamp)	7.50	15.00

■ 1993 to date

Printed by Harrisons, then by De La Rue.

1p crimson (April 1, 1997)	0.20	0.15
2p deep green (May 27, 1997)	0.25	0.20
4p new blue (May 27, 1997)	0.20	0.15
5p claret (May 27, 1997)	0.20	0.15
6p lime green (April 1, 1997)	0.25	0.20
7p light grey (April 20, 1999)	0.40	0.40
7p bright magenta (April 1, 2004)	0.20	0.15
8p deep yellow (April 25, 2000)	0.35	0.30
9p deep orange (April 5, 2005)	0.25	0.25
10p orange (May 8, 1997)	0.40	0.35
12p turquoise (August 1, 2006)	0.30	0.30
14p salmon pink (August 1, 2006)	0.35	0.35
15p shocking pink (April 1, 2008)	0.35	0.35
16p bright pink (March 27, 2007)	0.40	0.35
19p olive (Oct 26, 1993) (one phos band)	0.45	0.40
20p bright green		
(June 25, 1996) (centre phos band)	0.45	0.50
(September 23, 1997) (phos band at right)	1.00	1.10
(April 20, 1999) (two phos bands)	0.45	0.50
25p salmon-pink		
(October 26, 1993) (phos coated paper)	0.60	0.60
(December 20, 1994)	0.60	0.60
26p reddish brown (June 25, 1996)	0.60	0.60
26p gold (April 29, 1997)	0.60	0.55
30p grey-green (May 12, 1997)	0.65	0.65
31p deep mauve (August 26, 1997)	0.65	0.70
33p slate-blue (April 25, 2000)	0.65	0.65
35p yellow (Nov 1, 1993) (phos coated paper)	4.00	1.50
35p sepia (April 1, 2004)	0.70	0.75
35p lime-green (April 26, 2005)	0.70	0.75
37p amethyst (July 8, 1996)	1.00	1.05
37p bright mauve (August 7, 1997)	0.80	0.85
37p deep grey (July 4, 2002)	0.80	0.80
37p olive green (March 28, 2006)	0.65	0.70
38p ultramarine (April 20, 1999)	0.70	0.70
39p magenta (May 12, 1997)	0.80	0.85
39p grey (April 1, 2004)	0.80	0.80
40p greyish blue (April 20, 1999)	0.75	0.80
40p turquoise (April 1, 2004)	0.80	0.80
41p drab (Nov 1, 1993) (phos coated paper)	5.50	4.50
41p rosine (April 20, 1999)	0.95	0.90
42p olive-grey (July 4, 2002)	0.85	0.85
43p chocolate-brown (July 8, 1996)	1.10	1.10
43p brown (March 21, 1997)	0.90	0.90
43p emerald (April 1, 2004)	0.90	0.95
44p stone (April 20, 1999)	0.95	0.75
44p ultramarine (March 28, 2006)	0.75	0.75
45p mauve (April 20, 1999)	0.80	0.85
46p light brown (April 5, 2005)	0.75	0.80
47p turquoise green (July 4, 2002)	0.85	0.85
48p purple (March 27, 2007)	0.85	0.80
49p rust (March 28, 2006)	0.85	0.80
50p ochre (April 1, 1997)	1.00	0.95
50p grey (March 27, 2007)	1.00	0.95
54p rust (March 27, 2007)	1.00	0.90
56p lime green (April 1, 2008)	1.20	1.20
63p emerald (December 12, 1996)	1.20	1.10
64p sea green (April 20, 1999)	1.20	1.10
65p greenish blue (April 25, 2000)	1.20	1.10
68p grey-brown (July 4, 2002)	1.25	1.15
72p red (March 28, 2006)	1.20	1.20
78p emerald green (March 27, 2007)	1.20	1.20
81p sea green (April 1, 2008)	1.25	1.25
£1 bluish-violet (April 1, 1997)	1.90	1.90
£1 ruby (June 5, 2007)	1.50	1.25
Stamp cards (one of each value current in September 2008, including NVIs; 24 in total)	15.00	15.00

■ 1994-1996

Printed in litho by Questa. Two phosphor bands, except where stated.

1p crimson (July 8, 1995)		
from £1 booklets	1.00	0.55
6p lime-green (July 26, 1994)		
from Northern Ireland prestige stamp book	6.00	5.00
10p deep orange (April 25, 1995)		
from National Trust prestige stamp book	2.25	2.25

19p olive green (July 26, 1994) (phos band at left)
from Northern Ireland & National Trust PSBs 1.50   1.50
(April 25, 1995) (phos band at right)
from National Trust prestige stamp book   1.10   1.20
20p bright green (July 8, 1996) (centre phos band)
from £1 and £2 booklets   1.90   1.90
25p salmon-pink (July 26, 1994)
from £1 and £2 booklets, and Northern
Ireland & National Trust PSBs   1.00   1.00
26p red-brown (July 8, 1996)
from £1 and £2 booklets   0.90   0.90
30p grey-green (April 25, 1995)
from National Trust prestige stamp book   2.60   2.50
35p deep yellow (April 25, 1995)
from National Trust prestige stamp book   1.50   1.60
41p drab (April 25, 1995)
from National Trust prestige stamp book   2.00   2.00

■ **1998-1999**
Printed in gravure by Questa. Two phosphor bands, except
where stated.
1p crimson (December 1, 1998)
from £1 booklets and World Changers PSB   1.25   1.00
2p myrtle-green (April 26, 1999)
from £1 booklets   0.60   0.50
19p olive green (Apr 26, 1999) (centre phos band)
from £1 and £2 booklets
and World Changers PSB   1.00   1.00
20p bright green (Dec 1, 1998) (centre phos band)
from £1 and £2 stamp booklets   1.50   1.20
26p red-brown (December 1, 1998)
from £1 and £2 booklets and
World Changers prestige stamp book   2.00   1.50

■ **1993-1996**
Printed in litho by Walsall. Two phosphor bands.
25p salmon-pink (November 1, 1993)
from £1 booklets   1.30   1.10
35p deep yellow (November 1, 1993)
from £1.40 booklets   1.40   1.20
37p amethyst (July 8, 1996)
from £1.48 booklets   6.00   5.00
41p stone (November 1, 1993)
from £1.64 booklets   1.30   1.10
60p slate-blue (March 19, 1996)
from £2.40 booklets   2.50   2.30
63p emerald (July 8, 1996)
from £2.52 booklets   1.50   1.50

■ **1997-2000**
Printed in gravure by Walsall. Two phosphor bands, except
where stated.
10p deep orange (October 13, 1998)
from Breaking Barriers prestige stamp book   1.50   1.35
19p olive-green (Feb 15, 2000) (phos band at right)
from Special By Design prestige stamp book   1.00   1.10
30p grey-green (May 5, 1998)
from £1.20 booklet   0.70   0.70
37p amethyst (August 26, 1997)
from £1.48 booklets   0.85   0.80

38p ultramarine (April 26, 1999)
from £1.52 booklet   1.00   0.90
38p ultramarine (February 15, 2000) (perf: 14)
from Special By Design prestige stamp book   5.00   4.00
40p grey-blue (April 27, 2000)
from £1.60 booklets   1.00   1.00
43p chocolate brown (October 13, 1998)
from Breaking Barriers prestige stamp book   1.50   1.50
63p emerald (August 26, 1997)
from £2.52 booklets   1.50   1.50
64p sea-green (April 26, 1999)
from £2.56 booklets   1.50   1.50
65p greenish blue (April 27, 2000)
from £2.60 booklets   1.50   1.50

NON-VALUE INDICATORS WITH ELLIPTICAL PERFORATIONS, 1993-2000

Issued in booklets or coils. 2nd class stamps have one centre phosphor band; the others have two phosphor bands, except where stated.

■ **1993-1999**
Printed in photogravure by Harrison
2nd bright blue (September 7, 1993)   1.60   1.40
1st orange-red*
(April 6, 1993) (phos coated paper)   0.65   0.55
(April 4, 1995) (two phosphor bands)   0.75   0.65
1st gold (April 21, 1997)*   1.10   0.75
E deep blue (October 5, 1999)   0.80   0.85
Stamp card (1st gold)   0.75   3.00
(* The 1st class gold is also found in the 75 Years Of The BBC prestige stamp book, and the 1st class orange-red in the Profile On Print prestige stamp book.)

■ **1993**
Printed in litho by Walsall
2nd bright blue (April 6, 1993)   0.75   0.60
1st orange-red (April 6, 1993)   1.00   0.65

■ **1997-1999**
Printed in gravure by Walsall
2nd bright blue (April 29, 1997)   0.75   1.60
(Oct 13, 1998) (phos band at left, perf: 14)
from Breaking Barriers prestige stamp book   1.00   0.80
(Oct 13, 1998) (phos band at right, perf: 14)
from Breaking Barriers prestige stamp book   1.20   0.95
1st gold (April 21, 1997)   1.00   0.80
1st orange-red (August 26, 1997)   0.75   0.60
E deep blue (January 19, 1999)   0.80   0.70

■ **1993**
Printed in litho by Questa
2nd bright blue (April 6, 1993)   0.95   0.80
1st orange-red (April 6, 1993)   0.95   0.80

■ **1998-2000**
Printed in gravure by Questa
2nd bright blue (Dec 1, 1998) (perf: 14)   0.95   0.95

2nd bright blue (Apr 27, 2000) (perf: 15x14)	0.70	0.65
1st orange-red (Dec 1, 1998) (perf: 14)	0.95	0.90
1st orange-red (Apr 27, 2000) (perf: 15x14)	0.80	0.80

© The Post Office 1995

Valid for Royal Mail
First class up to 60g
within the UK

1ST

■ 1994-1997. Greetings card sheetlets
Small sheets including one 1st class orange-red stamp sold in conjunction with greetings cards, initially through Boots, and subsequently other retail outlets.

Printed in litho by Questa

1st sheetlet with Boots logo (Aug 17, 1994)	2.00	2.00
1st sheetlet with no logo (Sep 11, 1995)	1.50	1.50

Printed in litho by Enschedé

1st sheetlet with no logo (Apr 29, 1997)	0.95	0.95

SELF-ADHESIVES, 1993-date
All in vertical format except where otherwise stated.

1ST

■ 1993, October 19
Des: Jeffery Matthews. Printed in litho by Walsall. Horizontal format. Issued only in booklets of 20.

1st orange-red	0.80	0.80
Stamp card	7.50	10.00

■ 1997, March 18
Des; Jeffery Matthews. Printed in gravure by Enschedé. Horizontal format with 'st' or 'nd' in large size. Issued only in rolls of 100.

2nd bright blue	1.50	1.60
1st orange-red	1.60	1.70

2ND

■ 1998, April 6
Perf: 15 x 14. Printed in gravure by Enschedé in rolls of 200, by Walsall in business sheets of 100, by Questa in business sheets of 100 (1st class only) and by Enschedé in business sheets of 100.

2nd bright blue	1.00	1.00
2nd bright blue (Perf: 14½ x 14)	125.00	125.00
1st orange-red	1.00	1.00
1st orange-red (Perf: 14½ x 14)	125.00	125.00

(* Perf: 14½ x 14 stamps were printed only by Walsall, and sold only individually through Royal Mail's Tallents House)

■ 2002, June 5
Printed by gravure by De La Rue, Questa and Walsall in retail stamp booklets, and by Enschedé and Walsall in business sheets of 100.

1st gold	0.60	0.60

■ 2002, July 4
Printed in gravure by Walsall. Issued only in retail books.

E deep blue	1.50	1.50
42p olive-grey	2.25	2.25
68p grey-brown	2.50	2.50

Worldwide

postcard

■ 2003-2004. Overseas rates with airmail chevrons
Des: Sedley Place. Printed in gravure by Walsall. Issued only in booklets, although individual stamps were sold through Royal Mail's Tallents House.

Europe (March 27, 2003)	1.00	1.10
Worldwide (March 27, 2003)	1.75	1.90
Worldwide Postcard (April 1, 2004)	0.75	0.80
First day cover (March 27, 2003)		4.25
First day cover (April 1, 2004)		3.25
Stamp card	0.75	3.25

1ST

Large

■ 2006. Pricing in Proportion
Des: Mike Dempsey. Printed in gravure by De La Rue. Normal gum.

2nd blue (August 1, 2006)	0.50	0.55
2nd Large blue (August 1, 2006)	0.60	0.65
1st gold (August 1, 2006)	0.65	0.65
1st Large gold (August 1, 2006)	0.75	0.75

SPECIAL ISSUES

■ **1990, January 10. 150th Anniversary of the Penny Black**
Des: Jeffery Matthews. Issued in sheets and booklets; the stamps from booklets can have one or more edges imperforate.
Printed in photogravure by Harrison (from sheets and booklets)

15p bright blue (one centre phos band)	0.75	0.50
(one phos band at left)*	1.80	1.80
(one phos band at right)*	3.00	3.00
20p brownish-black and cream (phos paper)	0.60	0.65
(two phos bands)*	1.75	1.30
29p mauve (phosphor paper)	1.10	1.10
(two phosphor bands)*	6.00	6.00
34p blue-grey	1.00	1.10
37p rosine	1.20	1.25

(* these stamps come from the London Life prestige stamp book issued on March 20, 1990)
Printed in litho by Walsall (only from booklets)

15p bright blue (one centre phos band)	1.00	0.90
20p brownish-black and cream (phos paper)	1.00	1.00

Printed in litho by Questa (only from booklets)

15p bright blue (one centre phos band)	1.25	1.30
20p brownish-black (phos paper)	1.30	1.30

Printed in gravure by Walsall (only for the £7.50 Special by Design prestige stamp book issued on February 15, 2000)

1st brownish black and cream	1.00	1.05

■ **1999, February 6. Large-format definitives**
Issued only in the Profile On Print prestige stamp book.
Embossed and litho printed by Walsall. Self-adhesive.

1st pale grey	1.30	1.40

Recess printed by Enschedé. Engraved by C. Slania. Two phos bands.

1st grey-black	1.30	1.40

Printed in typography by Harrison. Two phos bands.

1st black	1.30	1.40

■ **2000, January 6. Millennium definitives**
The Machin portrait against a white background. Des: R. Scholey.
Printed in gravure by Harrison. Perf: 15 x 14. Issued in sheets.

1st olive-brown	0.80	0.75

Printed in gravure by Walsall. Perf: 15 x 14. Issued in retail books.

1st olive-brown	1.00	0.80

Printed in gravure by Walsall. Perf: 14. Issued in the Special By Design and Treasury Of Trees prestige stamp books.

1st olive-brown	1.00	0.75

Printed in gravure by Questa. Perf: 14. Issued in retail stamp booklets.

1st olive-brown	1.00	0.75

Printed in gravure by Questa. Perf: 15 x 14. Issued in the Queen Elizabeth The Queen Mother prestige stamp book.

1st olive-brown	1.00	1.00

■ **May 22, 2000. Stamp Show 2000 Exhibition Souvenir**
Des: Jeffery Matthews. Printed by De La Rue. Phosphor paper.
Miniature sheet comprising 4p blue, 5p claret, 6p lime green, 10p orange, 31p purple, 39p magenta, 64p sea-green, £1 bluish violet, plus the Royal Mail crest and the Jeffery Matthews colour palette.

Miniature sheet	13.00	13.00
First day cover		25.00

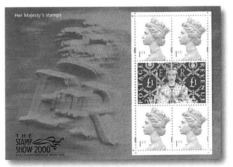

■ **2000, May 23. Her Majesty's Stamps Miniature Sheet. Stamp Show 2000.**
Des: Delaney Design Consultants. Printed in gravure by De La Rue. Comprising four 1st class Millennium definitives, plus the 1953 Coronation design by Edmund Dulac, with face value £1.

Miniature sheet	10.00	10.00
First day cover		20.00
Stamp cards	20.00	25.00

■ **1970, June 17**
Des: Arnold Machin. Printed in recess by Bradbury, Wilkinson.
No wmk. Perf: 12.

10p cerise, phos paper	0.70	0.70
20p olive-green	0.60	0.40
50p ultramarine	1.00	0.40
£1 black (Dec 6, 1972)	3.00	0.80

(* Initially the £1 was identical to that issued on March 5, 1969, but was printed in sheets of 100 instead of sheets of 40. However, on December 6, 1972 it was re-released with the denomination in a different typeface.)

■ **1977, February 2**
Des: Arnold Machin. Printed in photogravure by Harrison. Perf: 14x15.

£1 olive, deep green	2.00	0.30
£1.30 steel blue, buff (Aug 3, 1983)	4.50	4.50
£1.33 lilac, deep blue (Aug 28, 1984)	4.20	4.70
£1.41 deep blue, pale blue, green (Sep 17, 1985)	5.00	5.00
£1.50 rose-lilac, blue-black (Sep 2, 1986)	3.50	2.50
£1.60 buff, blue-green (Sep 15, 1987)	4.20	3.20
£2 emerald, deep purple	4.20	0.50
£5 pink, blue	9.00	1.90
Set	30.00	19.00
Gutter pair	70.00	
Traffic light gutter pair	82.00	
First Day Cover (£1, £2, £5)		10.00
First Day Cover (£1.30)		7.00
First Day Cover (£1.33)		6.00
First Day Cover (£1.41)		5.50
First Day Cover (£1.50)		5.00
First Day Cover (£1.60)		4.50

■ **March 9, 1999. Small format**
Printed in intaglio by Enschedé. Engraved by C. Slania.
£1.50, £2, £3, £5

Set	20.00	8.50
First Day Cover		17.50

■ **April 11, 2000**
Printed in intaglio by De La Rue.
£1.50, £2, £3, £5

Set	18.50	10.00
First Day Cover		20.00

■ **July 1, 2003**
Printed in gravure by De La Rue.
£1.50, £2, £3, £5

Set	18.00	10.00
First Day Cover		20.00

PROTECTIVE SHIELD

In a market filled with many pitfalls, it's good to know who you can rely on.

Members of the Philatelic Traders' Society agree to abide by a strict code of ethics, which ensures that you can deal with them in total confidence.

Established over 60 years, the PTS is the premier British dealer organisation with over 500 members respected throughout the philatelic community.

For more information on the society and its members, which also organises the world famous, twice yearly Stampex national stamp exhibitions held in London, go to
www.philatelic-traders-society.co.uk

The Philatelic Traders' Society Limited,
P.O. Box 371, Fleet, Hampshire GU52 6ZX.
Tel: 01252 628006 Fax: 01252 684674

QUEEN ELIZABETH II
DECIMAL SPECIAL ISSUES

In this section, prices are quoted in two columns: unmounted mint (left) and fine used (right).

Most issues are priced for complete sets only, except where a variety of an individual design has extra value. Gutter pairs, traffic light gutter pairs and stamp cards are also priced for a complete set except where stated.

Gutter pairs appear from November 1972, traffic light gutter pairs from November 1972 to January 1980, blue tinted polyvinyl alcohol dextrin (**PVAD**) gum from November 1973 and phosphor coated paper from September 1979.

'A Mountain Road' by Flanagan (3p)
'Deer's Meadow' by Carr (7½p)
'Slieve na brock' by Middleton (9p)

■ 1971, June 16. Ulster Paintings
Des: S. Rose.

Set	0.50	0.60
First day cover		1.00

John Keats (3p)
Thomas Gray (5p)
Sir Walter Scott (7½p)

■ 1971, July 28. Literary Anniversaries
Des: Rosalind Dease.

Set	0.50	0.60
First day cover		1.00

British Legion: Servicemen and a nurse (3p)
City of York: A Roman Centurion (7½p)
Rugby Football Union: Rugby Players (9p)

■ 1971, August 25. Anniversaries
Des: F. Wegner.

Set	0.50	0.60
First day cover		1.10

University College, Aberystwyth (3p)
University of Southampton (5p)
University of Leicester (7½p)
University of Essex (9p)

■ 1971, September 22. University Buildings
Des: N. Jenkins.

Set	0.75	1.00
First day cover		1.10

'Dream of the Wise Men' (2½p)
'Adoration of the Magi' (3p)
'Ride of the Magi' (7½p)

■ 1971, October 13. Christmas
Des: Clarke, Clement and Hughes based on stained glass windows at Canterbury Cathedral.

Set	0.30	0.40
First day cover		1.00

Sir James Clarke Ross (3p)
Sir Martin Frobisher (5p)
Henry Hudson (7½p)
Captain Scott (9p)

■ 1972, February 16. Polar Explorers
Des: Marjorie Seynor.

Set	0.60	0.75
First day cover		1.10

Tutankhamun (3p)
Coastguard (7½p)
Ralph Vaughan Williams (9p)

▪ 1972, April 26. Anniversaries
Des: Rosalind Dease (3p), F. Wegner (7½p), C. Abbott (9p)

Set	0.50	0.60
First day cover		1.10

St. Andrew's, Greensted-juxta-Ongar, Essex (3p)
All Saints, Earls Barton, Northants (4p)
St. Andrew's, Lethringsett, Norfolk (5p)
St. Andrew's, Helpringham, Lincs (7½p)
St. Mary the Virgin, Huish Episcopi, Somerset (9p)

▪ 1972, June 21. Village Churches
Des: R. Maddox.

Set	0.75	1.00
First day cover		1.50

Microphones (3p)
Horn Loudspeaker (5p)
Colour Television (7½p)
Oscillator and Spark Transmitter (9p)

▪ 1972, September 13. 50th Anniversary of the BBC
Des: D. Gentleman.

Set	0.75	0.80
First day cover		1.10

Angel with trumpet (2½p)
Angel with lute (3p)
Angel with harp (7½p)

▪ 1972, October 19. Christmas
Des: Sally Stiff.

Set	0.25	0.40
First day cover		0.60

Queen Elizabeth II and Prince Phillip (3p), (20p)

▪ 1972, November 20, Royal Silver Wedding
Des: J. Matthews from photograph by Norman Parkinson.
All-over phosphor (3p), no phosphor (20p).
i) Printed on a Rembrandt machine

Set	0.50	0.60
First day cover		0.60

ii) Printed on a Jumelle machine.

3p deep blue, brown, silver	0.20	0.20
Gutter pair	0.30	
Traffic light gutter pair	8.00	

(* The portraits tend to be lighter on the Jumelle printing)

Jigsaw pieces representing Europe (3p), (5p)

▪ 1973, January 3, European Communities
Des: P. Murdoch.

Set	0.50	0.75
First day cover		0.80

Oak Tree (9p)

■ **1973, February 28. British Trees**
Des: D. Gentleman.
9p multicoloured	0.25	0.25
First day cover		0.50

David Livingstone (3p)
H.M. Stanley (3p)
Francis Drake (5p)
Walter Raleigh (7½p)
Charles Sturt (9p)

■ **1973, April 18. British Explorers**
Des: Marjorie Seynor. All-over phosphor.
Set	1.10	1.00
First day cover		1.10

About to bat (3p)
Watching the ball (7½p)
Leaving the wicket (9p)

■ **1973, May 16. County Cricket**
Des: E Ripley, based on drawings by Harry Furniss of W.G.
Grace.
Set	1.00	1.00
First day cover		1.25
Stamp card (of 3p design)	50.00	

Self portrait of Joshua Reynolds (3p)
Self portrait of Henry Raeburn (5p)
'Nelly O'Brien' by Reynolds (7½p)
'Rev. R. Walker' by Raeburn (9p)

■ **1973, July. British Painters**
Des: S. Rose.
Set	0.55	0.65
First day cover		1.00

Court Masque Costumes (3p)
St Paul's church, Covent Garden (3p)
Prince's Lodging, Newmarket (5p)
Court Masque Stage Scene (5p)

■ **1973, August 15. 400th Anniversary of Birth of Inigo Jones**
Des: Rosalind Dease. Printed in litho and typo by Bradbury, Wilkinson.
Set	0.50	0.65
First day cover		0.90
Stamp card (of 3p St Paul's)	£125	£225

Palace of Westminster from Whitehall (8p)
Palace of Westminster from Millbank (10p)

■ **1973, September 12. Commonwealth Parliamentary Conference**
Des: R. Downer. Printed in recess and litho by Bradbury, Wilkinson.
Set	0.40	0.50
First day cover		0.75
Stamp card (of 8p design)	25.00	£150

Princess Anne and Captain Mark Phillips (3½p), (20p)

■ 1973, November 14. Royal Wedding

Des: C. Clements and E. Hughes based on photograph by Lord Lichfield

Set	0.50	0.55
Gutter pair	1.50	
Traffic light gutter pair	50.00	
First day cover		0.60
Stamp card (of 3½p design)	5.00	30.00

(*The 3½p exists from sheets guillotined in the wrong place giving incorrect inscriptions within the gutter: priced at £30.)

Good King Wenceslas (five different 3p designs)
Good King Wenceslas, the Page and the Peasant (3½p)

■ 1973, November 28. Christmas

Des: D. Gentleman. 3p values have one phosphor band. These stamps exist with either gum Arabic (3p), PVA gum (3½p) or dextrin gum (both values); prices are the same.

Set	1.00	1.50
First day cover		1.20

Horse Chestnut (10p)

■ 1974, February 27. British Trees

Des: D. Gentleman.

10p	0.20	0.25
Gutter pair	1.00	
Traffic light gutter pair	30.00	
First day cover		0.50
Stamp card	95.00	75.00

First Motor Fire Engine 1904 (3½p)
Fire Engine 1863 (5½p)
Steam Fire Engine (8p)
Fire Engine 1766 (10p)

■ 1974, April 24. Fire Engines

Des: D. Gentleman. Dextrin gum except where stated.

3½p with PVA gum	0.90	-
Set	0.75	0.80
Gutter pairs	1.75	
Traffic light gutter pairs	30.00	
First day cover		1.25
Stamp card (of 3½p)	75.00	75.00

P&O Packet Steamer 'Peninsular' (3½p)
Coronation Airmail 1911 (5½p)
Blue Airmail Van (8p)
Imperial Airways Flying boat (10p)

■ 1974, June 12. Centenary of the UPU

Des: Rosalind Dease.

Set	0.50	0.75
Gutter pairs	1.50	
Traffic light gutter pairs	25.00	
First day cover		0.75

Robert the Bruce (4½p)
Owain Glyndwr (5½p)
Henry V (8p)
The Black Prince (10p)

■ 1974, July 10. Famous Britons

Des: F. Wegner.

Set	0.55	0.75
Gutter pairs	2.50	
Traffic light gutter pairs	30.00	
First day cover		1.00
Stamp card (set)	16.00	50.00

Lord Warden of the Cinque Ports (4½p)
Prime Minister (5½p)
Secretary for War and Air (8p)
War Correspondent in South Africa (10p)

■ **1974, October 9. Birth Centenary of Winston Churchill**
Des: C. Clements and E. Hughes.

8p with PVA gum	1.25	-
Set	0.90	0.85
Gutter pairs	1.75	
Traffic light gutter pairs	17.50	
First day cover		1.00
Stamp card (of 5½p)	3.50	17.00

'Adoration of the Magi' (3½p)
'The Nativity' (4½p)
'Virgin and Child' (8p)
'Virgin and Child' (10p)

■ **1974, November 27. Christmas**
Des: Peter Hatch Partnership based on church roof bosses.

3½p with phos band to right	0.20	0.25
Set	0.50	0.60
Gutter pairs	2.25	
Traffic light gutter pairs	25.00	
First day cover		0.90

Invalid in Wheelchair (4½p + 1½p)

■ **1975, January 22. Health and Handicap Charities**
Des: P. Sharland. Surcharge donated to charity.

4½p + 1½p	0.15	0.15
Gutter pair	0.30	
Traffic light gutter pair	0.75	
First day cover		0.50

'Peace: Burial at Sea' (4½p)
'Snowstorm' (5½p)
'The Arsenal, Venice' (8p)
'St. Laurent' (10p)

■ **1975, February 19. Bicentenary of the Birth of Turner**
Des: S. Rose.

Set	0.50	0.60
Gutter pairs	1.25	
Traffic light gutter pairs	5.00	
First day cover		0.80
Stamp card (of 5½p)	6.00	17.00

Charlotte Square, Edinburgh (7p)
The Rows, Chester (7p)
Royal Observatory, Greenwich (8p)
St. George's Chapel, Windsor (10p)
National Theatre, London (12p)

■ **1975, April 23. European Architectural Heritage Year.**
Des: P. Gauld.

Set	0.80	1.00
Gutter pairs	2.25	
Traffic light gutter pairs	12.00	
First day cover		1.00
Stamp cards (7p and 8p)	6.00	22.00

Sailing Dinghies (7p)
Racing Keel Boats (8p)
Cruising Yachts (10p)
Multihulls (12p)

1975, June 11. Sailing

Des: A. Restall. Printed in photogravure and recess by Harrison.

Set	0.50	0.60
Gutter pairs	1.50	
Traffic light gutter pairs	12.00	
First day cover		0.90
Stamp card (of 8p)	4.00	15.00

(* The 7p exists from sheets guillotined in the wrong place, giving gutter pairs with the wrong inscriptions, priced at £45.)

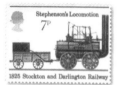

Stephenson's 'Locomotion' (7p)
Waverley Class (8p)
Caerphilly Class (10p)
High Speed Train (12p)

1975, August 13. Railways

Des: B. Cracker.

Set	0.80	0.75
Gutter Pairs	2.00	
Traffic light gutter pairs	6.00	
First day cover		1.00
Stamp cards (set)	35.00	35.00

Palace of Westminster (12p)

1975, September 3. Inter-Parliamentary Union Conference

Des: R. Downer

12p	0.25	0.25
Gutter pair	0.60	
Traffic light gutter pair	1.50	
First day cover		0.50

Emma and Mr. Woodhouse (8½p)
Catherine Morland (10p)
Mr. Darcy (11p)
Mary and Henry Crawford (13p)

1975, October 22. Jane Austen Birth Bicentenary

Des: Barbara Brown.

Set	0.65	0.70
Gutter pairs	1.40	
Traffic light gutter pairs	4.50	
First day cover		0.90
Stamp cards (set)	12.00	30.00

Angel with harp and lute (6½p)
Angel with mandolin (8½p)
Angel with horn (11p)
Angel with trumpet (13p)

1975, November 25. Christmas

Des: R. Downer. Dextrin gum except where stated. The 8½p has the phosphor in the green printing ink

6½p with PVA gum	0.50	-
Set	0.65	0.75
Gutter pairs	1.40	
Traffic light gutter pairs	5.00	
First day cover		0.75

Housewife with telephone (8½p)
Policeman with telephone (10p)
District Nurse with telephone (11p)
Industrialist with telephone (13p)

1976, March 10. Centenary of First Telephone Conversation

Des: P. Sharland.

Set	0.75	0.80
Gutter pairs	1.50	
Traffic light gutter pairs	5.00	
First day cover		0.75

Mining coal: Thomas Hepburn (8½p)
Machinery: Robert Owen (10p)
Sweeping a chimney: Lord Shaftesbury (11p)
Prison Bars: Elizabeth Fry (13p)

■ 1976, April 28. Social Reformers
Des: D. Gentleman.

Set	0.70	0.80
Gutter pairs	1.50	
Traffic light gutter pairs	5.00	
First day cover		0.75
Stamp card (of 8½p)	4.00	12.00

Benjamin Franklin (11p)

■ 1976, June 2. American Bicentennial
Des: P. Sharland.

11p	0.25	0.25
Gutter pair	0.50	
Traffic light gutter pair	1.50	
First day cover		0.50
Stamp card	3.50	12.00

Elizabeth of Glamis (8½p)
Grandpa Dickson (10p)
Rosa Mundi (11p)
Sweet Briar (13p)

■ 1976, June 30. Roses
Des: Kristin Rosenberg.

Set	0.70	0.80
Gutter pairs	1.50	
Traffic light gutter pairs	6.00	
First day cover		0.90
Stamp card	17.00	25.00

Archdruid (Royal National Eisteddfod) (8½p)
Morris Dancing (10p)
Highland Gathering (11p)
Harpist (Royal National Eisteddfod) (13p)

■ 1976, August 4. Cultural Traditions
Des: Marjorie Seynor.

Set	0.70	0.80
Gutter pairs	1.50	
Traffic light gutter pairs	5.50	
First day cover		0.75
Stamp card	9.00	17.00

'The Canterbury Tales' (8½p)
'The Tretyse of Love' (10p)
'The Game and Playe of Chesse (11p)
Printing Press (13p)

■ 1976, September 29. 500th Anniversary of British Printing
Des: R. Gay.

Set	0.70	0.75
Gutter pairs	1.50	
Traffic light gutter pairs	5.00	
First day cover		0.75
Stamp card	7.00	17.00

Virgin and Child (6½p)
Angel (8½p)
Angel with Shepherds (11p)
The Three Kings (13p)

■ **1976, November 24. Christmas.**
Des: Enid Marx (based on English embroideries)

6½p with one phos band	0.15	0.10
Set	0.60	0.70
Gutter pairs	1.50	
Traffic light gutter pairs	4.50	
First day cover		0.75
Stamp card	2.50	15.00

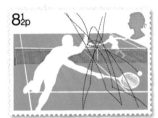

Lawn Tennis (8½p)
Table Tennis (10p)
Squash (11p)
Badminton (13p)

■ **1977, January 12. Racket Sports**
Des: A. Restall.

Set	0.65	0.60
Gutter pairs	1.75	
Traffic light gutter pairs	4.00	
First day cover		0.80
Stamp card	4.50	15.00

Steroids (8½p)
Vitamin C (10p)
Starch Chromatography (11p)
Salt Crystallography (13p)

■ **1977, March 2. Centenary of the Royal Institute of Chemistry**
Des: J. Karo.

Set	0.65	0.60
Gutter pairs	1.75	
Traffic light gutter pairs	4.00	
First day cover		0.75
Stamp card	4.50	10.00

ER (8½p, 9p, 10p, 11p, 13p)

■ **1977, May 11. Silver Jubilee.**
Des: Professor R. Guyatt. 9p issued on June 15.

Set	0.80	0.75
Gutter pairs	1.80	
Traffic light gutter pairs	3.50	
First day cover (8½p, 10p, 11p, 13p)		0.60
First day cover (9p)		0.50
Stamp card	7.00	11.00

Symbol of Pentagons (13p)

■ **1977, June 8. Commonwealth Heads of Government Meeting**
Des: P. Murdoch. Printed in photogravure and recess by Harrison.

13p	0.25	0.25
Gutter pair	0.50	
Traffic light gutter pair	1.00	
First day cover		0.50
Stamp card	3.00	4.00

Hedgehog (9p)
Hare (9p)
Red Squirrel (9p)
Otter (9p)
Badger (9p)

North Sea Oil (9p)
Coal Pithead (10½p)
Natural Gas Flame (11p)
Electricity (13p)

■ 1977, October 5. Wildlife.
Des: P Oxenham. All multicoloured

Se-tenant strip of five	0.75	0.90
Gutter strip	1.25	
Traffic light gutter strip	2.50	
First day cover		1.00
Stamp card	2.00	5.00

(* Gutter strips normally comprise a strip of four designs separated from the fifth design by the gutter.)

■ 1978, January 25. Energy
Des: P. Murdoch.

Set	0.65	0.75
Gutter pairs	1.50	
Traffic light gutter pairs	2.25	
First day cover		0.80
Stamp card	1.75	4.00

Three French Hens, two Turtle Doves and a Partridge in a Pear Tree (7p)
Six Geese, five Gold Rings, four Colley Birds (7p)
Eight Maids, seven Swans (7p)
Ten Pipers, nine Drummers (7p)
Twelve Lords, eleven Ladies (7p)
A Partridge and Pears (9p)

Tower of London (9p)
Holyroodhouse (10½p)
Caernarvon Castle (11p)
Hampton Court (13p)

■ 1977, November 23. Christmas
Des: D. Gentleman based on the Christmas song 'The Twelve Days of Christmas'. The 7p values, issued se-tenant, have one phosphor band.

Set	0.75	0.85
Gutter pairs	1.50	
Traffic light gutter pairs	4.00	
First day cover		0.80
Stamp card	2.00	4.50

(* Gutter pairs of the 7p values comprise two horizontal se-tenant strips of the stamps separated by a horizontal gutter.)

■ 1978, March 1. Historic Buildings
Des: R. Maddox.

Set	0.75	0.80
Gutter pairs	1.60	
Traffic light gutter pairs	2.25	
First day cover		0.90
Stamp card	2.00	4.00
Miniature sheet	0.80	0.85
Miniature sheet first day cover		1.00

(* The miniature sheet, designed by J. Matthews, was sold at 53½p, the extra 10p being donated to assist the finances of staging the International Stamp Exhibition. London 1980, which the sheet itself publicised.)

State Coach (9p)
St. Edward's Crown (10½p)
Sovereign's Orb (11p)
Imperial State Crown (13p)

■ 1978, May 31. 25th Anniversary of the Coronation
Des: J. Matthews.

Set	0.75	0.75
Gutter pairs	1.60	
Traffic light gutter pairs	2.25	
First day cover		0.75
Souvenir Pack	1.75	
Stamp card	2.00	3.00

Shire Horse (9p)
Shetland Pony (10½p)
Welsh Pony (11p)
Thoroughbred (13p)

■ 1978, July 5. Horses
Des: P. Oxenham.

Set	0.70	0.75
Gutter pairs	1.50	
Traffic light gutter pairs	2.25	
First day cover		0.75
Stamp card	1.75	3.00

Penny Farthing and Safety Bicycle of 1884 (9p)
Touring bicycles (10½p)
Small-Wheel Bicycles (11p)
Road-racers (13p)

■ 1978, August 2. Cycling
Des: F. Wegner.

Set	0.70	0.75
Gutter pairs	1.60	
Traffic light gutter pairs	2.25	
First day cover		0.75
Stamp card	1.50	3.00

Dancing around a Christmas Tree (7p)
The Waits (9p)
Carol Singers (11p)
Carrying the Boar's Head (13p)

■ 1978, November 22. Christmas
Des: Faith Jacques. 7p has one phos band.

Set	0.65	0.75
Gutter pairs	1.25	
Traffic light gutter pairs	2.25	
First day cover		0.75
Stamp card	2.25	3.00

Old English Sheepdog (9p)
Welsh Springer Spaniel (10½p)
West Highland Terrier (11p)
Irish Setter (13p)

■ 1979, February 7. British Dogs
Des: P. Barrett.

Set	0.70	0.75
Gutter pairs	1.25	
Traffic light gutter pairs	2.25	
First day cover		0.75
Stamp card	1.75	3.00

Primrose (9p)
Daffodil (10½p)
Bluebell (11p)
Snowdrop (13p)

■ 1979, March 21. Spring Flowers
Des: P. Newcombe.

Set	0.70	0.75
Gutter pairs	1.50	
Traffic light gutter pairs	2.25	
First day cover		0.75
Stamp card	1.50	3.00

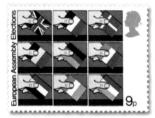

Hands placing 'flag' voting papers into ballot boxes
(9p, 10½p, 11p, 13p, designs vary slightly)

■ 1979, May 9. Direct Elections to the European Assembly
Des: S. Cliff.

Set	0.70	0.75
Gutter pairs	1.50	
Traffic light gutter pairs	2.25	
First day cover		0.75
Stamp card	1.50	3.00

Saddling Mahmoud for the Derby (9p)
The Liverpool Great National Steeple Chase (10½p)
The First Spring Meeting, Newmarket (11p)
Racing at Dorsett Ferry, Windsor (13p)

■ 1979, June 6. Horse Racing
Des: S. Rose.

Set	0.70	0.75
Gutter pairs	1.50	
Traffic light gutter pairs	2.25	
First day cover		0.75
Stamp card	1.50	3.00

The Tale of Peter Rabbit (9p)
The Wind in the Willows (10½p)
Winnie the Pooh (11p)
Alice's Adventures in Wonderland (13p)

■ 1979, July 11. International Year of the Child
Des: E. Hughes.

Set	0.85	0.80
Gutter pairs	1.75	
Traffic light gutter pairs	2.25	
First day cover		0.75
Stamp card	1.60	3.00

Sir Rowland Hill (10p)
London Post (11½p)
General Post (13p)
Penny Post (15p)

1979, August 22. Centenary of Death of Sir Rowland Hill

Des: E Stemp.

Set	0.75	0.75
Gutter pairs	1.60	
Traffic light gutter pairs	2.25	
First day cover		0.75
Stamp card	1.50	3.00
Miniature sheet	0.75	0.75
Miniature sheet first day cover		0.75

(* The miniature sheet, designed by J. Matthews and issued October 24, 1979, was sold at 59½p, the extra 10p being donated towards the finances of staging the International Stamp Exhibition, London 1980, which the sheet itself publicised.)

Policeman talking to two children (10p)
Street Patrol (11½p)
Policewoman on horseback (13p)
River police (15p)

1979, September 26. Metropolitan Police 150th Anniversary

Des: B. Sanders.

Set	0.80	0.85
Gutter pairs	1.60	
Traffic light gutter pairs	2.25	
First day cover		0.85
Stamp card	1.50	3.00

The Kings following the Star (8p)
The Angel appearing to the Shepherd (10p)
The Manger Scene (11½p)
Joseph and Mary travelling to Bethlehem (13p)
The Annunciation (15p)

1979, November 21. Christmas

Des: F. Wegner. 8p has one phosphor band.

Set	0.90	0.90
Gutter pairs	1.80	
Traffic light gutter pairs	2.25	
First day cover		0.90
Stamp card	1.50	3.00

Kingfisher (10p)
Dipper (11½p)
Moorhen (13p)
Yellow Wagtail (15p)

1980, January 16. Water Birds

Des: Michael Warren.

Set	0.80	0.80
Gutter pairs	2.00	
First day cover		0.90
Stamp card	1.50	3.00

The Rocket (12p)
First and second class carriages (12p)
Third class carriage and cattle truck (12p)
Open coach on truck and horsebox (12p)
Goods wagon and mail coach (12p)

1980, March 12. 150th Anniversary of the Liverpool & Manchester Railway

Des: D. Gentleman.

Se-tenant strip of five	0.85	1.00
Gutter pairs	2.25	
First day cover		1.00
Stamp card	1.50	3.50

(* The gutter pairs comprise two horizontal se-tenant strips of the stamps separated by a horizontal gutter.)

Charlotte Bronte (12p)
George Eliot (13½p)
Emily Bronte (15p)
Mrs. Gaskell (17½p)

■ **1980, July 9. Famous Women/Europa 1980**
Des: Barbara Brown.

Set	1.00	0.75
Gutter pairs	2.50	
First day cover		0.90
Stamp card	1.75	3.00

Montage of London buildings and monuments (50p)

■ **1980, April 9. London 1980, International Stamp Exhibition**
Des: J. Matthews. Printed by line-engraving. No phosphor.

50p	0.90	0.75
Gutter pair	2.00	
First day cover		0.75
Stamp card	0.50	1.50
Miniature sheet	0.90	1.25
Miniature sheet first day cover		1.25

(* The miniature sheet, issued on May 7, 1980, was sold at 75p, the extra 25p being donated towards the finances of staging the International Stamp Exhibition, London 1980.)
(* The stamp is known to exist in shades of green: the shades were caused by the speed of the ink-drying operation. Attempts have been made to create artificially the 'green' shades.)

Her Majesty Queen Elizabeth The Queen Mother (12p)

■ **1980, August 4. The Queen Mother's 80th Birthday**
Des: Jeffery Matthews.

12p	0.40	0.30
Gutter pair	1.00	
First day cover		0.60
Stamp card	0.60	1.00

Buckingham Palace (10½pp)
Albert Memorial (12p)
Royal Opera House (13½p)
Hampton Court (25p)
Kensington Palace (17½p)

■ **1980, May 7. London Landmarks**
Des: Sir Hugh Casson.

Set	1.00	1.00
Gutter pairs	2.50	
First day cover		1.00
Stamp card	1.50	3.50

Sir Henry Wood (12p)
Sir Thomas Beecham (13½p)
Sir Malcolm Sargent (15p)
Sir John Barbirolli (17½p)

■ 1980, September 10. Music: British Conductors
Des: Peter Gauld

Set	0.90	0.80
Gutter pairs	2.25	
First day cover		0.90
Stamp card	1.50	2.50

(* These stamps exist on paper which reveals differences in the degree of 'shine' on the surface.)

Athletics (12p)
Rugby (13½p)
Boxing (15p)
Cricket (17½p)

■ 1980, October 10. Sports
Des: Robert Goldsmith. Printed in litho by Questa.

Set	0.90	0.80
Gutter pairs	2.25	
First day cover		0.90
Stamp card	1.50	2.50

Christmas tree (10p)
Candles, ivy and ribbon (12p)
Mistletoe and apples (13½p)
Paper chains with crown and bell (15p)
Holly wreath and ornaments (17½p)

■ 1980, November 10. Christmas
Des: Jeffery Matthews. 10p has one phosphor band.

Set	1.00	1.00
Gutter pairs	2.50	
First day cover		1.00
Stamp card	1.50	2.50

(* These stamps exist on paper which reveals differences in the degree of 'shine' on the surface.)

St. Valentine's Day (14p)
Morris Dancers (18p)
Lammastide (22p)
Medieval Mummers (25p)

■ 1981, February 6. Folklore/Europa 1981
Des: Fritz Wegner.

Set	1.60	1.25
Gutter pairs	3.50	
First day cover		1.00
Stamp card	2.00	2.25

Blind Man and Guide Dog (14p)
Deaf and Dumb Alphabet (18p)
Person in Wheelchair (22p)
Foot Artist (25p)

■ 1981, March 25. International Year of Disabled People
Des: John Gibbs.

Set	1.20	1.20
Gutter pairs	3.00	
First day cover		0.90
Stamp card	1.50	2.25

Small tortoiseshell (14p)
Large Blue (18p)
Peacock (22p)
Chequered Skipper (25p)

■ 1981, May 13. Butterflies
Des: Gordon Beningfield.

Set	1.25	1.25
Gutter pairs	3.50	
First day cover		0.90
Stamp card	1.50	3.00

Glenfinnan, Scotland (14p)
Derwentwater, England (18p)
Stackpole Head, Wales (20p)
Giant's Causeway, Northern Ireland (22p)
St. Kilda, Scotland (25p)

■ 1981, June 24. National Trusts
Des: Michael Fairclough.

Set	1.30	1.40
Gutter pairs	3.50	
First day cover		1.20
Stamp card	1.50	3.00

Prince Charles and Lady Diana Spencer(14p and 25p)

■ 1981, July 22. Wedding of Prince Charles and Lady Diana Spencer
Des: Jeffery Matthews, from a portrait by Lord Snowdon.

Set	1.00	0.75
Gutter pair	2.50	
First day cover		1.50
Souvenir Pack	2.00	
Stamp card	1.75	3.00

(*A folder containing these two stamps with text printed in Japanese, was sold at the international stamp exhibition in Tokyo in 1981. A modified version of this was made available through the British Philatelic Bureau. A folder was also prepared for a promotion with Cadbury Typhoo.)

Expeditions (14p)
Skills (18p)
Service (22p)
Recreation (25p)

■ 1981, August 12. Duke of Edinburgh's Award 25th Anniversary
Des: Philip Sharland. Printed in Litho by Waddingtons.

Set	1.25	1.25
Gutter pairs	3.50	
First day cover		1.00
Stamp card	1.50	2.25

Cockle Dredging (14p)
Hauling Side Trawl (18p)
Lobster Potting (22p)
Hauling Seine Net (25p)

■ 1981, September 23. Fishing
Des: Brian Saunders.

Set	1.25	1.25
Gutter pairs	3.50	
First day cover		1.10
Stamp card	1.50	2.25

Father Christmas with sacks of toys (11½p)
The head of Christ (14p)
Angel in flight (18p)
Joseph and Mary with Donkey (22p)
The Three Wise Man on their camels following the star (25p)

■ 1981, November 18. Christmas
Des: Samantha Brown (11½p), Tracy Jenkins (14p), Lucinda Blackmore (18p), Stephen Moore (22p), Sophie Sharp (25p). The 11½p has one phosphor band

Set	1.25	1.20
Gutter pairs	3.00	
First day cover		1.10
Stamp card	1.50	3.00

Darwin and Giant Tortoises (15½p)
Darwin and Iguanas (19½p)
Darwin and Darwin's Finches (26p)
Darwin and Prehistoric Skulls (29p)

■ 1982, February 10. Centenary of the death of Charles Darwin.
Des: David Gentleman.

Set	1.20	1.10
Gutter pairs	3.00	
First day cover		1.20
Stamp cards	1.50	3.50

Boy's Brigade (15½p)
Girl's Brigade (19½p)
Scouts (26p)
Guides and Brownies (29p)

■ 1982, March 24. Youth Organisations
Des: Brian Sanders.

Set	1.20	1.10
Gutter pairs	3.00	
First day cover		1.20
Stamp cards	1.50	3.50

Ballet (15½p)
Pantomime (19½p)
Shakespearean drama (26p)
Opera (29p)

■ 1982, April 28. British Theatre/Europa
Des: Adrian George.

Set	2.00	1.10
Gutter pairs	6.00	
First day cover		1.20
Stamp cards	1.50	3.00

Henry VIII and 'Mary Rose' (15½p)
Admiral Blake and 'Triumph' (19½p)
Lord Nelson and 'HMS Victory' (24p)
Lord Fisher and 'HMS Dreadnought' (26p)
Viscount Cunningham and 'HMS Warspite' (29p)

■ 1982, June 16. Maritime Heritage
Des: Marjorie Seynor. Printed in recess and photogravure by Harrison.

Set	2.00	1.25
Gutter pairs	5.00	
First day cover		1.25
Stamp cards	1.75	4.00

'Strawberry Thief', 1883 by William Morris (15½p)
'Scarlet Tulips', 1906 by F. Steiner and Co (19½p)
'Cherry Orchard', 1930 by Paul Nash (26p)
'Chevrons', 1973 by Andrew Foster (29p)

■ 1982, July 23. British Textiles
Des: Peter Hatch Patnership.

Set	1.25	1.40
Gutter pairs	3.00	
First day cover		1.20
Stamp cards	1.75	3.50

'History of Communications (15½p)
'Technology Today' (26p)

■ 1982, September 8. Information Technology Year
Des: Brian Delaney and Darrell Ireland.

Set	0.75	0.80
Gutter pair	2.00	
First day cover		0.90
Stamp cards	1.00	2.50

Austin Seven and Metro (15½p)
Ford Model T and Escort (19½p)
Jaguar SS1 and XJ6 (26p)
Rolls Royce Silver Ghost and Silver Spirit (29p)

■ 1982, October 13. British Motor Cars
Des: Stanley Paine. Printed in litho by Questa.

Set	1.40	1.40
Gutter pairs	3.25	
First day cover		1.25
Stamp cards	1.75	3.50

While Shepherds Watched (12½p)
The Holly and the Ivy (15½p)
I Saw Three Ships (19½p)
We Three Kings of Orient Are (26p)
Good King Wenceslas (29p)

■ 1982, November 17. Christmas
Des: Barbara Brown. 12½p has one phosphor band.

Set	1.50	1.25
Gutter pairs	3.50	
First day cover		1.25
Stamp cards	1.75	4.00

Salmon (15½p)
Pike (19½p)
Trout (26p)
Perch (29p)

■ 1983, January 26. British River Fishes
Des: Alex Jardine.

Set	1.50	1.40
Gutter pairs	3.50	
First day cover		1.20
Stamp cards	1.75	4.00

COMMONWEALTH DAY 14 MARCH 1983

Tropical island (15½p)
Hot arid desert (19½p)
Lush arable land (26p)
Cold mountainous region (29p)

■ 1983, March 9. Commonwealth Day.

Des: Donald Hamilton Fraser based on an original idea by
Stafford Cliff.

Set	1.50	1.40
Gutter pairs	3.50	
First day cover		1.20
Stamp cards	1.75	3.50

The Humber Bridge (16p)
Thames Flood Barrier (20½p)
'Iolair' Emergency Support Vessel (28p)

■ 1983, May 25. Europa: Engineering Achievements

Des: Michael Taylor.

Set	1.50	1.50
Gutter pairs	4.00	
First day cover		1.20
Stamp cards	2.00	3.00

Musketeer and pikeman of the Royal Scots (16p)
The Royal Welch Fusiliers (20½p)
Riflemen of the 95th Rifles: The Royal Green Jacket (26p)
Irish Guards (28p)
The Parachute Regiment (31p)

■ 1983, July 6. The British Army

Des: Eric Stemp.

Set	1.60	1.60
Gutter pairs	4.00	
First day cover		1.50
Stamp cards	1.75	4.00

20TH CENTURY GARDEN
SISSINGHURST

Sissinghurst (16p)
Biddulph Grange (20½p)
Blenheim (28p)
Pitmedden (31p)

■ 1983, August 24. British Gardens

Des: Liz Butler. Printed in litho by Waddingtons.

Set	1.40	1.50
Gutter pairs	3.25	
First day cover		1.20
Stamp cards	1.75	3.50

Merry-go-round (16p)
Menagerie and fairground rides (20½p)
Side shows (28p)
Trading in farm produce (31p)

■ 1983, October 5. Fairs and Shows.

Des: Andrew Restall.

Set	1.40	1.50
Gutter pairs	3.25	
First day cover		1.20
Stamp cards	1.75	3.50

Flurry of birds posting Christmas greetings (12½p)
Chimney pots with a dove and cat (16p)
Dove and blackbird under an umbrella (20½p)
Dove and blackbird under a street lamp (28p)
Hedge sculpture in shape of dove (31p)

■ 1983, November 16. Christmas
Des: Tony Meeuwissen. 12½p has one phosphor band.

Set	1.50	1.60
Gutter pairs	3.50	
First day cover		1.30
Stamp cards	1.75	3.50

Arms of The College of Arms (16p)
Arms of Richard III (20½p)
Arms of The Earl Marshal (28p)
Arms of the City of London (31p)

■ 1984, January 17. Quincentenary of The College of Arms
Des: Jeffrey Matthews.

Set	1.40	1.50
Gutter pairs	3.25	
First day cover		1.25
Stamp cards	1.75	4.00

Highland Cow (16p)
Chillingham Wild Bull (20½p)
Hereford Bull (26p)
Welch Black Bull (28p)
Irish Moiled Cow (31p)

■ 1984, March 6. Cattle
Des: Barry Driscoll.

Set	1.60	1.50
Gutter pairs	4.00	
First day cover		1.25
Stamp cards	1.75	4.00

Liverpool: International Garden Festival (16p)
Durham: Milburngate Shopping Centre (20½p)
Bristol: Bush House, City Docks Area (28p)
Perth: Commercial Street Housing Scheme (31p)

■ 1984, April 19. Urban Renewal
Des: Trickett and Webb and Ronald Maddox.

Set	1.50	1.25
Gutter pairs	3.50	
First day cover		1.25
Stamp cards	1.75	3.50

Europa 'bridge' and CEPT emblem (16p, both values)
Europa abducted by Zeus in the shape of a bull and the emblem of the European Parliament (20½p, both values)

■ 1984, May 15. 25th Anniversary of CEPT and Second Direct Elections to the European Parliament
Des: J. Larriviere (16p), Fritz Wegner (20½p). The two designs were printed in se-tenant pairs throughout the sheet.

Set	2.00	2.50
Gutter pairs	5.00	
First day cover		2.00
Stamp cards	2.00	3.50

VENDING MACHINE LABELS

From May 1, 1984 until April 30, 1985, machines were installed at four locations, printing labels for the basic 1st class rate, 2nd class rate or any denomination from ½p to 16p (17p from August 28).

'Frama' labels had a red value and frame with the Queen's portrait printed on phosphor-coated white security paper with a grey-green background design.

Pack of 3½p, 12½p and 16p	1.25
Pack of 16½p and 17p labels	1.50
Pack of all values from ½p to 16p	11.00
First day cover bearing 3½p, 12½p and 16p	2.50

Lancaster House and flags of participating nations (31p)

■ 1984, June 5. London Economic Summit.
Des: Paul Hogarth.

31p	0.60	0.70
Gutter pair	1.75	
First day cover		1.00
Stamp cards	0.50	2.00

The Earth from space (16p)
Navigational chart of the English Channel (20½p)
Aerial photograph of the Greenwich Observatory (28p)
Airy's transit telescope (31p)

■ 1984, June 21. Centenary of the Greenwich Meridian
Des: Jerry Barney and Howard Walker. Printed in litho by Questa.

Set	1.50	1.50
Gutter pairs	3.50	
First day cover		1.25
Stamp cards	1.75	3.50

Original Bath Mail Coach of 1784 (16p)
Attack on the Exeter Mail in 1816 (16p)
The Norwich Mail in a thunderstorm 1827 (16p)
The Holyhead and Liverpool Mails 1828 (16p)
The Edinburgh Mail snowbound in 1831 (16p)

■ 1984, July 31. 200th Anniversary of the Frst Mail Coach Run from Bristol and Bath to London
Des: Keith Bassford and Stanley Paine. Printed in recess and photogravure by Harrison.

Set	1.50	1.50
Gutter pairs	3.50	
First day cover		1.25
Stamp cards	1.75	4.00

(* Gutter pairs comprise two horizontal se-tenant strips of the five stamps separated by a gutter.)

'Education for development' (17p)
'Promoting the arts' (22p)
'Technical training' (31p)
'Language and libraries' (34p)

■ 1984, September 25. 50th Anniversary of the British Council.
Des: Francis Newell, John Sorrell and Brian Sanders.

Set	1.50	1.50
Gutter pairs	3.50	
First day cover		1.25
Stamp cards	1.75	3.50

(* Sheets of these stamps sold at the international stamp exhibition held in Melbourne, Australia, in September 1984 had the gutter margins overprinted with the exhibition logo.)

Holy Family (13p)
Arrival in Bethlehem (17p)
Shepherd and Lamb (22p)
Virgin and Child (31p)
Offering of Frankincense (34p)

■ 1984, November 20. Christmas
Des: Yvonne Gilbert. 13p has one centre phosphor band.

Set	1.60	1.60
13p (stars printed on back)	0.60	
Gutter pairs	4.00	
First day cover		1.25
Stamp cards	1.75	3.00
Booklet (20 x 13p)	5.50	

(* The booklet, with a Manger Scene cover, sold at £2.30, a discount of 30p. The stamps had an all-over five-pointed star pattern printed on the back.)

Flying Scotsman (17p)
Golden Arrow (22p)
Cheltenham Flyer (29p)
Royal Scot (31p)
Cornish Riviera (34p)

■ **1985, January 22. Famous Trains**
Des: Terence Cuneo.

Set	2.75	2.25
Gutter pairs	7.00	
First day cover		2.25
Stamp cards	3.25	9.00

Buff-tailed Bumble Bee (17p)
Seven-Spotted Ladybird (22p)
Wart-biter Bush-cricket (29p)
Stag Beetle (31p)
Emperor Butterfly (34p)

■ **1985, March 12. Insects**
Des: Gordon Beningfield.

Set	2.00	1.80
Gutter pairs	4.00	
First day cover		1.60
Stamp cards	1.75	4.50

'Water Music' by Handel (17p)
'The Planet Suite' by Holst (22p)
'The First Cuckoo' by Delius (31p)
'Sea Picture' by Elgar (34p)

■ **1985, May 14. European Music Year. British Composers.**
Des: Wilson McLean.

Set	2.50	2.50
Gutter pairs	7.00	
First day cover		1.50
Stamp cards	1.75	4.00

RNLI Lifeboat and dinghy in distress (17p)
Beachy Head Lighthouse (22p)
Marecs A Satellite (31p)
Trinity House Buoy (34p)

■ **1985, June 18. Safety at Sea**
Des: Newell and Sorell. Printed in litho by Waddingtons.

Set	1.60	1.70
Gutter pairs	4.00	
First day cover		1.40
Stamp cards	1.75	3.50

Datapost motorcyclist and plane (17p)
Postbus in countryside (22p)
Parcel delivery (31p)
Postman delivering letters (34p)

■ **1985, July 30. 350th Anniversary of Royal Mail Service to the Public**
Des: Paul Hogarth.

Set	1.60	1.60
17p 'D' pattern printed on gummed side	0.60	
Gutter pairs	4.00	
First day cover		1.40
Stamp cards	1.75	3.50
Booklet (10 x 17p)	3.00	

(*The booklet sold at a discounted price of £1.53. Each stamp had a 'D' pattern printed on the gummed side. The cover shows a Datapost van and plane, and Concorde.)

King Arthur and Merlin (17p)
The Lady of the Lake (22p)
Guinevere and Lancelot of the Lake (31p)
Sir Galahad (34p)

■ 1985, September 3. Arthurian Legend

Des: Yvonne Gilbert.

Set	1.60	1.60
Gutter pairs	4.00	
First day cover		1.40
Stamp cards	1.75	4.00

Peter Sellers from photograph by Bill Brandt (17p)
David Niven by Cornel Lucas (22p)
Charles Chaplin by Snowdon (29p)
Vivien Leigh by Angus McBean (31p)
Alfred Hitchcock by Howard Coster (34p)

■ 1985, October 8. British Film Year

Des: Keith Bassford.

Set	2.25	2.50
Gutter pairs	6.00	
First day cover		2.25
Stamp cards	1.75	5.00

Principal Boy (12p)
Genie (17p)
Pantomime Dame (22p)
Good Fairy (31p)
Pantomime Cat (34p)

■ 1985, November 19. Christmas: Pantomime

Des: Adrian George. 12p has one phosphor band.

Set	1.60	1.60
12p ('stars' on gummed side)	0.55	
Gutter pairs	4.00	
First day cover		1.50
Stamp cards	1.75	4.50
Christmas card pack (50 x 12p)	30.00	
Booklet (20 x 12p)	5.00	

(* The booklet sold at £2.40. Cover shows Cinderella's slipper on a cushion.)

North Sea Drilling Rig and light bulb (17p)
Thermometer and laboratory (22p)
Garden hoe and steelworks (31p)
Loaf of bread and cornfield (34p)

■ 1986, January 14. Industry Year

Des: Keith Bassford. Printed in litho by Questa.

Set	1.50	1.60
Gutter pairs	4.00	
First day cover		1.40
Stamp cards	1.75	3.50

Edmund Halley as the Comet (17p)
The Giotto space probe (22p)
'Maybe twice in a lifetime' (31p)
The Comet's Orbit (34p)

■ 1986, February 18. Halley's Comet

Des: Ralph Steadman.

Set	1.50	1.60
Gutter pairs	4.00	
First day cover		1.40
Stamp cards	2.25	3.50

The Queen at the age of 2, 16 and 26 (17p and 34p)
The Queen at the age of 32, 47 and 56 (17p and 34p)

■ 1986, April 21. The Queen's 60th Birthday
Des: Jeffrey Matthews.

Set	2.25	2.00
Gutter pairs	5.00	
First day cover		2.20
Stamp cards	1.75	4.00

Barn Owl (17p)
Pine Marten (22p)
Wild Cat (31p)
Natterjack Toad (34p)

■ 1986, May 20. Europa: Nature Conservation
Des: Ken Lilly.

Set	2.00	1.80
Gutter pairs	6.00	
First day cover		1.75
Stamp cards	3.50	4.00

The peasant working on his land (17p)
The freeman and his craft (22p)
The knight and his retinue (31p)
The lord at head of table (34p)

■ 1986, June 17. Medieval Life. 900th Anniversary of the Domesday Book
Des: Tayburn.

Set	1.60	1.60
Gutter pairs	4.00	
First day cover		1.50
Stamp cards	1.75	3.50

Sprinter's feet on starting blocks (17p)
Oarsman (22p)
Weightlifter with bar (29p)
Man looking through the sights of a rifle (31p)
Hockey player (34p)

■ 1986, July 15. Sport
Des: Nick Cudworth.

Set	1.90	2.00
Gutter pairs	4.50	
First day cover		1.75
Stamp cards	2.25	4.50

Prince Andrew and Miss Sarah Ferguson (12p and 17p)

■ 1986, July 22. Royal Wedding
Des: Jeffery Matthews.

Set	0.75	0.75
Gutter pairs	2.00	
First day cover		1.00
Stamp cards	1.25	3.00

Ballot-paper cross (34p)

■ 1986, August 19. Commonwealth Parliamentary Association Conference
Des: John Gibbs. Printed in litho by Questa.

34p	0.75	0.80
Gutter pairs	2.00	
First day cover		0.80
Stamp cards	0.50	1.50

Lord Dowding and the Hurricane (17p)
Lord Tedder and the Typhoon (22p)
Lord Trenchard and the DH 9A (29p)
Sir Arthur Harris and the Lancaster (31p)
Lord Portal and the Mosquito (34p)

■ 1986, September 16. Royal Air Force
Des: Brian Sanders.

Set	2.25	2.25
Gutter pairs	5.00	
First day cover		2.00
Stamp cards	2.25	5.50

The Glastonbury Thorn (12p), (13p)
The Tanad Valley Plygain (18p)
The Hebrides Tribute (22p)
The Dewsbury Church Knell (31p)
The Hereford Boy Bishop (34p)

■ 1986, November 18. Christmas. Traditions
Des: Lynda Gray. 12p has one phosphor band and was issued on December 2, 1986; 13p has one phosphor band
13p ('stars' printed on gummerd side)0.50

Set	2.00	2.00
Gutter Pairs	5.00	
First day cover		2.50
Stamp cards	1.75	5.00
Pack (36 x 13p, stars on gum)	9.00	

Gaillardia (18p)
Echinops (22p)
Echeveria (31p)
Colchicum (34p)

■ 1987, January 6. Flowers
Des: Jeffery Matthews from photographs by Alfred Lammer.

Set	1.75	2.00
Gutter pairs	4.50	
First day cover		1.75
Stamp cards	1.75	4.00

(* A card with a Flowers design, stamped and cancelled with the 31p and 34p stamps, was made available at several stamp exhibitions, starting with Capex 87 in Toronto in June 1987.)

An apple (18p)
Planets moving around the sun (22p)
Flask of water and refraction of light (31p)
The earth and an artificial satellite (34p)

■ 1987, March 24. Sir Isaac Newton
Des: Sarah Goodwin.

Set	1.75	2.00
Gutter pairs	4.50	
First day cover		1.75
Stamp cards	1.75	3.50

Willis Faber Dumas Building, Ipswich (18p)
Pompidou Centre, Paris (22p)
Staatgalerie, Stuttgart (31p)
European Investment Bank, Luxembourg (34p)

■ 1987, May 12. British Architects in Europe.
CEPT
Des: Minale Tattersfield Studio.

Set	2.00	2.00
Gutter pairs	6.00	
First day cover		1.70
Stamp cards	2.00	3.50

First aid duties in 1887 (18p)
First aid in wartime (22p)
First aid at events (31p)
Transplant organs flights (34p)

■ 1987, June 16. St John Ambulance
Centenary
Des: Debbie Cook. Printed in litho by Questa.

Set	1.75	2.00
Gutter pairs	4.50	
First day cover		1.70
Stamp cards	1.75	3.50

Arms of the Lord Lyon, King of Arms (18p)
Arms of His Royal Highness The Duke of
Rothesay (22p)
Arms of the Royal Scottish Academy of Painting,
Sculpture and Architecture (31p)
Arms of The Royal Society of Edinburgh (34p)

■ 1987, July 21. Scottish Heraldry
Des: Jeffery Matthews.

Set	1.75	2.00
Gutter pairs	4.50	
First day cover		1.70
Stamp cards	1.75	4.00

Landseer's painting 'Monarch of the Glen', the Great Exhibition,
Grace Darling's Rescue (18p)
Launching of Brunel's 'Great Eastern', Mrs Beeton's Book of
Household Management, Prince Albert (22p)
The Albert Memorial, Benjamin Disraeli, the first ballot
box (31p)
Marconi's broadcast to Paris, Queen Victoria's diamond jubilee,
the Boer War (34p)

■ 1987, September 8. Victorian Britain
Des: Carroll and Dempsey Studio. Printed in recess and
photogravure by Harrison.

Set	2.00	2.25
Gutter pairs	6.00	
First day cover		1.70
Stamp cards	1.75	4.00

Pottery by Bernard Leach (18p)
Pottery by Elizabeth Fritsch (26p)
Pottery by Lucie Rie (31p)
Pottery by Hans Coper (34p)

■ 1987, October 13. Studio Pottery
Des: Tony Evans.

Set	1.75	2.00
Gutter pairs	4.50	
First day cover		1.70
Stamp cards	1.75	3.50

Decorating the Christmas tree (13p)
Child looking out of a window (18p)
Father Christmas in sleigh and child asleep (26p)
A child reading a book surrounded by toys (31p)
Child playing a recorder and a snowman (34p)

■ 1987, November 17. Christmas
Des: M. Foreman. 13p has one phosphor band.

Set	1.75	2.00
13p (double lined star on gummed side)	0.50	
Gutter pairs	4.00	
First day cover		1.60
Stamp cards	1.75	3.50
Folder (36 x 13p with star on gum)	8.50	

Bull-rout *Myoxocephalus scorpius*
THE LINNEAN SOCIETY 1788/1988

Short-spined seascorpion (18p)
Yellow waterlily (26p)
Bewick's Swan (31p)
Morchella esculenta (34p)

■ 1988, January 19. Bicentenary of Linnean Society
Des: E. Hughes.

Set	1.60	1.75
Gutter pairs	4.00	
First day cover		1.50
Stamp cards	1.75	3.25

Revd William Morgan (18p)
William Salesbury (26p)
Bishop Richard Davies (31p)
Bishop Richard Parry (34p)

■ 1988, March 1. 400th Anniversary of the Welsh Bible
Des: K. Bowen.

Set	1.60	1.75
Gutter pairs	4.00	
First day cover		1.50
Stamp cards	1.75	3.25

Gymnastics (18p)
Downhill skiing (26p)
Tennis (31p)
Football (34p)

■ 1988, March 22. Sports Organisations
Des: J. Sutton.

Set	1.60	1.75
Gutter pairs	4.00	
First day cover		1.50
Stamp cards	1.50	3.25

'Mallard' (18p)
'Queen Elizabeth' (26p)
Glasgow tram (31p)
Handley Page H.P.45 'Horatius' (34p)

■ **1988, May 10. Transport and Mail Services. Europa**
Des: M. Dempsey.

Set	2.00	1.75
Gutter pairs	5.00	
First day cover		1.70
Stamp cards	2.00	3.00

Settler and clipper (18p)
British and Australian Parliament Buildings
and Queen Elizabeth II (18p)
W. G. Grace and tennis racquet (34p)
Shakespeare, John Lennon and Sydney Opera House (34p)

■ **1988, June 21. Australian Bicentenary**
Des: G. Emery. Printed in litho by Questa.

Set of four in two se-tenant pairs	1.50	1.75
Gutter pairs	4.00	
First day cover		1.50
Stamp cards	1.25	3.50

Spanish off The Lizard (18p)
English Fleet leaving Plymouth (18p)
Fighting off the Isle of Wight (18p)
English attacking at Calais (18p)
Armada in the North Sea (18p)

■ **1988, July 19. Spanish Armada**
Des: G. Evernden.

Set of five in se-tenant strip	1.50	1.90
Gutter pairs	4.00	
First day cover		1.75
Stamp cards	1.50	4.50

The Owl and the Pussy cat (19p)
Edward Lear as a bird (27p)
'Cat' (32p)
There was a Young Lady whose bonnet (35p)

■ **1988, September 6. Centenary of the Death of Edward Lear**
Des: M. Swatridge and S. Dew.

Set	1.75	1.90
Gutter pairs	4.00	
First day cover		1.75
Stamp cards	1.25	3.50
Miniature sheet	2.75	3.00
First day cover		3.75

(* The miniature sheet, containing one of each value, was sold with a surcharge to help fund the international stamp exhibition, Stamp World London 90, Issued on September 27, 1988.)

Carrickfergus Castle (£1)
Caernarfon Castle (£1.50)
Edinburgh Castle (£2)
Windsor Castle (£5)

■ **1988, October 18. Castle high value definitives**
Engraved by C. Matthews from photographs by Prince Andrew.
Recess printed by Harrison.

Set	16.00	4.50
Gutter pairs	35.00	
Gutter blocks of four (centre cross)	75.00	
First Day Cover		20.00

Journeying to Bethlehem (14p)
Shepherds following the Star (19p)
Three Wise Men (27p)
The Nativity (32p)
The Annunciation (35p)

■ **1988, November 15. Christmas**
Des: L. Trickett. 14p has one phosphor band.

Set	1.75	2.00
Gutter pairs	4.00	
First day cover		1.75
Stamp cards	1.50	3.50

Atlantic Puffin (19p)
Avocet (27p)
Oystercatcher (32p)
Northern Gannet (35p)

■ **1989, January 17. Centenary of the Royal Society for the Protection of Birds**
Des: D. Cordery.

Set	1.75	2.00
Gutter pairs	4.00	
First day cover		1.75
Stamp cards	1.50	4.25

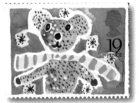

Teddy Bear (19p)
Rose (19p)
Cupid (19p)
Yachts (19p)
Fruit (19p)

■ **1989, January 31. Greetings stamps**
Des: P. Sutton. Se-tenant strip of five Issued in booklets in panes of ten containing two of each design.

Se-tenant strip	12.00	12.00
Booklet pane (of 10)	15.00	
Booklet		30.00
First day cover		12.00
Stamp cards	5.00	10.00

Fruit and vegetables (19p)
Meat (27p)
Dairy products (32p)
Cereals (35p)

■ **1989, March 7. Food and Farming Year**
Des: Sedley Place Ltd.

Set	1.75	2.00
Gutter pairs	4.00	
First day cover		1.60
Stamp cards	1.25	3.25

Firework display: Mortar board (19p)
Firework display: Cross on ballot paper (19p)
Firework display: Posthorn (35p)
Firework display: Globe (35p)

■ **1989, April 11. Anniversaries & Events**
Des: Lewis Moberly. 19p and 35p issued in se-tenant pairs.

Set (of two se-tenant pairs)	1.75	2.25
Gutter pairs	4.00	
First day cover		1.60
Stamp cards	1.25	4.00

Toy aeroplane and locomotive (19p)
Building bricks (27p)
Board games and dice (32p)
Robot, boat and doll's house (35p)

■ **1989, May 16. Toys and Games. Europa**
Des: D. Fern.

Set	2.00	1.75
Gutter pairs	5.00	
First day cover		1.50
Stamp cards	3.00	3.25

Ironbridge, Shropshire (19p)
Tin mine, St Agnes Head, Cornwall (27p)
Cotton Mills, New Lanark, Strathclyde (32p)
Pontcysylite Aqueduct, Clwyd (35p)

■ **1989, July 4. Industrial Archaeology**
Des: R. Maddox.

Set	1.60	1.75
Gutter pairs	4.00	
First day cover		1.50
Stamp cards	1.50	2.50
Miniature sheet	2.50	2.50
First day cover		3.50

(*The miniature sheet contained one of each value, but with the designs in a horizontal format, with a surcharge to help fund the international stamp exhibition, Stamp World London 90. Issued on July 25, 1989.)

Snowflake (19p)
Fly (27p)
Blood cells (32p)
Microchip (35p)

■ **1989, September 5. 150th Anniversary of the Microscopical Society**
Des: K. Bassford. Printed in litho by Questa.

Set	1.60	1.70
Gutter pairs	4.00	
First day cover		1.50
Stamp cards	1.25	3.25

Royal Mail coach (20p)
The Blues and Royals (20p)
Lord Mayor's coach (20p)
St Paul's Cathedral (20p)
Blues and Royals Drum Horse (20p)

■ **1989, October 17. Lord Mayor's Show.**
Des: P. Cox.

Set in se-tenant strip	1.50	1.90
Gutter pairs	4.00	
First day cover		1.50
Stamp cards	1.50	4.00

Peasants, from stained glass window (15p)
Arches and Roundels, West Front (15p + 1p)
Octagon Tower (20p + 1p)
Arcade from West Transept (34p + 1p)
Triple Arch from West Front (37p + 1p)

■ **1989, November 14. Christmas. 800th Anniversary of Ely Cathedral**
Des: D. Gentleman. 15p and 15+1p have one phosphor band.

Set	1.75	1.90
Gutter pairs	4.25	
First day cover		1.75
Stamp cards	1.50	4.00

(* Four of the stamps carried a surcharge for charity.)

■ **1990, January 10. 150th Anniversary of the Penny Black**
See under Machin decimal definitives

Kitten (20p)
Rabbit (29p)
Duckling (34p)
Puppy (37p)

■ **1990, January 23. 150th Anniversary of the Royal Society for the Prevention of Cruelty to Animals**
Des: T. Evans. Printed in litho by Questa.

Set	1.75	1.80
Gutter pairs	4.50	
First day cover		1.75
Stamp cards	2.50	4.50

Teddy Bear (20p)
Dennis the Menace (20p)
Punch (20p)
Cheshire Cat (20p)
The Man in the Moon (20p)
The Laughing Policeman (20p)
Clown (20p)
Mona Lisa (20p)
Queen of Hearts (20p)
Stan Laurel (20p)

■ **1990, February 6. Greetings stamps: Smiles.**
Des: Michael Peters and Partners. Stamps se-tenant in booklet panes of ten containing one of each design.

Booklet pane (of 10)	14.00	14.00
Booklet	17.50	
First day cover		14.00

Alexandra Palace (20p)
Glasgow School of Art (20p)
British Philatelic Bureau, Edinburgh (29p)
Templeton Carpet Factory, Glasgow (37p)

■ **1990, March 6. Europa and Glasgow 1990 European City of Culture**
Des: P. Hogarth.

Set	2.00	2.00
Gutter pairs	6.00	
First day cover		1.75
Stamp cards	2.50	3.50

(* The two 20p designs were issued in separate sheets, not as se-tenant pairs. The 20p Alexandra Palace design also appears as a pane of four in the £5 'London Life' prestige stamp booklet issued on March 20, 1990.)

Export Achievement Award (20p and 37p)
Technological Achievement Award (20p and 37p)

■ **1990, April 10. 25th Anniversary of The Queen's Awards for Export and Technology**
Des: S. Broom. Printed in litho by Questa.

Set (in two se-tenant pairs)	1.60	1.80
Gutter pairs	4.00	
First day cover		1.60
Stamp cards	1.50	3.50

Portraits of Queen Victoria and Queen Elizabeth II (20p)

■ **1990, May 3. Stamp World London 90 International Exhibition**
Des: Sedley Place Design; engraved by C. Matthews. Printed in recess and photogravure by Harrison. Issued only as a miniature sheet.

Miniature sheet	1.75	2.25
First day cover		2.75

(* The border of the sheet includes the Penny Black and Britannia from the 1913-1934 'Seahorse' design. The sheets were sold at £1 each, the surcharge being used to help fund the exhibition.)

Cycad and Sir Joseph Banks Building (20p)
Stone Pine and Princess of Wales Conservatory (29p)
Willow Tree and Palm House (34p)
Cedar Tree and Pagoda (37p)

■ **1990, June 5. 150th Anniversary of Kew Gardens**
Des: P. Leith.

Set	1.60	2.00
Gutter pairs	4.00	
First day cover		1.60
Stamp cards	1.50	3.50

Thomas Hardy and Clyffe Clump, Dorset (20p)

■ **1990, July 10. 150th Anniversary of the Birth of Thomas Hardy**
Des: J. Gibbs.

20p	0.40	0.40
Gutter pair	1.00	
First day cover		0.70
Stamp card	0.50	2.50

Queen Elizabeth The Queen Mother (20p)
Queen Elizabeth (29p)
Elizabeth, Duchess of York (34p)
Lady Elizabeth Bowes-Lyon (37p)

■ 1990, August 2. 90th Birthday of Queen Elizabeth, The Queen Mother

Des: J. Gorham from photographs by Norman Parkinson, Dorothy Wilding, B. Park and Rita Martin.

Set	3.00	2.25
Gutter pairs	7.50	
First day cover		2.25
Stamp cards	2.75	6.00

(* The same designs were used in 2002 in memory of the Queen Mother although the borders were changed to black.)

Victoria Cross (20p)
George Cross (20p)
Distinguished Service Cross and Distinguished Service Medal (20p)
Military Cross and Military Medal (20p)
Distinguished Flying Cross and Distinguished Flying Medal (20p)

■ 1990, September 11. Gallantry Awards

Des: J. Gibbs and J. Harwood.

Set	2.50	2.00
Gutter pairs	6.00	
First day cover		1.70
Stamp cards	1.75	4.00

(* The 20p also appears on the miniature sheet and in the Prestige stamp book for the Victoria Cross issued on September 21, 2006.)

Armagh Observatory, Jodrell Bank & La Palma Telescopes (22p)
Early telescope and diagram of Moon & Tides by Newton (26p)
Greenwich Old Observatory and astronomical equipment (31p)
Stonehenge, Gyroscope and Navigation by the stars (37p)

■ 1990, October 16. Astronomy

Des: J. Fisher. Printed in litho by Questa.

Set	2.00	2.00
Gutter pairs	5.00	
First day cover		1.75
Stamp cards	1.50	4.00

Building a snowman (17p)
Fetching a Christmas tree (22p)
Carol singers (26p)
Tobogganing (31p)
Ice-skating (37p)

■ 1990, November 13. Christmas

Des: J. Gorham and A. Davidson. 17p has one phosphor band.

Set	2.00	2.00
Gutter pairs	5.00	
First day cover		1.75
Booklet (20 x 17p)	7.00	
Stamp cards	1.75	4.00

(* The 17p was also sold in £3.40 booklets containing a pane of 20 stamps.)

King Charles Spaniel (22p)
Pointer (26p)
Two Hounds in a landscape (31p)
A Rough Dog (33p)
Fino and Tiny (37p)

■ 1991, January 8. Dogs: Paintings by George Stubbs

Des: Carroll, Dempsey and Thirkell Ltd.

Set	2.25	2.00
Gutter pairs	5.50	
First day cover		2.00
Stamp cards	2.25	4.00

Thrush's Nest (1st)
Shooting Star and Rainbow (1st)
Magpies and Charm Bracelet (1st)
Black cat (1st)
Kingfisher and key (1st)
Mallard and frog (1st)
Four-leaf clover, boot and matchbox (1st)
Pot of Gold at the end of the Rainbow (1st)
Butterflies (1st)
Wishing Well and sixpence (1st)

Man looking at Space (design over two se-tenant 22p values)
Space looking at Man (design over two se-tenant 37p values)

■ 1991, February 5. Greetings stamps: Good luck
Des: J. Meeuwissen. Issued in booklets in panes of ten containing one of each design.

Booklet pane (of 10)	7.00	7.00
Booklet	7.00	
First day cover		7.00

■ 1991, April 23. Europe in Space. Europa
Des: J-M. Folon.

Set of two se-tenant pairs	2.50	2.00
Gutter pairs	7.00	
First day cover		1.80
Stamp cards	2.00	3.50

Michael Faraday (22p)
Charles Babbage (22p)
Sweep of radar of East Anglia (31p)
Gloster Whittle E28/39 airplane over East Anglia (37p)

Fencing (22p)
Hurdling (26p)
Diving (31p)
Rugby (37p)

■ 1991, March 5. Scientific Achievements
Des: P. Till (22p values), J. Harwood (31p, 37p).

Set	1.75	1.75
Gutter pairs	4.25	
First day cover		1.75
Stamp cards	1.75	3.50

■ 1991, June 11. World Student Games, Sheffield and World Cup Rugby Championships, London
Des: Huntley Muir Partners.

Set	1.75	1.80
Gutter pairs	4.25	
First day cover		1.75
Stamp cards	1.50	3.50

■ 1991, March 26. Greetings stamps: Smiles
Designs as for the Greetings stamps of February 6, 1990, but the values in each case changed to 1st. Issued in booklets in panes of ten containing one of each design.

Booklet pane (of 10)	5.50	5.50
Booklet	6.00	
First day cover		5.50

(* These designs were also used for Smilers sheets in 2000 and 2001.)

Silver Jubilee (22p)
Mme Alfred Carrière (26p)
Rosa Moyesii (31p)
Harvest Fayre (33p)
Mutabilis (37p)

■ 1991, July 16. Ninth World Conference of Roses, Belfast
Des: Yvonne Skargon. Printed in litho by Questa.

Set	2.00	2.25
Gutter pairs	5.00	
First day cover		2.00
Stamp cards	1.75	4.50

Iguanodon (22p)
Stegosaurus (26p)
Tyrannosaurus (31p)
Protoceratops (33p)
Triceratops (37p)

■ 1991, August 20. 150th Anniversary of the identification of Dinosaurs by Owen
Des: B. Kneale.

Set	2.25	2.50
Gutter pairs	5.00	
First day cover		1.75
Stamp cards	1.75	4.50

Map of Hamstreet in 1816 (24p)
Map of Hamstreet in 1906 (28p)
Map of Hamstreet in 1959 (33p)
Map of Hamstreet in 1991 (39p)

■ 1991, September 17. Bicentenary of Ordnance Survey
Des: H. Brown. Printed in recess and litho by Harrison (24p), in litho by Harrison (28p) and in litho by Questa (33p, 39p).

Set	2.00	2.00
Gutter pairs	5.00	
First day cover		1.75
Stamp cards	1.75	3.25

(* Examples of the 28p are known with the denomination of 26p, from supplies printed before an increase in postage rates affected the denominations of this set.)

Adoration of the Magi (18p)
Mary with Jesus in stable (24p)
The Holy Family and angel (28p)
The Annunciation (33p)
The Flight into Egypt (39p)

■ 1991, November 12. Christmas
Des: D. Driver. 18p has one phosphor band.

Set	2.00	2.00
Gutter pairs	5.00	
First day cover		1.75
Booklet (20 x 18p)	6.25	
Stamp cards	1.75	4.00

(* The 18p was also sold in £3.60 booklets containing a pane of 20 stamps.)

Fallow deer (18p)
Hare (24p)
Fox (28p)
Redwing (33p)
Welsh Mountain sheep (39p)

■ 1992, January 14. Wintertime (The Four Seasons)
Des: J. Gorham and K. Bowen. 18p has one phosphor band.

Set	2.25	2.25
Gutter pairs	5.00	
First day cover		1.75
Stamp cards	2.75	4.50

(* The 39p also appears as a pane of four in the Cymru Wales prestige stamp booklet issued on February 25, 1992.)

Spray of flowers (1st)
Double locket (1st)
Key (1st)
Toy car and cigarette cards (1st)
Compass and map (1st)
Pocket watch (1st)
Penny red stamp and pen (1st)
Pearl necklace (1st)
Marbles (1st)
Starfish and a bucket and spade (1st)

■ 1992, January 28. Greetings stamps: Memories
Des: Trickett and Webb Ltd. Issued in booklets in panes of ten
containing one of each design.

Booklet pane (of 10)	6.50	6.50
Booklet	7.00	
First day cover		6.50

Queen Elizabeth II,
In Coronation robes (24p)
In Garter robes (24p)
With Prince Andrew as a baby (24p)
At Trooping the Colour (24p)
With emblem of the Commonwealth (24p)

■ 1992, February 6. 40th Anniversary of the Accession
Des: Why Not Associates. Printed in litho by Questa.

Set (in se-tenant strip)	3.00	3.25
Gutter pairs	7.50	
First day cover		2.50
Stamp cards	2.75	5.50

Tennyson in 1888 (24p)
In 1856 (28p)
In 1864 (33p)
As a young man (39p)

■ 1992, March 10. Centenary of the Death of Alfred,
Lord Tennyson
Des: Irene von Treskow.

Set	2.00	2.00
Gutter pairs	5.00	8.00
First day cover		1.75
Stamp cards	2.50	3.50

British Olympic Association logo (24p)
British Paralympic Association symbol (24p)
Santa Maria, Christopher Columbus (24p)
Kaisei, Operation Raleigh (39p)
British Pavilion at Expo '92 in Seville (39p)

■ 1992, April 7. International Events
Des: K. Bassford (BOA, BPA and Expo), K. Bassford and S. Paine
(Santa Maria and Kaisei). Printed in litho by Questa and in
recess and litho by Harrison. The BOA and BPA designs were
issued as a se-tenant pair.

Set	2.50	2.60
Gutter pairs	6.50	
First day cover		1.75
Stamp cards	3.00	5.00

Carrickfergus Castle (£1)
Caernarfon Castle (£1.50)
Edinburgh Castle (£2)
Windsor Castle (£5)

■ 1992, March 24. Castle definitives

As issue of October 18, 1988, but Queen's head is in silhouette printed in optically variable ink which changes colour from gold to green depending on the angle at which it is viewed. In addition, an elliptical perforation is included along the side of each stamp.

Set	19.50	4.00
Gutter pairs	40.00	
Gutter blocks of four (centre cross)	85.00	
First day cover		15.00
Stamp cards	10.00	40.00

(* The £1.50, £2 and £5 exist with either blue tinted PVAD gum, or white PVA gum. The date of release of the stamp cards is not the day of issue of the stamps.)

Pikeman (24p)
Drummer (28p)
Musketeer (33p)
Standard bearer (39p)

■ 1992, June 16. 350th Anniversary of the Civil War

Des: J. Sancha.

Set	1.85	1.75
Gutter pairs	4.50	
First day cover		1.75
Stamp cards	2.50	3.25

Gilbert and Sullivan operas:
The Yeoman of the Guard (18p)
The Gondoliers (24p)
The Mikado (28p)
The Pirates of Penzance (33p)
Iolanthe (39p)

■ 1992, July 21. 150th Anniversary of the birth of Sir Arthur Sullivan

Des: Lynda Gray. 18p has one phosphor band.

Set	2.00	2.00
Gutter pairs	5.00	
First day cover		1.75
Stamp cards	2.75	3.25

Acid rain kills (24p)
Ozone layer (28p)
Greenhouse effect (33p)
Bird of hope (39p)

■ 1992, September 15. Protection of the Environment

Des: C. Hall (24p), L. Fowler (28p), S. Warren (33p) and A. Newton-Mold (39p). All paintings by children, in conjunction with the BBC Television programme Blue Peter.

Set	1.75	2.00
Gutter pairs	4.50	
First day cover		1.75
Stamp cards	2.75	3.00

European Star (24p)

■ 1992, October 13. Single European Market

Des: D. Hockney.

24p	0.50	0.45
Gutter pair	1.50	
First day cover		0.65
Stamp card	0.50	2.00

Angel Gabriel (18p)
Madonna and Child (24p)
King carrying Gold (28p)
Shepherds (33p)
Kings with Frankincense and Myrrh (39p)

■ **1992, November 10. Christmas**
Des: Carroll, Dempsey and Thirkell Ltd. 18p has one phosphor band.

Set	2.25	2.25
Gutter pairs	6.00	
First day cover		1.75
Booklet (20 × 18p)	6.25	
Stamp cards	2.75	4.00

(* The 18p was also sold in £3.60 booklets containing a pane of 20 stamps.)

Mute Swan Cob (18p)
Cygnet and Decoy (24p)
Swans and Cygnet (28p)
Eggs in nest (33p)
Young swan (39p)

■ **1993, January 19. 600th Anniversary of Abbotsbury Swannery**
Des: David Gentleman. 18p has one phosphor band.

Set	3.50	3.00
Gutter pairs	8.50	
First day cover		3.00
Stamp cards	4.25	5.50

William (1st)
Long John Silver (1st)
Tweedledum and Tweedledee (1st)
Mole and Toad (1st)
Teacher and Wilfred (1st)
Peter Rabbit and Mrs Rabbit (1st)
Snowman and Father Christmas (1st)
The Big Friendly Giant and Sophie (1st)
Bill Badger and Rupert Bear (1st)
Aladdin and the Genie (1st)

■ **1993, January 28. Greetings stamps: Gift Giving**
Des: Newell and Sorell. Issued in booklets in panes of ten containing one of each design.

Booklet pane (of 10)	6.00	5.50
Booklet	6.50	
First day cover		5.50
Stamp cards	10.00	15.50

(* The Peter Rabbit and Mrs Rabbit design also appears as a pane of four in the Story of Beatrix Potter prestige stamp book issued on August 10, 1993.)

Decorated dial (24p)
Escapement, Remontoire and Eusée (28p)
Balance, Spring and Temperature compensator (33p)
Movement seen from back (39p)

■ **1993, February 16. 300th Anniversary of the birth of John Harrison**
Des: H. Brown and D. Penny. Printed in litho by Questa.

Set	2.00	2.25
Gutter pairs	5.00	
First day cover		1.75
Stamp cards	3.25	4.50

Britannia (£10)

1993, March 2. £10 Definitive.

Des: B. Craddock and Roundel Design Group. Printed in litho by Questa, also including die-stamping and embossing of Braille.

£10	20.00	7.50
First Day Cover		15.00
Stamp card	4.50	50.00

Dendrobium hellwigianum (18p)
Paphiopedilum Maudiae 'Magnificum' (24p)
Cymbidium lowianum (28p)
Vanda Rothschildiana (33p)
Dendrobium vexillarius var albiviride (39p)

1993, March 16. 14th World Orchid Conference, Glasgow

Des: Pandora Sellars. 18p has one phosphor band.

Set	2.25	2.25
Gutter pairs	5.50	
First day cover		1.75
Stamp cards	3.25	5.50

'Family Group' by Henry Moore (24p)
'Kew Gardens' by Edward Bawden (28p)
'St Francis and the Birds' by Stanley Spencer (33p)
'Still Life: Odyssey I' by Ben Nicholson (39p)

1993, May 11. Contemporary Art. Europa

Des: A. Dastor.

Set	2.50	2.25
Gutter pairs	6.50	
First day cover		1.75
Stamp cards	3.25	4.50

Emperor Claudius (24p)
Emperor Hadrian (28p)
Goddess Roma (33p)
Christ (39p)

1993, June 15. Roman Britain

Des: J. Gibbs.

Set	2.00	2.25
Gutter pairs	5.50	
First day cover		1.75
Stamp cards	3.25	4.50

Grand Union Canal (24p)
Stainforth and Keadby Canal (28p)
Brecknock and Abergavenny Canal (33p)
Crinan Canal (39p)

1993, July 20. Inland Waterways

Des: T. Lewery. Printed in litho by Questa.

Set	1.80	2.25
Gutter pairs	4.50	
First day cover		1.75
Stamp cards	3.25	4.50

Horse Chestnut (18p)
Blackberry (24p)
Hazel (28p)
Rowan (33p)
Pear (39p)

1993, September 14. Autumn (The Four Seasons)

Des: Charlotte Knox. 18p has one phosphor band.

Set	2.25	2.25
Gutter pairs	6.00	
First day cover		1.75
Stamp cards	4.25	5.50

SHERLOCK HOLMES & DR.WATSON
"THE REIGATE SQUIRE"

The Reigate Square (24p)
The Hound of the Baskervilles (24p)
The Six Napoleons (24p)
The Greek Interpreter (24p)
The Final Problem (24p)

■ **1993, October 12. Sherlock Holmes**
Des: A. Davidson. Printed in litho by Questa.

Set (in se-tenant strip of five)	2.00	2.50
Gutter pairs	5.00	
First day cover		2.50
Stamp cards	4.25	5.50

Bob Cratchit and Tiny Tim (19p)
Mr and Mrs Fezziwig (25p)
Scrooge (30p)
The Prize Turkey (35p)
Scrooge's nephew (41p)

■ **1993, November 9. Christmas: 'A Christmas Carol' by Charles Dickens**
Des: Q. Blake. 19p has one phosphor band.

Set	2.25	2.25
Gutter pairs	6.00	
First day cover		2.00
Booklet (20 x 19p)	7.00	
Booklet (10 x 25p)	5.75	
Stamp cards	4.25	5.50

Class 5 and Class B1 on the West Highland Line (19p)
Class A1 at Kings Cross (25p)
Class 4 at Blythe North (30p)
Class 4 near Wigan Central (35p)
Castle Class crossing Worcester and Birmingham Canal (41p)

■ **1994, January 18. The Age of Steam**
Des: B. Delaney, from photographs by Colin Gifford. 19p has one phosphor band.

Set	2.50	2.25
Gutter pairs	7.00	
First day cover		2.25
Stamp cards	4.25	5.50

Dan Dare (1st)
The Three Bears (1st)
Rupert Bear (1st)
Alice (1st)
Noggin and the Ice Dragon (1st)
Peter Rabbit (1st)
Little Red Riding Hood (1st)
Orlando the Marmalade Cat (1st)
Biggles (1st)
Paddington Bear (1st)

■ **1994, February 1. Greetings stamps: Messages**
Des: Newell and Sorell. Issued in booklets in panes of ten containing one of each design.

Booklet pane (of 10)	6.50	5.50
Booklet	7.00	
First day cover		5.50
Stamp cards	10.00	15.50

Castell Y Waun /Chirk Castle, Clwyd, Cymru /Wales

Castell Y Waun/Chirk Castle, Clwyd, Wales (19p)
Ben Arkle, Sutherland, Scotland (25p)
Mourne Mountains, County Down, Northern Ireland (30p)
Dersingham, Norfolk, England (35p)
Dolwyddelan, Gwynedd, Wales (41p)

1994, March 1. 25th Anniversary of the Investiture of The Prince of Wales

Paintings by the Prince of Wales. 19p has one phosphor band.

Set	2.25	2.25
Gutter pairs	6.00	
First day cover		2.00
Stamp cards	4.25	5.50

(*The 30p also appears as a pane of four in the Northern Ireland prestige stamp book issued on July 26, 1994.)

Bathing at Blackpool (19p)
Where's My Little Lad (25p)
Wish You Were Here (30p)
Punch and Judy Show (35p)
'The Tower Crane' machine (41p)

1994, April 12. Centenary of Picture Postcards

Des: M. Dempsey and B. Dare. Printed in litho by Questa. 19p has one phosphor band, others have two.

Set	2.25	2.25
Gutter pairs	6.00	
First day cover		2.25
Stamp cards	4.25	5.50

British Lion and French Cockerel (25p and 41p)
Hands over a train (25p and 41p)

1994, May 3. Opening of Channel Tunnel

Des: G. Hardie (Lion & Cockerel), J.-P. Cousin (Hands & train)

Set of two se-tenant pairs	2.25	2.50
Gutter pairs	6.00	
First day cover		2.25
Stamp cards	3.25	4.50

Douglas Boston and groundcrew (25p)
HMS Warspite (25p)
Commandos on Gold Beach (25p)
Infantry on Sword Beach (25p)
Tank and infantry (25p)

1994, June 6. 50th Anniversary of D-Day

Des: K. Bassford. Printed in litho by Questa.

Set of five in se-tenant strip	2.50	2.25
Gutter pairs	6.00	
First day cover		2.25
Stamp Cards	4.25	5.50

St Andrew's (19p)
Muirfield (25p)
Carnoustie (30p)
Royal Troon (35p)
Turnberry (41p)

1994, July 5. British Golf Courses

Des: P. Hogarth. 19p has one phosphor band.

Set	2.25	2.25
Gutter pairs	6.00	
First day cover		2.25
Stamp cards	4.25	5.50

Royal Welsh Show, Llanelwedd (19p)
Wimbledon Tennis Championships (25p)
Cowes Week (30p)
Test Match at Lord's (35p)
Braemar Gathering (41p)

1994, August 2. Summertime (The Four Seasons)

Des: M. Cook. 19p has one phosphor band.

Set	2.25	2.25
Gutter pairs	6.00	
First day cover		2.25
Stamp cards	4.25	5.50

Ultrasonic imaging (25p)
Scanning electron microscopy (30p)
Magnetic resonance imaging (35p)
Computed tomography (41p)

■ 1994, September 27. Medical Discoveries. Europa
Des: P.Vermier and J.-P.Tibbles. Printed in photogravure by
Enschedé.

Set	2.25	2.25
Gutter pairs	6.00	
First day cover		2.25
Stamp cards	3.25	4.50

Mary and Joseph (19p)
Three Wise Men (25p)
Mary with doll (30p)
Shepherds (35p)
Angels (41p)

■ 1994, November 1. Christmas: Children's Nativity Plays
Des: Yvonne Gilbert. 19p has one phosphor band.

Set	2.00	2.25
Gutter pairs	5.00	
First day cover		2.00
Booklet (20 x 19p)	6.75	
Booklet (10 x 25p)	4.25	
Stamp cards	4.25	5.50

Black cat (19p)
Siamese and tabby cat (25p)
Ginger cat (30p)
Tortoiseshell and Abyssinian cat (35p)
Black and white cat (41p)

■ 1995, January 17. Cats
Des: Elizabeth Blackadder. Printed in litho by Questa. 19p has
one phosphor band, other two phosphor bands.

Set	2.25	2.25
Gutter pairs	6.00	
First day cover		2.25
Stamp cards	5.00	7.50

Dandelion (19p)
Chestnut leaves (25p)
Garlic leaves (30p)
Hazel leaves (35p)
Spring grass (41p)

■ 1995, March 14. Springtime (The Four Seasons)
Plant sculptures by Andy Goldsworthy. 19p has one phosphor
band, other two phosphor bands.

Set	2.25	2.25
Gutter pairs	6.00	
First day cover		2.25
Stamp cards	5.00	6.50

'La Danse à la Campagne' by Renoir (1st)
'Troilus and Criseyde' by Peter Brookes (1st)
'The Kiss' by Rodin (1st)
'Girls on the Town' by Beryl Cook (1st)
'Jazz' by Andrew Mockett (1st)
'Girls performing a Kathak Dance' (1st)
'Alice Keppel with her daughter' by Alice Hughes (1st)
'Children Playing' by L. S. Lowry (1st)
'Circus Clowns' by Emily Firmin and Justin Mitchell (1st)
'All the Love Poems of Shakespeare' (detail) by Eric Gill (1st)

■ **1995, March 21. Greetings Stamps: Art**
Des: Newell and Sorell. Printed in litho by Walsall. Issued in booklets in panes of ten containing one of each design.

Booklet pane (of 10)	5.25	5.50
Booklet	6.00	
First day cover		6.00
Stamp cards	10.00	15.50

■ 1995, April 11. Centenary of The **National Trust**
Des: T. Evans. One phosphor band (19p), two phosphor bands (25p, 35p), phosphor paper (30p, 41p).

Set	2.25	2.25
Gutter pairs	6.00	
First day cover		2.25
Stamp cards	5.00	6.50

(* The 25p also appeared in a pane of six in the National Trust prestige stamp book issued on April 25, 1995.)

British troops and French civilians (19p)
Hands and Red Cross (19p)
Searchlights in a 'V' over St Paul's Cathedral 25p)
Hand releasing Dove of Peace (25p)
Symbolic hands (30p)

■ **1995, May 2. Peace & Freedom. Europa**
Des: J-M. Folon (Red Cross 19p, Dove 25p, 30p), J. Gorham (Troops 19p, Seachlights 25p), One phosphor band (19p), two phosphor bands (others).

Set	2.25	2.50
Gutter pairs	6.00	
First day cover		2.25
Stamp cards	5.00	6.50

(* The design with St Paul's Cathedral was also used as a 1st class stamp in a miniature sheet in 2005.)

The Time Machine (25p)
The First Men in the Moon (30p)
The War of the Worlds (35p)
The Shape of Things to Come (41p)

■ **1995, June 6. Novels of H. G. Wells**
Des: Siobhan Keaney. Printed in litho by Questa.

Set	2.25	2.25
Gutter pairs	6.00	
First day cover		2.25
Stamp cards	4.25	5.50

The Swan, 1595 (25p)
The Rose, 1592 (25p)
The Globe, 1599 (25p)
The Hope, 1613 (25p)
The Globe, 1614 (25p)

■ **1995, August 8. Reconstruction of Shakespeare's Globe Theatre**
Des: C. Hodges. Printed in litho by Walsall.

Set of five in se-tenant strip	2.25	2.25
Gutter pairs	6.00	
First day cover		2.25
Stamp cards	5.00	6.50

■ 1995, August 22. Castle high-value definitive

As issue of March 24, 1992, but new value, replacing the £1.

£3	8.50	1.35
Gutter pair	18.00	
Gutter block of four (centre cross)	40.00	
First day cover		5.00
Stamp card	10.00	21.00

(* This stamp exists with either blue tinted PVAD gum or white PVA gum.)

Sir Rowland Hill and Uniform Penny Postage Petition (19p)
Sir Rowland Hill and Penny Black (25p)
Marconi and early wireless (41p)
Marconi and 'Titanic' (60p)

■ 1995, September 5. Pioneers of Communications

Des: The Four Hundred; engraved by C. Slania. Printed in recess and litho by Harrison. 19p has one phosphor band.

Set	2.25	2.25
Gutter pairs	6.00	
First day cover		2.25
Stamp cards	4.25	5.50

Harold Wagstaff (19p)
Gus Risman (25p)
Jim Sullivan (30p)
Billy Batten (35p)
Brian Bevan (41p)

■ 1995, October 3. Centenary of Rugby League

Des: C. Birmingham. One phosphor band (19p), two phosphor bands (others).

Set	2.25	2.25
Gutter pairs	6.00	
First day cover		2.25
Stamp cards	5.00	7.50

Robin in letter box (19p)
Robin on railings (25p)
Robin on milk bottles (30p)
Robin on road sign (35p)
Robin on front door handle (41p)

■ 1995, October 30. Christmas. Robins

Des: K. Lilly. One phosphor band (19p), two phosphor bands (others).

Set	2.25	2.25
Gutter pairs	6.00	
First day cover		2.40
Booklet (20 × 19p)	7.00	
Booklet (10 × 25p)	4.25	
Booklet (4 × 60p)	4.25	
Stamp cards	5.00	6.50

(* The 19p design was also used in Smilers sheets in 2000 and 2001.)

Wee, fleeket, cowran, tim'rous beastie (19p)
O, my Love's like a red, red rose (25p)
Scots, Wha hae wi Wallace bled (41p)
Should auld acquaintance be forgot (60p)

■ 1996, January 25. Bicentenary of Death of Robert Burns

Des: Tayburn Design Consultancy. Printed in litho by Questa. One phosphor band (19p), two phosphor bands (others).

Set	2.25	2.25
Gutter pairs	6.00	
First day cover		2.25
Stamp cards	4.25	5.50

I'm writing to you because you don't listen to a word I say .. (1st)
More! Love (1st)
Sincerely (1st)
Do you have something for the human condition? (1st)
Mental floss (1st)
4:55pm. Don't ring (1st)
Dear lottery prize winner (1st)
Fetch this, fetch that. Let the cat do it. (1st)
My day starts before I'm ready for it (1st)
The cheque in the post (1st)

■ **1996, February 26. Greetings Stamps: Cartoons**
Des: M. Wolff. Printed in litho by Walsall. All-over phosphor.
Issued in booklets in panes of ten containing one of each design.

Booklet pane (of 10)	6.50	5.50
Booklet	6.00	
First day cover		5.50
Stamp cards	10.00	15.50

Muscovy Duck (19p)
Lapwing (25p)
White-front Goose (30p)
Bittern (35p)
Whooper Swan (41p)

■ **1996, March 12. 50th Anniversary of the Wildfowl and Wetlands Trust**
Des: Moseley Webb, from paintings by C. F. Tunnicliffe. 19p has one phosphor band.

Set	2.25	2.50
Gutter pairs	6.00	
First day cover		2.75
Stamp cards	5.00	6.50

Odeon (19p)
Laurence Olivier and Vivien Leigh (25p)
Cinema ticket (30p)
Pathé News (35p)
'Big Screen Showing' (41p)

■ **1996, April 16. Centenary of Cinema**
Des: The Chase. One phosphor band (19p), two phosphor bands (others).

Set	2.25	2.25
Gutter pairs	6.00	
First day cover		2.60
Stamp cards	5.00	6.50

Dixie Dean (19p)
Bobby Moore (25p)
Duncan Edwards (30p)
Billy Wright (35p)
Danny Blanchflower (41p)

■ **1996, May 14. European Football Championships**
Des: H. Brown. Printed in litho by Questa. One phosphor band (19p), two phosphor bands (others).

Set	3.00	2.50
Gutter pairs	7.50	
First day cover		2.25
Stamp cards	5.00	6.50

(* All of the stamps in this set also appeared as panes in the European Football Championships prestige stamp booklet, issued on May 14, 1996.)

Athlete (26p)
Throwing the Javelin (26p)
Basketball (26p)
Swimming (26p)
Athlete and Olympic rings (26p)

■ 1996, July 9. Olympic Games and Paralympic Games
Des: N. Knight. Printed in litho by Questa.

Set (in se-tenant strip of five)	2.25	2.25
Gutter pairs	6.00	
First day cover		2.25
Stamp cards	5.00	6.50

Dorothy Hodgkin (20p)
Margot Fonteyn (26p)
Elizabeth Frink (31p)
Daphne du Maurier (37p)
Marea Hartman (43p)

■ 1996, August 6. Famous Women. Europa
Des: Stephanie Nash. One phosphor band (20p), two phosphor
bands (others).

Set	2.50	2.50
Gutter pairs	6.50	
First day cover		2.50
Stamp cards	3.75	6.50

Muffin the Mule (20p)
Sooty (26p)
Stingray (31p)
The Clangers (37p)
Dangermouse (43p)

■ 1996, September 3. 50th Anniversary of Children's
Television
Des: Tutssels. Printed in photogravure by Enschedé. One
phosphor band (20p), two phosphor bands (others).

Set	2.25	2.50
Gutter pairs	6.00	
First day cover		2.50
Stamp cards	5.00	6.50

(*The 20p also appeared in the 75th Anniversary of the BBC
prestige stamp booklet issued on September 23, 1997, but
printed in photogravure by Harrison; priced at 60p mint.)

Triumph TR3 (20p)
MG TD (26p)
Austin Healey 100 (37p)
Jaguar XK120 (43p)
Morgan Plus 4 (63p)

■ 1996, October 1. Classic Sports Cars
Des: S. Clay. One phosphor band (20p), two phosphor bands
(others).

Set	3.00	2.75
Gutter pairs	7.50	
First day cover		2.50
Stamp cards	3.75	6.50

The Three Kings (2nd)
The Annunciation (1st)
The Journey to Bethlehem (31p)
The Nativity (43p)
The Shepherds (63p)

■ **1996, October 28. Christmas**
Des: Laura Stoddart. One phosphor band (2nd), two phosphor bands (others).

Set	2.50	2.50
Gutter pairs	6.50	
First day cover		2.75
Booklet (20 x 2nd)	7.00	
Booklet (10 x 1st)	4.25	
Stamp cards	5.00	6.50

■ **1996, November 11. Greetings Stamps: Cartoons**
As issue of February 26, but with two phosphor bands. Issued in booklets in panes of ten containing one of each design

Booklet pane (of 10)	25.00	25.00
Booklet	25.00	

(* These designs were also used for Smilers sheets in 2001 and 2002.)

Iris latifolia (1st)
Gentiana acaulis (1st)
Magnolia grandiflora (1st)
Camellia japonica (1st)
Tulipa (1st)
Fuchsia 'Princess of Wales' (1st)
Tulipa gesneriana (1st)
Gazania splendens (1st)
Hippeastrum rutilum (1st)
Passiflora coerulea (1st)

■ **1997, January 6. Greetings stamps: Flower Paintings**
Des: Tutssls. Printed in litho by Walsall. Two phosphor bands. Issued in booklets in panes of ten containing one of each design.

Booklet pane (of 10)	6.50	6.00
Booklet	7.00	
First day cover		6.00
Stamp cards	10.00	15.50

(* The Gentiana acaulis, Tulipa and Iris latifolia designs also appear in the Glory of the Garden prestige stamp book of 2004. The designs were also used for a Smilers sheet in 2003.)

King Henry VIII (26p)
Catherine of Aragon (26p)
Anne Boleyn (26p)
Jane Seymour (26p)
Anne of Cleves (26p)
Catherine Howard (26p)
Catherine Parr (26p)

■ **1997, February. 450th Anniversary of the Death of King Henry VIII**
Des: Kate Stephens. Two phosphor bands. King Henry VIII design issued as a separate stamp in sheets, wives designs in a se-tenant strip

Set	3.00	3.25
Gutter pairs	7.50	
First day cover		3.75
Stamp cards	5.25	8.50

St Columba in boat (26p)
St Columba on Iona (37p)
St Augustine with King Ethelbert (43p)
St Augustine with a model of a cathedral (63p)

■ **1997, March 11. Religious Anniversaries**
Des: Claire Melinsky. Printed in photogravure by Enschedé. Two phosphor bands.

Set	2.25	2.50
Gutter pairs	6.00	
First day cover		2.75
Stamp cards	4.25	5.50

Dracula

Dracula (26p)
Frankenstein (31p)
Dr Jekyll and Mr Hyde (37p)
The Hound of the Baskervilles (43p)

■ 1997, May 13. Tales of Horror. Europa
Des: J. Pollock. Printed in photogravure by Walsall. Two phosphor bands.

Set	2.50	2.50
Gutter pairs	6.50	
First day cover		2.50
Stamp cards	4.25	5.50

Supermarine Spitfire MkIIA and Reginald Mitchell (20p)
Avro Lancaster MkI and Roy Chadwick (26p)
De Havilland Mosquito B MkXVI and Ronald Bishop (37p)
Gloster Meteor T Mk7 and George Carter (43p)
Hawker Hunter FGA Mk9 and Sir Sydney Camm (63p)
The faces of the aircraft designers feature in the cloud formations

■ 1997, June 10. British Aircraft Designers
Des: Turner Duckworth. One phosphor band (20p), two phosphor bands (others).

Set	3.00	2.75
Gutter pairs	7.50	
First day cover		2.75
Stamp cards	3.75	6.50

(*The 20p also appears in the Pilot To Plane: RAF Uniforms prestige stamp book issued on September 18, 2008)

Carriage horse (20p)
Lifeguards horse (26p)
Blues and Royals drum horse (43p)
Duke of Edinburgh's horse (63p)

■ 1997, July 8. All The Queen's Horses. 50th Anniversary of the British Horse Society
Des: J.-L. Benard. Printed in litho by Walsall. One phosphor band (20p), two phosphor bands (others).

Set	2.40	2.50
Gutter pairs	6.00	
First day cover		2.50
Stamp cards	4.25	5.50

■ 1997, July 29. Castle high-value definitives
As £1.50, £2 and £5 of March 24, 1992, and £3 of August 8, 1995, but printed in recess and silk screen (for Queen's portrait) by Enschedé. Engraved by Inge Madlé.

Set	45.00	10.00
Gutter pairs	£125	
Gutter blocks of four (centre cross)	£275	
First day cover		25.00

Haroldswick, Shetland (20p)
Painswick, Gloucestershire (26p)
Beddgelert, Gwynedd (43p)
Ballyroney, County Down (63p)

■ 1997, August 12. Sub Post Offices
Des: T. Millington. Printed in photogravure by Enschedé. One phosphor band (20p), two phosphor bands (others).

Set	2.40	2.50
Gutter pairs	6.00	
First day cover		2.50
Stamp cards	4.00	5.50

Enid Blyton's *Malory Towers*

Malory Towers (63p)
Noddy (20p)
Famous Five (26p)
Secret Seven (37p)
Faraway Tree (43p)

■ **1997, September 9. Centenary of the birth of Enid Blyton**
Des: C. Birmingham. Printed in photogravure by Enschedé. One phosphor band (20p), two phosphor bands (others).

Set	2.50	2.50
Gutter pairs	6.50	
First day cover		2.50
Stamp cards	5.00	6.50

Children and Father Christmas pulling Christmas cracker (2nd)
Father Christmas with Christmas cracker (1st)
Father Christmas riding on a Christmas cracker (31p)
Father Christmas with a snowball (43p)
Father Christmas on a chimney (63p)

■ **1997, October 27. Christmas. 150th Anniversary of the Christmas Cracker**
Des: M. Thomas (1st) and J. Gorham (others). One phosphor band (2nd), two phosphor bands (others).

Set	2.50	2.75
Gutter pairs	6.50	
First day cover		2.50
Booklet (20 x 2nd)	6.75	
Booklet (10 x 1st)	5.00	
Stamp cards	5.00	6.50

(*The 1st class design was also used for Smilers sheets in 2000 and 2001.)

Queen Elizabeth II and Prince Philip Wedding photograph of 1947 (20p and 43p)
Queen Elizabeth II and Prince Philip photographed in 1997 (26p and 63p)

■ **1997, November 13. Royal Golden Wedding**
Des: D. Driver (20p, 43p), Lord Snowdon (26p, 63p). One phosphor band (20p), two phosphor bands (others).

Set	2.50	2.50
Gutter pairs	6.50	
First day cover		2.50
Stamp cards	5.00	5.50

Common Dormouse (20p)
Lady's Slipper Orchid (26p)
Song Thrush (31p)
Shining Ram's-horn Snail (37p)
Mole Cricket (43p)
Devil's Bolette (63p)

■ **1998, January 20. Endangered Species**
Des: R. Maude. Printed in litho by Questa. One phosphor band (20p), two phosphor bands (others).

Set	3.25	3.00
Gutter pairs	8.00	
First day cover		3.00
Stamp cards	6.25	7.50

By Lord Snowdon (26p)
At British Lung Foundation function (26p)
Wearing tiara (26p)
During visit to Birmingham (26p)
In evening dress (26p)

■ **1998, February 3. Diana, Princess of Wales Memorial**
Des: B. Robinson. Two phosphor bands.

Set (in se-tenant strip of five)	2.00	2.25
Gutter pairs	5.00	
First day cover		2.25

Lion of England and Griffin of Edward III (26p)
Flacon of Plantagenet and Bull of Clarence (26p)
Lion of Mortimer and Yale of Beaufort (26p)
Greyhound of Richmond and Dragon of Wales (26p)
Unicorn of Scotland and Horse of Hanover (26p)

■ **1998, February 24. The Queen's Beasts. 650th
Anniversary of the Order of the Garter**
Des: Jeffery Matthews. Printed in recess and litho by Harrison.
Two phosphor bands.

Set (in se-tenant strip of five)	2.40	2.50
Gutter pairs	6.00	
First day cover		2.50
Stamp cards	5.00	6.50

■ **1998, March 10. Wilding definitives**
Des: Dew Gibbons Design Group, from original design by G.
Knipe. Printed in gravure by Walsall. Issued only in the £7.49 The
Wilding Definitives prestige stamp book.

20p light green (phos band at left)	0.70	0.75
20p light green (phos band at right)	0.70	0.75
26p red-brown	0.75	0.80
37p light purple	1.75	1.85

St John's Point Lighthouse (20p)
Smalls Lighthouse (26p)
Needles Rock Lighthouse (37p)
Bell Rock Lighthouse (43p)
Eddystone Lighthouse (63p)

■ **1998, March 24. Lighthouses**
Des: D. Davis and J. Boon. Printed in litho by Questa. One
phosphor band (20p), two phosphor bands (others).

Set	3.00	2.50
Gutter pairs	7.50	
First day cover		2.60
Stamp cards	5.00	6.50

Tommy Cooper (20p)
Eric Morecambe (26p)
Joyce Grenfell (37p)
Les Dawson (43p)
Peter Cook (63p)

■ **1998, April 23. Comedians**
Des: Gerald Scarfe. Printed in litho by Questa. One phosphor
band (20p), two phosphor bands (others).

Set	3.00	2.50
Gutter pairs	7.50	
First day cover		2.60
Stamp cards	5.00	6.50

(* Examples exist of the 37p design but with the denomination
30p, printed before an increase in postal rates, and issued in
error.)

Hands forming the shape of a heart (20p)
Adult holding the hand of a child (26p)
Hands forming a cradle (43p)
Hand taking a pulse (63p)

■ 1998, June 23. 50th Anniversary of the National Health Service

Des: V. Frost, using photographs by A. Wilson. Printed in litho by Questa. One phosphor band (20p), two phosphor bands (others).

Set	2.25	2.50
Gutter pairs	5.50	
First day cover		2.60
Stamp cards	4.25	5.50

The Hobbit (20p)
The Lion, The Witch and the Wardrobe (26p)
The Phoenix and the Carpet (37p)
The Borrowers (43p)
Through The Looking Glass (63p)

■ 1998, July 21. Children's Fantasy Novels

Des: P. Malone. Printed in photogravure by De La Rue. One phosphor band (20p), two phosphor bands (others).

Set	2.75	2.75
Gutter pairs	6.50	
First day cover		2.75
Stamp cards	6.00	6.50

Woman in costume of yellow feathers (20p)
Woman in blue costume (26p)
Children in white and gold robes (43p)
Child dressed as a tree (63p)

■ 1998, August 25. Notting Hill Carnival. Europa

Des: T. Hazael. Printed in photogravure by Walsall. One phosphor band (20p), two phosphor bands (others).

Set	2.50	2.50
Gutter pairs	6.50	
First day cover		2.60
Stamp cards	4.25	5.50

Bluebird of Sir Malcolm Campbell (20p)
Sunbeam of Sir Henry Segrave (26p)
Babs of John G. Parry Thomas (30p)
Railton Mobil Special of John R. Cobb (43p)
Bluebird CN7 of Donald Campbell (63p)

■ 1998, September 29. British Land Speed Records

Des: Roundel Design Group. Printed in photogravure by De La Rue. One centre phosphor band (20p), two phosphor bands (others).

Set	2.60	2.75
Gutter pairs	6.50	
First day cover		2.75
Stamp cards	5.00	6.50

(* The 26p also appears in the Breaking Barriers prestige stamp book issued on October 13, 1988, but printed in photogravure by Walsall, and with one phosphor band printed on the left or right of the stamp; priced at £1.00 mint.)

Angel with hands in blessing (20p)
Angel praying (26p)
Angel playing lute (30p)
Angel playing flute (43p)
Angel praying (63p)

■ **1998, November 2. Christmas. Angels**
Des: Irene von Treskow. Printed in photogravure by De La Rue.
One phosphor band (20p), two phosphor bands (others).

Set	2.50	2.75
Gutter pairs	5.50	
First day cover		2.70
Booklet (20 x 20p)	6.50	
Booklet (10 x 26p)	4.50	
Stamp cards	5.00	6.50

During 1999 and 2000 Royal Mail embarked on a
programme of special stamp issues to mark the
new Millennium. Each design includes the inscription
'Millennium' and the year, and a serial number.

The designs for 1999 looked back over the previous
Millennium, by exploring twelve different 'tales'. The
designs for 2000 are of photographs of projects
undertaken to celebrate the Millennium.

Greenwich Meridian and clock (20p)
Worker and blast furnace (26p)
Photograph of leaves (43p)
Computer inside head (63p)

■ **1999, January 12. The Inventors' Tale**
Des: David Gentleman (20p), P. Howson (26p), Z. and Barbara
Baran (43p), E. Paolozzi (63p). Printed in photogravure by
Enschedé (26p), or De La Rue (others). One phosphor band
(20p), two phosphor bands (others).

Set	2.50	2.60
Gutter pairs	6.25	
First day cover		3.25
Stamp cards	4.25	6.50

(* The 63p also appears in the World Changers prestige
stamp book issued on September 21, 1999, but printed in
photogravure by Questa; priced at £1.75 mint.)

Globe surrounded by aircraft (20p)
Woman on bicycle (26p)
Railway Station (43p)
Captain Cook and man (63p)

■ **1999, February 2. The Travellers' Tale**
Des: G. Hardie (20p), Sara Fanelli (26p), J. Lawrence (43p), A.
Klimowski (63p). Printed in photogravure by Enschedé (20p
and 63p), by De La Rue (26p), or litho by Enschedé (43p). One
phosphor band (20p), two phosphor bands (others).

Set	2.50	2.60
Gutter pairs	6.25	
First day cover		3.25
Stamp cards	4.25	6.50

Cow with markings of child being vaccinated (20p)
Patient on trolley (26p)
Penicillin mould (43p)
Test tube baby (63p)

■ 1999, March 2. The Patients' Tale

Des: P. Brookes (20p), Susan Macfarlane (26p), M. Dempsey (43p), A. Gormley (63p. Printed in photogravure by Questa. One phosphor band (20p), two phosphor bands (others).

Set	2.50	2.60
Gutter pairs	6.25	
First day cover		3.25
Stamp cards	4.25	6.50

(* The 20p also appears in the World Changers prestige stamp book issued on September 21, 1999.)

Norman and dove (20p)
Pilgrim Fathers and Red Indian (26p)
Sailing ship and emigration to Australia (43p)
Face superimposed on hummingbird (63p)

■ 1999, April 6. The Settlers' Tale

Des: J. Byrne (20p), W. McLean (26p), J. Fisher (43p), G. Powell (63p). Printed in litho (20p) or photogravure (others) by Walsall. One phosphor band (20p), two phosphor bands (others).

Set	2.50	2.60
Gutter pairs	6.25	
First day cover		3.25
Stamp cards	4.25	6.50

(* The 26p also appears in a booklet issued on May 12, 1999.)

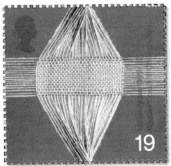

Woven threads (19p)
Salts Mill, Saltaire (26p)
Hull of ship on slipway (44p)
Lloyd's Building (64p)

■ 1999, May 4. The Workers' Tale

Des: P. Collingwood (19p), D. Hockney (26p), R. Sanderson (44p), B. Neiland (64p). Printed in litho (19p) or photogravure (others) by De La Rue. One phosphor band (19p), two phosphor bands (others).

Set	2.50	2.60
Gutter pairs	6.25	
First day cover		3.25
Stamp cards	4.25	6.50

(* The 26p from this set also appears in a booklet issued on May 12, 1999, printed in photogravure by Walsal; priced at £1.50 mint.)

Freddie Mercury (19p)
Bobby Moore holding the World Cup (26p)
Dalek (44p)
Charlie Chaplin (64p)

■ 1999, June 1. The Entertainers' Tale

Des: P. Blake (19p), M. White (26p), Lord Snowdon (44p), R. Steadman (64p). Printed in photogravure by Enschedé. One phosphor band (19p), two phosphor bands (others).

Set	2.50	2.60
Gutter pairs	6.25	
First day cover		3.25
Stamp cards	4.25	6.50

Prince Edward and Miss Sophie Rhys-Jones facing front (26p)
Facing sideways (64p)

■ 1999, June 15. Royal Wedding

Des: J. Gibbs from photographs by John Swannell. Printed in photogravure by De La Rue.

Set	1.50	1.50
Gutter pairs	4.00	
First day cover		2.25
Stamp cards	2.50	3.50

Suffragette behind bars (19p)
Tap (26p)
Children (44p)
Magna Carta (64p)

■ 1999, July 6. The Citizens' Tale

Des: Natasha Kerr (19p), M. Craig-Martin (26p), A. Drummond (44p), A. Kitching (64p). Printed in photogravure by De La Rue. One phosphor band (19p), two phosphor bands (others).

Set	2.50	2.60
Gutter pairs	6.25	
First day cover		3.25
Stamp cards	4.25	6.50

DNA (19p)
Galapagos Finch and skeleton (26p)
Light polarised by magnetism (44p)
Saturn, from Hubble Space Telescope (64p)

■ 1999, August 3. The Scientists' Tale

Des: M. Curtis (19p), R. Harris Ching (26p), C. Gray (44p), photograph (64p). Printed in photogravure (19p, 64p) or litho (others) by Questa. One phosphor band (19p), two phosphor bands (others).

Set	2.50	2.60
Gutter pairs	6.25	
First day cover		3.25
Stamp cards	4.25	6.50

(*The 26p and 44p also appear in the World Changers prestige stamp book of September 21, 1999; priced at £3 for the pair. The 64p also appears on a miniature sheet of August 11.)

Saturn, from Hubble Space Telescope (64p)

■ 1999, August 11. Solar Eclipse

Printed in photogravure by De La Rue. Miniature sheet, comprising four 64p values from issue of August 3.

Miniature sheet	12.00	12.00
First day cover		12.00

Upland landscape (19p)
Horse-drawn seed drill (26p)
Peeling potato (44p)
Combine harvester in field (64p)

■ 1999, September 7. The Farmers' Tale

Des: D. Tress (19p), C. Wormell (26p), Tessa Traeger (44p), R. Cooke (64p). Printed in photogravure by De La Rue. One phosphor band (19p), two phosphor bands (others).

Set	2.50	2.60
Gutter pairs	6.25	
First day cover		3.25
Stamp cards	4.25	6.50

(*The 26p also appears in a booklet issued on September 21, 1999, printed in photogravure by Walsall; priced at £1.50 mint.)

Robert the Bruce (19p)
Cavalier and horse (26p)
War Graves Cemetery (44p)
Soldiers with boy (64p)

■ 1999, October 5. The Soldiers' Tale

Des: A. Davidson (19p), R. Kelly (26p), D. McCullin (44p), C. Corr (64p). Printed in litho (19p) or photogravure (others) by Walsall. One phosphor band (19p), two phosphor bands (others).

Set	2.50	2.60
Gutter pairs	6.25	
First day cover		3.25
Stamp cards	4.25	6.50

'Hark the Herald Angels Sing' (19p)
King James I and Bible (26p)
St Andrews Cathedral, Fife (44p)
Nativity (64p)

■ 1999, November 2. The Christians' Tale
Des: B. Neuenschwander (19p), Claire Melinsky (26p), Catherine
Yass (44p), C. Aitchison (64p). Printed in photogravure by De La
Rue. One phosphor band (19p), two phosphor bands (others).

Set	2.50	2.60
Gutter pairs	6.25	
First day cover		3.25
Booklet (20 x 19p)	6.75	
Booklet (10 x 26p)	4.75	
Stamp cards	4.25	6.50

'World of the Stage' (19p)
'World of Music' (26p)
'World of Literature' (44p)
'New Worlds' (64p)

■ 1999, December 7. The Artists' Tale
Des: Allen Jones (19p), Bridget Riley (26p), Lisa Milroy (44p),
Sir Howard Hodgkin (64p). Printed in photogravure by Walsall.
One phosphor band (19p), two phosphor bands (others).

Set	2.50	2.60
Gutter pairs	6.25	
First day cover		3.25
Stamp cards	4.25	6.50

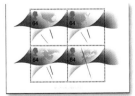

Globe showing North America (64p)
Globe showing Asia (64p)
Globe showing Middle East (64p)
Globe showing Europe (64p)

■ 1999, December 14. Millennium Timekeeper
Des: David Gentleman. Printed in gravure by De La Rue.
Miniature sheet containing 64p, 64p, 64p, 64p

Miniature sheet	14.00	11.00
First day cover		11.00
Stamp cards	12.50	18.50

(* The miniature sheet exists with the margin overprinted 'Earls
Court, London 22-28 May 2000 The Stamp Show 2000' sold
with tickets to The Stamp Show 2000 at £10: first put on sale
on March 1, 2000. Price: £15.00 mint.)

Barn owl (19p)
Night sky (26p)
River Goyt and textile mills (44p)
Cape Gannets (64p)

■ 2000, January 18. Above and Beyond
Printed in litho (44p) and gravure (others) by Questa. One
phosphor band (19p), two phosphor bands (others).

Set	2.50	2.60
Gutter pairs	6.25	
First day cover		3.25
Stamp cards	4.25	6.50

(* The 26p also appears as a 1st class value in a £2.70 stamp
booklet issued on May 26, 2000, printed in gravure by Walsall.
Priced at £1.50 mint.)

Millennium beacon (19p)
Garratt locomotive and train (26p)
Lightning (44p)
Floodlighting (64p)

■ 2000, February 1. Fire and Light
Printed in gravure by De La Rue. One phosphor band (19p),
two phosphor bands (others).

Set	2.50	2.60
Gutter pairs	6.25	
First day cover		3.25
Stamp cards	4.25	6.50

Pebbles (19p)
Frog's legs and water lilies (26p)
Cliff Broadwalk (44p)
Reflections in water (64p)

■ 2000, March 7. Water and Coast

Printed in litho (44p) or gravure (others) by Walsall. One phosphor band (19p), two phosphor bands (others).

Set	2.50	2.60
Gutter pairs	6.25	
First day cover		3.25
Stamp cards	4.25	6.50

River Braid (2nd)
South American leaf-cutter ants (1st)
Solar sensors (44p)
Hydroponic leaves (64p)

■ 2000, April 4. Life and Earth

Printed in gravure by De La Rue. One phosphor band (2nd), two phosphor bands (others).

Set	2.50	2.60
Gutter pairs	6.25	
First day cover		3.25
Stamp cards	4.25	6.50

(*The 1st also appears in a booklet issued on May 26, 2000.)

Pottery glaze (2nd)
Tate Modern (1st)
Road marking for bicycle (45p)
People in Salford (65p)

■ 2000, May 2. Art and Craft

Printed in gravure by Enschedé. One phosphor band (2nd), two phosphor bands (others).

Set	2.50	2.60
Gutter pairs	6.25	
First day cover		3.25
Stamp cards	4.25	6.50

Children playing (2nd)
Millennium Bridge, Gateshead (1st)
Daisies (45p)
African hut and thatched cottage (65p)

■ 2000, June 6. People and Places

Printed in gravure (2nd, 45p) or litho (others) by Walsall. One phosphor band (2nd), two phosphor bands (others).

Set	2.50	2.60
Gutter pairs	6.25	
First day cover		3.25
Stamp cards	4.25	6.50

Raising the Stone (2nd)
Horse's hooves (1st)
Cyclist and reflection (45p)
Bluebell wood (65p)

■ **2000, July 4. Stone and Soil**

Printed in gravure in Enschedé. One phosphor band (2nd), two phosphor bands (others).

Set	2.50	2.60
Gutter pairs	6.25	
First day cover		3.25
Stamp cards	4.25	6.50

(* The 1st also appears in a £2.70 stamp booklet issued on September 5, 2000, printed in gravure by Walsall. Priced at 75p mint. The 65p also appears in the Treasury of Trees prestige stamp book issued on September 18, 2000, printed in gravure by Walsall; priced at £1.50 mint.)

Roots of trees (2nd)
Sunflower (1st)
Sycamore seeds (45p)
Doire Dach Forest (65p)

■ **2000, August 1. Tree and Leaf**

Printed in gravure in De La Rue. One phosphor band (2nd), two phosphor bands (others).

Set	2.50	2.60
Gutter pairs	6.25	
First day cover		3.25
Stamp cards	4.25	6.50

(* The 2nd, 45p and 65p also appear in the Treasury of Trees prestige stamp book issued on September 18, 2000, printed in gravure by Walsall; priced at £3 mint.)

Queen Elizabeth II (27p)
Prince William (27p)
The Queen Mother (27p)
Prince Charles (27p)

■ **2000, August 4. 100th birthday of The Queen Mother**

Des: J. Gibbs. Photograph by J. Swannell. Printed in gravure by De La Rue. Miniature sheet containing four 27p designs as part of the entire photograph.

Miniature sheet	4.00	4.00
First day cover		5.00
Stamp cards	9.50	10.50

(* The 27p design showing the Queen Mother, and the entire miniature sheet but in a slightly larger size, also appeared in the Life of the Century prestige stamp book issued on August 4, 2000, printed in gravure by Questa; stamp priced at £1.25 mint.)

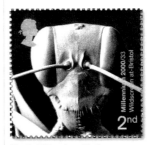

Head of Gigantiops (2nd)
Gathering water lilies on Norfolk Broads (1st)
X-Ray of hand with computer mouse (45p)
Tartan wool holder (65p)

■ **2000, September 5. Mind and Matter**

Printed in litho by Walsall. One phosphor band (2nd), two phosphor bands (others).

Set	2.50	2.60
Gutter pairs	6.25	
First day cover		3.25
Stamp cards	4.25	6.50

Acrobats (2nd)
Footballers (1st)
Bather (45p)
Hen's egg (magnified) (65p)

■ **2000, October 3. Body and Bone**

Printed in litho (2nd) or gravure by Questa. One phosphor band (2nd), two phosphor bands (others).

Set	2.50	2.60
Gutter pairs	6.25	
First day cover		3.25
Stamp cards	4.25	6.50

Virgin and Child stained glass window (2nd)
Floodlit church (1st)
Latin gradual (45p)
Chapter House ceiling of York Minster (65p)

■ 2000, November 7. Spirit and Faith

Printed in gravure by De La Rue. One phosphor band (2nd), two phosphor bands (others).

Set	2.50	2.60
Gutter pairs	6.25	
First day cover		3.25
Booklet (20 x 2nd)	6.25	
Booklet (10 x 1st)	4.75	
Stamp cards	4.25	6.50

Church bells (2nd)
Eye (1st)
Top of a harp (45p)
Figure in latticework (65p)

■ 2000, December 5. Sound and Vision

Printed in gravure by De La Rue. One phosphor band (2nd), two phosphor bands (others).

Set	2.50	2.60
Gutter pairs	6.25	
First day cover		3.25
Stamp cards	4.25	6.50

Children's face painting: Flower (2nd)
Tiger (1st)
Owl (45p)
Butterfly (65p)

■ 2001, January 16. Looking to the Future

Des; Why Not Associates. Printed in gravure by De La Rue. One phosphor band (2nd), two phosphor bands (others).

Set	2.60	2.60
Gutter pairs	6.50	
First day cover		3.25
Stamp cards	5.00	6.50

Hallmarks: Love (1st)
Thanks (1st)
abc (1st)
Welcome (1st)
Cheers (1st)

■ 2001, February 6. Occasions stamps

Des: Springpoint Design. Printed in gravure by Enschedé.

Set	3.50	3.00
Gutter pairs	8.50	
First day cover		3.25
Stamp cards	8.00	7.50

(* These designs were also used for Smilers sheets in 2001.)

Dog in bath (1st)
Dog and man sitting on bench (1st)
Boxer (1st)
Cat handbag (1st)
Cat on gate (1st)
Dog in car (1st)
Cat at window (1st)
Dog looking over fence (1st)
Cat watching bird (1st)
Cat in wash basin (1st)

■ 2001, February 13. Cats and Dogs

Des: Johnson Banks. Printed in gravure by Walsall. Issued as a self-adhesive sheetlet which could be folded to form a booklet containing one of each of the ten designs.

Sheetlet	7.50	8.00
First day cover		6.50
Stamp cards	10.00	15.50

(* The ten designs, with two 1st class definitives, were also issued in a £3.24 Cats and Dogs booklet on February 13, 2001.)

Sections of a barometer:
Rain (19p)
Fair (27p)
Stormy (45p)
Very dry (65p)

■ 2001, March 13. The Weather

Des: H. Brown and T. Meeuwissen. Printed in gravure by De La Rue. One phosphor band (19p), two phosphor bands (others).

Set	3.00	3.00
Gutter pairs	7.50	
First day cover		3.50
Stamp cards	5.00	8.50
Miniature sheet (1 x each value)	8.50	8.50
Miniature sheet first day cover		8.50

Vanguard Class submarine (2nd)
Swiftsure Class submarine (1st)
Utility Class submarine (45p)
Holland type submarine (65p)

■ 2001, April 10. Centenary of Royal Navy Submarine Service

Des: D. Davis. Printed in gravure by Questa. One phosphor band (2nd), two phosphor bands (others). Perf: 15 x 14. PVA gum.

Set	2.75	2.50
Gutter pairs	7.00	
First day cover		3.50
Stamp cards	4.75	6.50

(* The four stamps are also in the Unseen & Unheard prestige stamp book issued on October 22, 2001. Perf: 15 x 15; priced at £10.00 mint or used. The 1st class design also appears twice in self-adhesive form, together with four 1st class definitives, in a £1.62 stamp booklet issued on April 17, 2001; priced at £35 mint, £20 used. See also the issue of October 22)

Leyland X2, B Type, Leyland Titan TD1, AEC Regent I (1st)
AEC Regent I, Daimler COG5, Guy Arab II, AEC Regent III (1st)
AEC Regent III, Bristol K, AEC Routemaster, Bristol Lodekka FSF (1st)
Bristol Lodekka FSF, Leyland PD3, Leyland Atlantean, Daimler Fleetline (1st)
Daimler Fleetline, MCW Metrobus, Leyland Olympian, Dennis Trident (1st)

■ 2001, May 15. Double-deck Buses

Des: M. English. Printed in gravure by Questa. The illustrations extend into the sheet margins, and across the sheet, so that some of the illustrations span two stamps.

Set of five in se-tenant strip	2.50	2.60
Gutter pairs	6.50	
First day cover		3.25
Miniature sheet (1 x each value)	5.50	5.00
Miniature sheet first day cover		6.00
Stamp cards	10.50	15.50

Toque hat (1st)
Butterfly hat (E)
Top hat (45p)
Spiral hat (65p)

■ 2001, June 19. Hats

Des: Rose Design, from photographs by N. Knight. Printed in litho by Enschedé.

Set	2.75	2.75
Gutter pairs	7.00	
First day cover		3.25
Stamp cards	4.75	6.50

Common frog (1st)
Great diving beetle (E)
Three-spined stickleback (45p)
Southern Hawker Dragonfly (65p)

■ 2001, July 10. Pond Life. Europa
Des: J. Gibbs. Printed in gravure by De La Rue.

Set	3.25	3.00
Gutter pairs	8.50	
First day cover		3.50
Stamp cards	4.75	6.50

Policeman (1st)
Mr Punch (1st)
Clown (1st)
Judy (1st)
Beadle (1st)
Crocodile (1st)

■ 2001, September 4. Punch and Judy
Des: K. Bernstein, from puppets made by Bryan Clarkez. Printed in gravure by Walsall. PVA gum. Perf: 14 x 15.

Set (in se-tenant strip of six)	2.75	2.75
Gutter pairs	7.00	
First day cover		3.25
Stamp cards	6.25	8.50

(* The Mr Punch and Judy designs also appear in self-adhesive form with four 1st class definitives in a £1.62 stamp booklet issued on September 4, 2001, printed in gravure by Questa. Perf: 14 x 15; priced at £15 mint, £10 used per pair.)

Carbon molecule, printed in litho and silk screen (2nd)
Globe, printed in litho and recess (1st)
Dove, printed in litho and embossing (E)
Crosses, printed in litho (40p)
'The Ad-dressing of Cats' by T. S. Eliot, printed in litho (45p)
Boron molecule, printed in litho with hologram (65p)

■ 2001, October 2. Nobel Prizes
Des: P. Vermier; engraved by Inge Madle (1st). Printed by Enschedé. One phosphor band (2nd), phosphor band around stamp (others).

Set	6.00	3.75
Gutter pairs	17.00	
First day cover		5.00
Stamp cards	6.25	8.50

White Ensign (1st)
Union Jack (1st)
Jolly Roger (1st)
Flag of Chief of Defence Staff (1st)

■ 2001, October 22. Centenary of Royal Navy Submarine Service. Flags
Printed in gravure by Questa. PVA gum.

Miniature sheet (1 x each value)	4.50	4.50
First day cover		4.50
Stamp cards	10.50	14.00

(* The White Ensign and Jolly Roger designs also appear in self adhesive form with four 1st class definitives in a £1.62 stamp booklet issued on October 22, 2001; priced at £11 mint, £11 used per pair. The Union Jack and White Ensign designs have been used for Smilers sheets from 2005, and also appear in the Ian Fleming's James Bond prestige stamp book issued on January 8, 2008. See also the issue of April 10.)

Robins with snowman (2nd)
Robins on bird table (1st)
Robins skating on bird bath (E)
Robins with Christmas pudding hanging from tree (45p)
Robins in nest made of paper chains (65p)

■ **2001, November 6. Christmas. Robins**
Des: A. Robins and H. Brown. Printed in gravure by De La Rue.
Self-adhesive.

Set	3.25	3.25
First day cover		5.00
Booklet (20 x 2nd)	7.50	
Booklet (10 x 1st)	5.50	
Stamp cards	5.25	7.50

(* The 2nd and 1st class values were also issued in separate
stamp books, in the form of folders. The same designs were
used for Smilers stamps in 2004.)

The Elephant's Child (1st)
How the Whale got his Throat (1st)
How the Camel got his Hump (1st)
How the Rhinoceros got his Skin (1st)
How the Leopard got his Spots (1st)
The Sing Song of Old Man Kangaroo (1st)
The Beginning of the Armadillos (1st)
The Crab that played with the Sea (1st)
The Cat that walked by Himself (1st)
The Butterfly that stamped (1st)

■ **2002, January 15. The Just So Stories by Rudyard
Kipling**
Des: I. Cohen. Printed in gravure by Walsall. Issued as a self-
adhesive sheetlet containing one of each of the ten designs.

Sheetlet	5.25	5.50
First day cover		5.50
Stamp cards	7.00	21.00

Queen Elizabeth II in 1952, by Dorothy Wilding (2nd)
In 1968, by Cecil Beaton (1st)
In 1978, by Lord Snowden (E)
In 1984, by Yousef Karsh (45p)
In 1996, by Tim Graham (65p)

■ **2002, February 6. Golden Jubilee**
Des: Kate Stephens. Printed in gravure by De La Rue. One phos
band (2nd), two phos bands (others). Wmk: 50 (sideways).

Set	3.50	3.00
Gutter pairs	8.50	
First day cover		3.75
Stamp cards	4.00	7.00

(* The stamps are also in the Gracious Accession prestige stamp
book, but with the Wmk upright; priced £7.50 mint, £8.00 used.)

Wilding design (1st)
Wilding design (2nd)

■ **2002, February 6. Wilding Design Decimal Definitives**
Des: M. Farrar-Bell (2nd), Enid Marx (1st). Printed in gravure
by Enschedé. Wmk: 50. One phosphor band (2nd) or two
phosphor bands (1st). Only issued in the £7.29 A Gracious
Accession prestige stamp book issued on February 6, 2002.
One pane included a tilted 2nd, resulting in a diagonal
watermark.

2nd carmine-red	0.90	1.00
2nd carmine-red (Wmk diagonal)	2.50	2.50
1st green	0.90	1.00

Love (1st)
Rabbits, inscribed 'a new baby' (1st)
'Hello' written in sky (1st)
Bear pulling topiary tree in shape of house (1st)
Flowers inscribed 'best wishes' (1st)

■ **2002, March 5. Occasions**
Des: I. Bilby (Rabbits and Flowers), A. Kitching (Love), Hoop
Associates (Hello), G. Percy (Bear). Printed in litho by Questa.

Set	2.75	2.75
Gutter pairs	7.00	
First day cover		3.25
Stamp cards	4.00	7.00

(* The 'Hello' design also appears in a self-adhesive booklet, with
four 1st gold definitives, issued on March 4, 2003; priced at £3.
The designs were also used for Smilers sheets in 2002.)

Studland Bay (27p)
Luskentyre (27p)
Cliffs of Dover (27p)
Padstow Harbour (27p)
Broadstairs (27p)
St Abb's Head (27p)
Dunster Beach (27p)
Newquay (27p)
Portrush (27p)
Sand-spit (27p)

■ 2002, March 19. British Coastlines

Des: R. Cooke. Printed in litho by Walsall.

Set of ten in se-tenant block	4.75	5.00
Gutter pairs	13.00	
First day cover		5.25
Stamp cards	6.50	13.50

Slack wire act (2nd)
Lion tamer (1st)
Trick tri-cyclists (E)
Krazy kar (45p)
Equestrienne (65p)

■ 2002, April 10. Circus. Europa

Des: R. Fuller. Printed in gravure by Questa. One phosphor band (2nd), two phosphor bands (others).

Set	3.50	3.25
Gutter pairs	9.00	
First day cover		3.75
Stamp cards	4.00	7.00

20p design from the Queen Mother issue of 1990 (1st)
29p design (E)
34p design (45p)
37p design (65p)

■ 2002, April 25. The Queen Mother Memorial Issue

Des: J. Gorham. Printed in gravure by De La Rue.

Set	2.75	3.00
Gutter pairs	7.00	
First day cover		4.00

Airbus A340-600 (2nd)
Concorde (1st)
Trident (E)
VC 10 (45p)
Comet (65p)

■ 2002, May 2. Airliners

Des: Roundel. Printed in gravure by De La Rue. One phosphor band (2nd), two phosphor bands (others).

Set	3.50	3.25
Gutter pairs	9.00	
First day cover		3.75
Miniature sheet	6.00	6.00
Miniature sheet first day cover		7.50
Stamp cards	4.00	14.00

(*The 1st class design also appears twice in self-adhesive form with four 1st class definitives in a £1.62 stamp booklet issued on May 2, 2002, printed in gravure by Questa; priced at £3 mint or used.)

Lion with shield of St George (1st)
Football with quarters: top left (1st)
Top right (1st)
Bottom left (1st)
Bottom right (1st)

■ **2002, May 21. World Cup Football Championships**
Des: Sedley Place (Lion), H. Brown (flag). Printed in gravure by Walsall.

1st (St George design)	1.25	1.25
Gutter pair	3.00	
First day cover		2.75
Miniature sheet	3.50	3.75
Miniature sheet first day cover		5.00
Stamp cards	4.00	11.00

(*The 1st class designs showing the top left and top right of the English flag also appear twice in self-adhesive form with four 1st class definitives in a £1.62 stamp booklet issued on May 21, 2002; priced at £4 per pair. The design showing the bottom right of the flag also appeared on Smilers sheets.)

Swimming (2nd)
Running (1st)
Cycling (E)
Long jump (47p)
Wheelchair racing (68p)

■ **2002, July 16. 17th Commonwealth Games, Manchester**
Des: Madeleine Bennett. Printed in gravure by Enschedé. One phosphor band (2nd), two phosphor bands (others).

Set	3.25	3.25
Gutter pairs	9.00	
First day cover		4.00
Stamp cards	4.00	10.00

Tinkerbell (2nd)
Wendy, John and Michael Darling flying by Big Ben (1st)
Crocodile and the alarm clock (E)
Captain Hook (47p)
Peter Pan (68p)

■ **2002, August 20. Peter Pan**
Des: Tutsells. Printed in gravure by De La Rue. One phosphor band (2nd), two phosphor bands (others).

Set	4.00	3.25
Gutter pairs	10.00	
First day cover		4.00
Stamp cards	5.00	8.00

Millennium Bridge (2nd)
Tower Bridge (1st)
Westminster Bridge (E)
Blackfriars Bridge (47p)
London Bridge (68p)

■ **2002, September 10. Bridges of London**
Des: Sarah Davies and Robert Maude. Printed in litho by Questa. One phosphor band (2nd), two phosphor bands (others).

Set	4.00	3.50
Gutter pairs	10.00	
First day cover		4.00
Stamp cards	4.00	10.00

(*The 1st class design also appears twice in self-adhesive form with four 1st class definitives in a £1.62 booklet issued on September 10, 2002. Printed in gravure by Questa; priced at £3 mint or used.)

Planetary nebula in Aquila (1st)
Seyfert 2 galaxy in Pegasus (1st)
Planetary nebula in Norma (1st)
Seyfert 2 galaxy in Circinus (1st)

■ **2002, September 24. Astronomy**
Des: Rose Design. Printed in gravure by Questa.
Miniature sheet, containing the four designs.

Miniature sheet	2.75	3.00
First day cover		4.50
Stamp cards	4.00	10.00

(*The design of the miniature sheet also appears in a larger size in the Across The Universe prestige stamp book issued on September 21, 2002.)

Pillar box of 1857 in green (2nd)
Pillar box of 1874 (1st)
Air mail box of 1934 (E)
Pillar box of 1939 (47p)
Pillar box of 1980 (68p)

■ 2002, October 8. 150th Anniversary of the first Pillar Box

Des: Silk Pearce; engraved by C. Slania. Printed in recess and litho by Enschedé. One phosphor band (2nd), two phosphor bands (others).

Set	4.25	3.25
Gutter pairs	11.00	
First day cover		4.00
Stamp cards	3.25	7.50

Blue spruce (2nd)
Holly (1st)
Ivy (E)
Mistletoe (47p)
Pine cone (68p)

■ 2002, November 5. Christmas. Christmas Flowers

Des: Rose Design. Printed in gravure by De La Rue. One phosphor band (2nd), two phosphor bands (others). Self-adhesive.

Set	3.25	3.25
First day cover		4.00
Booklet (24 x 2nd)	7.50	
Booklet (12 x 1st)	5.25	
Stamp cards	3.25	7.50

(* The 2nd and 1st class stamps also appear in folded stamp booklets.)

The Wilding definitives collection 1 ~ 1952 - 1953

Wilding Designs (1p, 2p, 5p, 2nd, 1st, 33p, 37p, 47p, 50p)

■ 2002, December 5. 50th Anniversary of the Wilding Definitives, 1st issue

Des: Rose Design (based on the original designs). Miniature sheet. Printed in gravure by De La Rue. One phosphor band (2nd), two phosphor bands (others). Wmk: 50.

Miniature sheet	5.50	5.00
First day cover		7.50
Stamp cards	5.00	15.00

Barn Owl about to land, five different views (1st)
Kestrel in flight, five different views (1st)

■ 2003, January 14. Birds of Prey

Des: J. Gibbs from photographs by S. Dakon. Printed in litho by Walsall.

Set (in se-tenant block of ten)	6.00	5.50
Gutter pairs	15.00	
First day cover		5.50
Stamp cards	5.00	15.00

Gold star, See me, Playtime (1st)
I 'love' U (1st)
Angel, Poppet, Little terror (1st)
Yes, No, Maybe (1st)
Oops! Sorry, Will try harder (1st)
I did it! You did it! We did it! (1st)

2003, February 4. Occasions

Des: UNA, Sarah Wiegand and M. Exon. Printed in litho by Questa.

Set (in se-tenant block of six)	3.75	3.50
Gutter pairs	8.00	
First day cover		4.00
Stamp cards	3.25	8.75

(*These designs also appeared as Smilers sheets.)

Genome **The End of the Beginning**

The genetic jigsaw (2nd)
Ape looking at scientist behind bars (1st)
DNA snakes and ladders (E)
Animals dressed as scientists (47p)
Looking into a DNA crystal ball (68p)

2003, February 25. 50th Anniversary of the Discovery of DNA

Des: William Murray Hamm and P. Brookes. Printed in litho by Enschedé. One phosphor band (2nd), two phosphor bands (others).

Set	3.25	3.25
Gutter pairs	8.00	
First day cover		4.25
Stamp cards	3.00	8.50

(*The 2nd and E designs also appear in the Microcosmos prestige stamp book issued on February 25, 2003.)

Red Pepper (1st)
Strawberry (1st)
Potato (1st)
Apple (1st)
Pear (1st)
Orange (1st)
Tomato (1st)
Lemon (1st)
Brussels sprout (1st)
Aubergine (1st)

2003, March 25. Fruit and Veg

Des: Johnson Banks. Printed in gravure by Walsall. Self-adhesive.

Set (in se-tenant block of six)	5.50	5.50
Gutter pairs	12.50	
First day cover		5.50
Stamp cards	10.50	25.00

(*These stamps were issued with various self-adhesive stickers, such as of eyes, ears and mouths, so that the fruit and vegetables could be made to resemble faces. These designs were also used for a Smilers sheet in 2006.)

Amy Johnson with bi-plane (2nd)
1953 Everest team (1st)
Freya Stark in the desert (E)
Ernest Shackleton (42p)
Francis Chichester with Gipsy Moth IV (47p)
Robert Falcon Scott at the South Pole (68p)

2003, April 29. Extreme Endeavours

Des: H. Brown. Printed in gravure by Questa. One phosphor band (2nd), two phosphor bands (others). Perf: 15 x 14½.

Set	4.50	4.50
Gutter pairs	12.00	
First day cover		5.00
Stamp cards	4.00	9.50

(*The 1st class design also appears twice, in self adhesive form, with four 1st class definitives in a £1.62 stamp booklet issued on April 29, 2003. Printed in gravure by De La Rue. Perf: 14½; priced at £2.75 mint, £2.75 used.)

The Wilding definitives collection II ~ 1953 - 1959

Wilding Designs (4p, 8p, 10p, 20p, 28p, 34p, E, 42p, 68p)

2003, May 20. 50th Anniversary of the Wilding Definitives, 2nd issue

Des: Rose Design (based on the original designs). Miniature sheet. Printed in gravure by De La Rue. One phosphor band (20p), two phosphor bands (others). Wmk: 50.

Miniature sheet	5.00	5.50
First day cover		6.50

Coronation procession (1st)
Children reading poster (1st)
The Queen seated in the Coronation Chair (1st)
Children producing Royal montage (1st)
The Queen in Coronation robes – by Cecil Beaton (1st)
Children racing during street party (1st)
Coronation Coach passing through Admiralty Arch (1st)
Children in fancy dress (1st)
Coronation Coach outside Buckingham Palace (1st)
Children at street party (1st)

■ 2003, June 2. 50th Anniversary of the Coronation
Des: Kate Stephens. Printed in gravure by De La Rue.

Set of ten in se-tenant block	4.75	4.75
Gutter pairs	12.00	
First day cover		5.25
Stamp cards	8.50	20.00

(* Eight of these designs also appear in the A Perfect Coronation prestige stamp book issued on June 2, 2003.)

■ 2003, June 2. Wilding design decimal definitives
Des: as issue of March 10, 1998. Printed in gravure by Walsall. Wmk: 50. Issued only in the £7.46 A Perfect Coronation prestige stamp book.

47p bistre-brown	3.00	3.25
68p grey-blue	3.00	3.25

(* The booklet pane comprised two of each value, plus the 1953 Coronation design by Edmund Dulac with face value £1. This stamp with Wmk: 50 priced at £25.00 mint, £25.00 used.)

Photographs of Prince William:
By Brendan Beirne (28p)
By Tim Graham (2000) (E)
By Camera Press (47p)
By Tim Graham (2001) (68p)

■ 2003, June 17. 21st Birthday of Prince William
Des: Madeleine Bennett. Printed in gravure by Walsall.

Set	7.00	3.00
Gutter pairs	19.00	
First day cover		4.00
Stamp cards	6.50	20.00

Loch Assynt, Sutherland (2nd)
Ben More, Isle of Mull (1st)
Rothiemurchus, Cairngorms (E)
Dalveen Pass, Lowther Hills (42p)
Glenfinnan Viaduct, Lochaber (47p)
Papa Little, Shetland Islands (68p)

■ 2003, July 15. A British Journey: Scotland
Des: Phelan Barker. Printed in gravure by De La Rue. One phosphor band (2nd), two phosphor bands (others).

Set	4.25	4.25
Gutter pairs	11.00	
First day cover		5.00
Stamp cards	3.50	9.00

(* The 1st class design also appears twice, in self adhesive form, with four 1st class definitives in a £1.68 stamp booklet issued on July 15, 2003; priced at £3 mint, £3 used.)

The Station (1st)
Black Swan (E)
The Cross Keys (42p)
The Mayflower (47p)
The Barley Sheaf (68p)

■ 2003, August 12. Pub Signs. Europa
Des: Elmwood. Printed in gravure by De La Rue.

Set	5.00	4.25
Gutter pairs	12.50	
First day cover		4.50
Stamp cards	4.00	7.50

(* The 1st class design also appears in a Letters by Night prestige stamp book issued on March 16, 2004.)

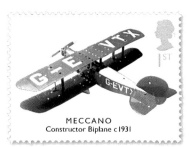

MECCANO
Constructor Biplane c1931

Meccano Constructor Biplane (1st)
Wells-Brimtoy bus (E)
Hornby M1 locomotive (42p)
Dinky Toys Ford Zephyr (47p)
Mettoy Space Ship Eagle (68p)

■ 2003, September 18. Toys
Des: Trickett and Webb. Printed in gravure by Enschedé.

Set	4.25	4.25
Gutter pairs	11.00	
First day cover		4.50
Stamp cards	3.50	13.50
Miniature sheet (1x each value)	4.25	4.50
Miniature sheet first day cover		7.50

(* The 1st class design also appears twice, in self adhesive form, with four 1st class definitives in a £1.68 stamp booklet issued on September 18, 2003. Printed in gravure by De La Rue; priced at £2.75 mint, £2.75 used.)

Coffin of Denytenamun (2nd)
Alexander the Great (1st)
Sutton Hoo helmet (E)
Sculpture of Parvati (42p)
Mask of Xiuhtecuhtli (47p)
Hoa Hakananai'a (68p)

■ 2003, October 7. Treasures from the British Museum
Des: Rose Design. Printed in gravure by Walsall. One phosphor band (2nd), band at right (42p, 68p), two phosphor bands (others).

Set	5.50	4.25
Gutter pairs	14.00	
First day cover		5.00
Stamp cards	3.25	9.00

Spiral (2nd)
Star (1st)
Wall (E)
Ball (42p)
Hole (47p)
Pyramids (68p)

■ 2003, November 4. Christmas. Ice Sculptures
Des: D. Davis, from ice Sculptures by Andy Goldsworthy. Printed in gravure by De La Rue. One phosphor band (2nd), two phosphor bands (others). Self-adhesive.

Set	5.00	5.25
First day cover		5.50
Booklet (24 x 2nd)	8.00	
Booklet (12 x 1st)	5.50	
Stamp cards	3.25	12.00

(* The 1st class and 2nd class design also appear in folded stamp booklets, and as Smilers sheets.)

England fans and England flag (1st)
England team standing in a circle (1st)
The Rugby World Cup (1st)
The England team after winning the Rugby World Cup (1st)

■ 2003, December 19. England Winning the Rugby World Cup
Des: Why Not Associates. Printed in litho by Walsall. Miniature sheet, containing one of each design.

Miniature sheet	12.00	7.00
First day cover		10.00

'Dolgoch' on the Rheilffordd Tayllyn Railway (20p)
CR 439 on the Bo'ness and Kinneil Railway (28p)
GCR 8K on the Grand Central Railway (E)
GWR Manor on the Severn Valley Railway (42p)
SR West Country on the Bluebell Railway (47p)
BR Standard on the Keighley and Worth Valley Railway (68p)

■ **2004, January 13. Classic Locomotives**
Des: Roundel. Printed in litho by De La Rue. One phosphor band (2nd), two phosphor bands (others).

Set	4.50	4.50
Gutter pairs	12.00	
First day cover		5.00
Stamp cards	8.50	15.50
Miniature sheet (1 x each value)	15.00	12.00
Miniature sheet first day cover		15.00

(*The 28p, E and 42p designs also appear in the Letters by Night prestige stamp book issued on March 16, 2004.)

Postman (1st)
Face (1st)
Duck (1st)
Baby (1st)
Aircraft (1st)

■ **2004, February 3. Occasions.**
Des: S. Kambayashi. Printed in litho by De La Rue.

Set (in se-tenant strip of five)	2.25	2.50
Gutter pairs	6.00	
First day cover		3.50
Stamp cards	2.25	7.50

(*These designs also appear as a Smilers sheet.)

Middle Earth (1st)
Forest of Lothlórien (1st)
The Fellowship of the Ring (1st)
Rivendell (1st)
The Hall at Bag End (1st)
Orthanc (1st)
Doors of Durin (1st)
Barad-dûr (1st)
Minas Tirth (1st)
Fangorn Forest (1st)

■ **2004, February 26. The Lord of The Rings by J. R. R. Tolkien**
Des: HGV Design. Printed in litho by Walsall.

Set (in se-tenant block of ten)	6.00	6.00
Gutter pairs	17.00	
First day cover		6.00
Stamp cards	7.50	15.00

Ely Island, Lower Lough Erne (2nd)
Giant's Causeway, Antrim coast (1st)
Slemish, Antrim Mountains (E)
Banns Road, Mourne Mountains (42p)
Glenelly Valley, Sperrins (47p)
Islandmore, Strangford Lough (68p)

■ **2004, March 16. A British Journey: Northern Ireland**
Des: Phelan Barker. Printed in gravure by Enschedé. One phosphor band (2nd), two phosphor bands (others).

Set	3.75	4.00
Gutter pairs	9.00	
First day cover		5.00
Stamp cards	2.75	9.50

(*The 28p design also appears twice in self-adhesive form in a £1.68 stamp booklet issued on March 16, 2004; priced at £3.00.)

'Lace 1 (trial proof) 1968' by Sir Terry Frost (28p)
'Coccinelle' by Sonia Delaunay (57p)

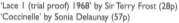

2004, April 6. Entente Cordiale
Des: Rose Design. Printed in gravure by Walsall.

Set	1.50	1.50
Gutter pairs	4.00	
Traffic light gutter pairs	7.50	
First day cover		2.50
Stamp cards	4.00	4.00

(* Stamps in the same designs were issued by France.)

RMS Queen Mary 2 (1st)
SS Canberra (E)
RMS Queen Mary (42p)
RMS Mauretania (47p)
SS City of New York (57p)
PS Great Western (68p)

2004, April 13. Ocean Liners
Des: J. Gibbs. Printed in gravure by De La Rue.

Set	4.50	4.50
Gutter pairs	12.00	
First day cover		5.25
Stamp cards	4.00	15.50
Miniature sheet (1 x each value)	6.00	5.50
Miniature sheet first day cover		7.50

(* The 1st class design also appears in self-adhesive form with four 1st class definitives in a £1.68 stamp booklet issued on April 13, 2004; priced at £3.00 mint, £3.00 used.)

Dianthus Allwoodii group (2nd)
Dahlia Garden Princess (1st)
Clematis Arabella (E)
Miltonia French Lake (42p)
Lilium Lemon Pride (47p)
Delphinium Clifford Sky (68p)

2004, May 25. Bicentenary of the Royal Horticultural Society
Des: Rose Design. Printed in gravure by Enschedé. One phosphor band (2nd), two phosphor bands (others).

Set	4.25	4.25
Gutter pairs	11.00	
First day cover		5.00
Stamp cards	4.00	15.50
Miniature sheet (1 x each value)	5.00	5.50
Miniature sheet first day cover		7.50

(* All values are also in the Glory of the Garden prestige stamp book of May 25, 2004, and the 1st class on Smilers sheets.)

Barmouth Bridge (2nd)
Hyddgen, Plynlimon (1st)
Brecon Beacons (40p)
Pen-pych, Rhondda Valley (43p)
Rhewl, Dee Valley (47p)
Marloes Sands (68p)

2004, June 15. A British Journey: Wales. Europa
Des: Phelan Barker. Printed in gravure by De La Rue. One phosphor band (2nd), two phosphor bands (others).

Set	3.75	3.75
Gutter pairs	9.00	
First day cover		5.00
Stamp cards	2.75	9.00

(* The 1st class design also appears in self-adhesive form in a £1.68 stamp booklet of June 15, 2004; priced at £4.00.)

Penny Black with citation to Sir Rowland Hill (1st)
William Shipley (40p)
R, S and A as typewriter keys (43p)
Brush for sweeping chimneys (47p)
Typeface by Eric Gill (57p)
Zero Waste (68p)

2004, August 10. 250th Anniversary of the Royal Society of Arts
Des: D. Birdsall. Printed in litho by Walsall.

Set	5.25	5.25
Gutter pairs	14.00	
First day cover		6.00
Stamp cards	2.75	9.50

DECIMAL QEII

Pine Marten (1st)
Roe Deer (1st)
Badger (1st)
Yellow-necked mouse (1st)
Wild Cat (1st)
Red Squirrel (1st)
Stoat (1st)
Natterer's Bat (1st)
Mole (1st)
Fox (1st)

■ **2004, September 16. Woodland Animals**
Des: Kate Stephens. Printed in gravure by Enschedé.

Set (in se-tenant block of ten)	5.00	5.00
Gutter pairs	13.00	
Traffic light gutter blocks	17.50	
First day cover		5.75
Stamp cards	7.00	15.00

Scotland definitives (40p, 1st, 2nd, 1st, 40p)

■ **2004, October 5. Opening of the Scottish Parliament Building**
Des: H. Brown. Printed in gravure by De La Rue.
Miniature sheet, comprising one 2nd, two 1st and two 40p Scotland definitives.

Miniature sheet	3.25	3.50
First day cover		4.50

Pte McNamara (2nd)
Piper Muir (1st)
Sgt Major Edwards (40p)
Sgt Powell (57p)
Sgt Major Poole (68p)
Sgt Glasgow (£1.12)

■ **2004, October 12. The Crimean War**
Des: Atelier Works, from photographs taken during The Crimean War. Printed in litho by Walsall. One phosphor band (**2nd**), two phosphor bands (others).

Set	5.25	5.25
Gutter pairs	12.50	
Traffic light gutter pairs	15.00	
First day cover		8.00
Stamp cards	2.75	9.00

Father Christmas on roof (2nd)
Father Christmas welcoming the sunrise (1st)
Father Christmas battling against the wind (40p)
Father Christmas holding umbrella (57p)
Father Christmas holding torch (68p)
Father Christmas sheltering by a chimney (£1.12)

■ **2004, November 2. Christmas**
Des: R. Briggs. Printed in gravure by De La Rue. One phosphor band (2nd), two phosphor bands (others).

Set	5.25	5.25
First day cover		8.50
Booklet (24 x 2nd)	7.00	
Booklet (12 x 1st)	4.75	
Stamp cards	3.25	15.00
Miniature sheet (1 x each value, but conventionally gummed)	5.50	6.00
First day cover		7.50

(* The 1st class and 2nd class designs also appear in folded stamp booklets, and in Smilers sheets.)

Embden geese (1st)
British Saddleback pigs (1st)
Khaki Campbell ducks (1st)
Clydeside mare with foal (1st)
Dairy Shorthorn cattle (1st)
Border Collie (1st)
Light Sussex chickens (1st)
Suffolk sheep (1st)
Bagot goat (1st)
Norfolk Black turkeys (1st)

■ **2005, January 11. Farm Animals**
Des: C. Wormell. Printed in gravure by Enschedé.

Set of ten in se-tenant block	5.00	5.00
Gutter pairs	12.50	
Traffic light gutter blocks	17.50	
First day cover		5.25
Stamp cards	7.50	15.50

Old Harry Rocks, Studland Bay (2nd)
Wheal Coates, St Agnes (1st)
Start Point, start Bay (40p)
Horton Down, Wiltshire (43p)
Chiselcombe, Exmoor (57p)
St James's Stone, Lundy (68p)

■ **2005, February 8. A British Journey: South-West England**
Des: J. Phelan and Lissa Barker. Printed in gravure by De La Rue. One phosphor band (2nd), two phosphor bands (others).

Set	4.25	4.25
Gutter pairs	11.00	
First day cover		5.50
Stamp cards	2.75	9.00

Mr Rochester (2nd)
Come to me (1st)
In the comfort of her bonnet (40p)
La Ligne des Rats (57p)
Refectory (68p)
Inspection (£1.12)

■ **2005, February 24. 150th Anniversary of the Death of Charlotte Brontë**
Des: P. Willberg, from illustrations by Paula Rego. Printed in litho by Walsall. One phosphor band (2nd), two phosphor bands (others).

Set	5.50	5.50
Gutter pairs	14.00	
Traffic light gutter blocks	21.00	
First day cover		7.00
Stamp cards	3.25	15.00
Miniature sheet (1 x each value)	5.50	5.75
First day cover		7.00

(* All designs also appear in the Brontë Sisters prestige stamp book issued on February 24, 2005.)

Heads or Tails (1st)
Rabbit and Top Hat (40p)
Coloured scarves and tube (47p)
Ace of Hearts (68p)
Three fezzes and pyramids (£1.12)

■ **2005, March 15. Magic**
Des: Tathem Design; illustration by George Hardie. Printed in gravure by Walsall. The designs include 'magical' features; rubbing the 1st class stamp with a coin reveals either the head or tail of a coin.

Set	5.50	5.50
Gutter pairs	14.00	
First day cover		6.50
Stamp cards	2.25	7.50

(* The 1st class design is also found in a Smilers sheet issued on March 15, 2005.)

Carrickfergus Castle (50p)
Caernarvon Castle (£1)
Edinburgh Castle (£1) •
Windsor Castle (50p)

■ **2005, March 22. The Castle Definitives of 1955**
Des: Sedley Place (original illustrations by Lynton Lamb). Miniature sheet. Printed by intaglio and litho by Enschedé.

Miniature sheet	4.50	5.00
First day cover		6.50
Stamp cards	5.00	16.00

At the Mey Games in the Scottish Highlands (30p)
At Birkhall (68p)

■ 2005, April 8. The Wedding of Prince Charles and Mrs Camilla Parker Bowles

Des: Rose Design,, from photographs by Christopher Furlong (30p) and Carolyn Robb (68p). Printed in litho by Enschedé. Miniature sheet, containing two of the 30p and two of the 68p design.

Miniature sheet	3.25	3.50
First day cover		5.00

(* Whilst the first day handstamps and the miniature sheet are dated April 8, the wedding took place on April 9)

Hadrian's Wall (2nd)
Uluru Kata Tjuta National Park (2nd)
Stonehenge (1st)
Wet Tropics of Queensland (1st)
Blenheim Palace (47p)
Greater Blue Mountains Area (47p)
Heart of Neolithic Orkney (68p)
Pumululu National Park (68p)

■ 2005, April 21. World Heritage Sites

Des: Jason Godfrey from photographs by Peter Marlow. Litho printed by Enschedé. One phosphor band (2nd), two phosphor bands (others).

Set of four se-tenant pairs	5.25	5.50
Gutter pairs	12.50	
Traffic light gutter blocks	21.00	
First day cover		7.50
Stamp cards	3.50	12.50

(* This is a joint issue with Australia Post.)

Ensign of the Scots Guards (2nd)
The Queen taking the salute (1st)
Trumpeter of the Household Cavalry (42p)
Welsh Guardsman (60p)
The Queen on horseback (68p)
The Queen with Duke of Edinburgh in an open carriage (£1.12)

■ 2005, June 7. Trooping the Colour

Des: Why Not Associates. Printed in litho by Walsall. One phosphor band (2nd), two phosphor bands (others).

Set	5.50	5.75
Gutter pairs	14.00	
First day cover		7.00
Stamp cards	3.25	10.00
Miniature sheet (1 x each value)	5.50	5.75
Miniature sheet first day cover		6.50

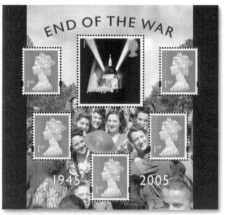

Searchlights in a 'V' over St Paul's Cathedral (1st)
Definitives (1st, 1st, 1st, 1st, 1st)

■ 2005, July 5. End of the War
Des: Jeffery Matthews, using a stamp designed by J. Gorham and originally issued on May 2, 1995. Printed in gravure by Enschedé. Miniature sheet containing St Paul's Cathedral design plus five 1st class definitives.

Miniature sheet	3.00	3.25
First day cover		5.00

1991 **Norton F.1** road version of a race winner

Norton F.1 (1st)
BSA Rocket 3 (40p)
Vincent Black Shadow (42p)
Triumph Speed Twin (47p)
Brough Superior (60p)
Royal Enfield (68p)

■ 2005, July 19. Motorcycles
Des: Atelier works, with illustrations by Michael English. Printed in litho by Walsall.

Set	4.50	4.75
Gutter pairs	12.00	
First day cover		6.50
Stamp cards	2.75	10.00

Athletes (1st, 1st, 1st, 1st, 1st, 1st, 1st)

■ 2005, August 12. London 2012
Printed in litho by Walsall. Miniature sheet containing one of each of the five designs issued for the Olympic and Paralympic Games stamps of 1996, plus a second of the Athlete with Olympic rings design, but all inscribed 'Ist'

Miniature sheet	3.25	3.50
First day cover		4.50

Eating rice (2nd)
Drinking tea (1st)
Eating sushi (42p)
Eating pasta (47p)
Eating chips (60p)
Eating an apple (68p)

■ 2005, August 23. Changing Tastes in Britain. Europa
Des: Rose Design, with illustrations by Catell Ronca. Printed in gravure by Enschedé. One phosphor band (2nd), two phosphor bands (others).

Set	4.25	4.50
Gutter pairs	12.00	
First day cover		5.50
Stamp cards	2.75	10.00

Inspector Morse (2nd)
Emmerdale (1st)
Rising Damp (42p)
The Avengers (47p)
The South Bank Show (60p)
Who Wants To Be A Millionaire? (68p)

■ 2005, September 15. Classic ITV
Des: Kate Stephens.. Printed in litho by De La Rue. One phosphor band (2nd), two phosphor bands (others).

Set	4.25	4.50
Gutter pairs	12.00	
First day cover		5.50
Stamp cards	2.75	10.00

(* The 1st class design is also found on a Smilers sheet.)

Gazania splendens (1st)
Hello (1st)
Love (1st)
Union flag (1st)
Teddy bear (1st)
Robin looking through pillar box slit (1st)

■ **2005, October 4. Pictorial definitives**
Printed by litho by Walsall. Self-adhesive. Issued in booklets
containing one of each of the six designs.

Booklet	2.75	
Booklet (with PiP information)	2.75	
First day cover		4.00

(* These designs were made available as a generic Smilers sheet
on July 4, 2006. For the same designs with elliptical perforations,
see the issues of January 16, 2007, and February 28, 2008.)

England team celebrating (two 1st designs)
England team in action (two 68p designs)

■ **2006, October 6. England Winning The Ashes**
Des: Why Not Associates. Printed in litho by Cartor.
Miniature sheet, comprising two 1st and two 68p.

Miniature sheet	3.50	4.00
First day cover		6.00

The Entrepreante with British Belle Isle (1st)
Nelson wounded (1st)
Entrepreante and the French Achille (42p)
The schooner Pickle (42p)
Nelson attacking in two columns (68p)
Putting to sea from Cadiz (68p)

■ **2005, October 18. Battle of Trafalgar**
Des: Dick Davis from a painting by William Heath. Printed in
litho by Walsall.

Set (of three se-tenant pairs)	4.75	4.75
Gutter pairs	13.00	
First day cover		6.00

Stamp cards	3.50	16.00
Miniature sheet (1 x each value)	4.50	4.75
Miniature sheet first day cover		6.00

(* The stamps also appear in a Battle of Trafalgar prestige stamp
book issued on October 18, 2005.)

Haiti (2nd)
European (1st)
European (42p)
North American Indian (60p)
India (68p)
Australian Aborigine (£1.12)

■ **2005, November 1. Christmas. Madonna and Child**
Des: Irene von Treskow. Printed in gravure by De La Rue. One
phosphor band (2nd), two phoshor bands (others). Self-adhesive.

Set	5.50	5.50
First day cover		7.00
Booklet (24 x 2nd)	7.00	
Booklet (12 x 1st)	4.75	
Stamp cards	6.00	17.50
Miniature sheet (1 x each value, but with conventional gumming)	5.50	5.50
First day cover		7.00

(* The 2nd and 1st class stamps also appear in stamp books.)

The Tale of Mr Jeremy Fisher (2nd)
Kipper (2nd)
The Enormous Crocodile (1st)
More About Paddington (1st)
Comic Adventures of Boots (42p)
Alice's Adventures in Wonderland (42p)
The Very Hungry Caterpillar (68p)
Maisy's ABC (68p)

■ **2006. January 10. Animal Tales**
Des: Rose Design. Printed in litho by De La Rue.

Set	5.25	5.50
Gutter pairs	12.50	
Traffic light gutter blocks	21.00	
First day cover		7.00
Stamp cards	7.50	15.00

Carding Mill Valley, Shropshire (1st)
Beachey Head, Sussex (1st)
St Paul's Cathedral (1st)
Brancaster, Norfolk (1st)
Derwent Edge, Peak District (1st)
Robin's Hood Bay, Yorkshire (1st)
Buttermere, Lake District (1st)
Chipping Campden, Cotswolds (1st)
St Boniface Down, Isle of Wight (1st)
Chamberlain Square, Birmingham (1st)

■ **2006, February 7. England: A British Journey**
Des: Phelan Parker Design Consultants. Printed in gravure by De La Rue.

Set (in se-tenant block of 10)	5.00	5.50
Gutter pairs	12.50	
First day cover		7.00
Stamp cards	5.00	15.00

Royal Albert Bridge (1st)
Box Tunnel (40p)
Paddington Station (42p)
PSS Great Britain (47p)
Clifton Suspension Bridge (60p)
Maidenhead Bridge (68p)

■ **2006, February 23. Bicentenary of the birth of Isambard Kingdom Brunel**
Des: Hat-trick Design. Printed in litho by Enschedé.

Set	4.50	4.75
Gutter pairs	12.00	
First day cover		6.00
Stamp cards	5.50	15.00
Miniature sheet (1 x each value)	4.50	4.75
Miniature sheet first day cover	6.00	

Wales definitives (68p, 1st, 2nd, 1st, 68p)

■ **2006, March 1. Welsh Assembly**
Des: Silk Pearce. Printed in gravure by De La Rue.
Miniature sheet, comprising one 2nd, two 1st and two 68p Welsh definitives.

Miniature sheet	4.50	4.50
First day cover		5.00

Sabre-tooth Cat (1st)
Giant Deer (42p)
Woolly Rhino (47p)
Woolly Mammoth (68p)
Cave Bear (£1.12)

■ **2006, March 21. Ice Age Animals**
Des: Howard Brown (illustrations by Andrew Davidson). Printed in litho by Enschedé.

Set	5.00	5.25
Gutter pairs	12.50	
First day cover		6.50
Stamp cards	4.00	15.00

The Queen in 1972 (2nd)
The Queen in 1985 (2nd)
The Queen in 1931 (1st)
The Queen in 2001 (1st)
The Queen in 1951 (44p)
The Queen in 1960 (44p)
The Queen in 1940 (72p)
The Queen in 1950 (72p)

■ **2006, April 18. The Queen's 80th birthday**
Des: Sedley Place. Printed in gravure by Enschedé.

Set	5.50	5.75
Gutter pairs	14.00	
First day cover		7.00
Stamp cards	4.50	17.00

World Cup
Winners

42

England (1st)
Italy (42p)
Argentina (44p)
Germany (50p)
France (64p)
Brazil (72p)

■ 2006, June 6. World Cup Winners
Des: Getty Images. Printed in litho by Walsall.

Set	5.00	5.25
Gutter pairs	12.50	
First day cover		6.50
Stamp cards	5.00	11.00

Downland Gridshell, Chichester (50p)
30 St Mary Axe, London (1st)
Maggie's Centre, Dundee (42p)
Selfridges, Birmingham (44p)
An Turas Isle of Tiree (64p)
The Deep, Hull (72p)

■ 2006, June 20. Modern Architecture
Des: Roundel. Printed in gravure by Walsall.

Set	4.75	5.00
Gutter pairs	12.50	
First day cover		6.25
Stamp cards	3.00	10.00

T. S. Eliot (1st)
Sir Winston Churchill (1st)
Sir Joshua Reynolds (1st)
Emmeline Pankhurst (1st)
Virginia Woolf (1st)
Sir Walter Scott (1st)
Mary Seacole (1st)
William Shakespeare (1st)
Dame Cicely Saunders (1st)
Charles Darwin (1st)

■ 2006, July 18. 150th Anniversary of the National Portrait Gallery
Des: Peter Willberg. Printed in gravure by De La Rue.

Set (in se-tenant block of 10)	5.25	5.50
Gutter pairs	14.00	
Traffic light gutter blocks	21.00	
First day cover		7.00
Stamp cards	5.00	16.00

Definitive (£3)

■ 2006, August 31. The Year of the Three Kings
Des: Together Design. Printed in gravure by De La Rue.
Miniature sheet comprising £3 Machin definitive, and illustrating the 1d stamps of the reigns of King George V, King Edward VIII and King George VI.

Miniature sheet	5.50	6.00
First day cover		7.50

Agansing Rai, a Gurkha (1st)
Boy Seaman First Class Jack Cornwell (1st)
Midshipman Charles Lucas (64p)
Captain Noel Chavasse (64p)
Captain Alan Ball (72p)
Captain Charles Upham (72p)

2006, September 21. Victoria Cross

Des: Atelier Works. Printed in litho by Enschedé.

Set	5.50	6.00
Gutter pairs	11.00	
First day cover		6.50
Stamp cards	3.50	15.00
Miniature sheet (1 x each value, plus the 20p Victoria Cross from September 1990)	6.50	7.00
Miniature sheet first day cover		6.50

Asian sitar (1st)
Caribbean base player (42p)
Latin American maracas (44p)
Irish fiddle (50p)
Black American Blues (72p)

2006, October 3. Sounds of Britain

Des: CDT. Printed in litho by Cartor

Set	5.50	5.50
Gutter pairs	10.00	
Traffic light gutter blocks	21.00	
First day cover		6.50
Stamp cards	3.50	8.00

New baby (1st)
Best wishes (1st)
Thank you (1st)
Balloons (1st)
Firework (1st)
Champagne, flowers and butterflies (1st)

2006, October 17. Pictorial definitives

Printed by litho by Walsall. Self-adhesive. Issued in booklets containing one of each of the six designs.

Booklet	3.50	
First day cover		4.50
Stamp cards	4.00	7.00

(*These designs were also available as a generic Smilers sheet. For the same designs with elliptical perforations, see the issue of February 28, 2008.)

Poppies (1st), Country definitives (72p, 72p, 72p, 72p)

2006, November 6. Lest We Forget

Des: Hat-Trick Design. Printed in gravure by De La Rue. Miniature sheet with 1st class Poppies design, and 72p definitives of England, Northern Ireland, Scotland and Wales.

Miniature sheet	5.50	5.50
First day cover		7.50

(* The 1st Poppies design was also made available as a generic Smilers sheet.)

Snowman (2nd and 2nd Large)
Father Christmas sitting on chimney (1st and 1st Large)
Reindeer (72p)
Christmas tree (£1.19)

2006, November 7. Christmas

Des: CDT. Printed in litho by De La Rue. Self-adhesive.

Set	5.50	5.50
Gutter pairs	11.00	
First day cover		7.00
Stamp cards	3.25	18.00
Miniature sheet (normal gum)	6.50	6.50
Miniature sheet first day cover		6.75

Scottish flag (1st)
St Andrew (72p)
Edinburgh Castle (72p)
Scotland definitive (1st)

2006, November 30. Celebrating Scotland

Des: P. Crowther, Claire Melinsky, Silk Pearce. Printed in gravure by De La Rue. Miniature sheet.

Miniature sheet	3.75	3.75
First day cover		5.00
Stamp cards	2.50	10.00

(* The 1st Scotland definitive, self-adhesive, was also used for a generic Smilers sheet issued on November 30, 2007.)

With The Beatles (1st)
Sgt Pepper's Lonely Hearts Club Band (1st)
Help! (64p)
Abbey Road (64p)
Revolver (72p)
Let It Be (72p)

■ 2007, January 9. The Beatles
Des: Johnson Banks, from album sleeve covers. Printed in gravure by Walsall. Self-adhesive. Issued in se-tenant pairs.

Set	5.50	5.75
First day cover		7.50
Stamp cards (set & miniature sheet)	7.00	20.00

Guitar (1st)
Yellow Submarine lunch box (1st)
Love Me Do (1st)
Tea Tray (1st)

■ 2007, January 9. The Beatles
Miniature sheet, containing four at 1st: printed in litho by Walsall. Normal gum.

Miniature sheet	2.50	2.50
First day cover		4.00

■ 2007, January 16. Pictorial Definitive
As the 'Love' design of October 4, 2005, but with elliptical perforations along vertical sides.

1st	0.60	0.60

(*This design was also issued in booklets released on January 16, 2007, and January 15, 2008.)

Moon Jellyfish (1st)
Common Starfish (1st)
Beadlet Anemone (1st)
Bass (1st)
Thornback Ray (1st)
Lesser Octopus (1st)
Common Mussels (1st)
Grey Seal (1st)
Shore Carb (1st)
Common Sun Star (1st)

■ 2007, February 1. Sea Life
Des: A. Ross. Printed in litho by Cartor.

Set (in se-tenant block of ten)	5.25	5.50
Gutter pairs	12.50	
First day cover		7.00
Stamp cards	4.75	16.00

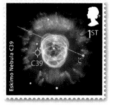

Saturn Nebula (1st)
Eskimo Nebula C39 (1st)
Cat's Eye Nebula C6 (50p)
Helix Nebula (50p)
Flaming Star Nebula C31 (72p)
The Spindle (72p)

■ 2007, February 13. The Sky at Night
Des: D. Davis, Printed in gravure by Walsall. Self-adhesive. Issued in se-tenant pairs. Stamps have description of designs on the backing paper.

Set	5.00	5.25
First day cover		6.50
Stamp cards	3.00	12.50

Railway Bridge (1st)
Locomotive with railway track as 'steam' (1st)
Map of British Isles and Australia (64p)
Television and camera (64p)
Globe (72p)
Carrying suitcases on the Moon (72p)

■ 2007, March 1. World of Invention
Des: P. Willberg. Printed in gravure by De La Rue. Self-adhesive.
Issued in se-tenant pairs. Stamps have description of designs on
the backing paper. Miniature sheet has normal gum.

Set	5.25	5.50
Gutter pairs	12.50	
First day cover		7.00
Miniature sheet	5.25	5.50
Miniature sheet first day cover	7.00	
Stamp cards	3.50	18.00

(*The same designs were also issued as normal gummed
stamps in the World of Invention prestige stamp book issued on
March 1, 2007.)

William Wilberforce (1st0
Olaudah Equiano (1st)
Granville Sharp (50p)
Thomas Clarkson (50p)
Hannah More (72p)
Ignatius Sancho (72p)

■ 2007, March 22. Abolition of the Slave Trade
Des: Howard Brown. Printed in litho by Cartor. Issued in
se-tenant pairs.

Set	5.00	5.25
Gutter pairs	12.00	
Traffic light gutter blocks	21.00	
First day cover		6.75
Stamp cards	2.75	11.00

England definitive (1st)
Flag of England (1st)
St George (78p)
Houses of Parliament (78p)

■ 2007, April 23. Celebrating England
Des; P. Crowther, Claire Melinsky, Silk Pearce. Printed in gravure
by De La Rue. Miniature sheet with 1st class England definitive
plus above three designs.

Miniature sheet	3.75	3.75
First day cover		5.00
Stamp cards	2.50	14.00

(*The 1st England definitive, self-adhesive, was also used for a
generic Smilers sheet.)

Ice cream cone (1st)
Sand castle (46p)
Merry-go-round (48p)
Beach huts (54p)
Deckchairs (69p)
Donkeys (78p)

■ 2007, May 15. Beside the Seaside
Des: Phelan Barker Design Consultants. Printed in gravure by
De La Rue.

Set	5.50	5.50
Gutter pairs	11.00	
First day cover		7.00
Stamp cards	3.00	11.00

(*The 1st class design also appears, as a self-adhesive, in a
booklet issued on May 13, 2008: priced at £1 mint.)

Lion with shield of St George (1st)
England definitives (2nd, 2nd, 78p, 78p)

■ 2007, May 17. Opening of the New Wembley Stadium
Des: Roundel. Printed in gravure by De La Rue. Miniature sheet.

Miniature sheet	4.00	4.00
First day cover		6.00

(*The 1st Lion design was previously issued on May 21, 2002
with an inscription, and was also used for a Smilers sheet.)

Arnold Machin (1st)
4d Machin olive sepia-brown (1st)
Definitive (£1 bluish-violet)
Definitive (£1 ruby)

■ 2007, June 5. 40th Anniversary of the Machin Definitives

Des: J. Matthews and Together Design. Printed in gravure by De La Rue. Miniature sheet.

Miniature sheet	4.50	4.50
Press sheet	75.00	
First day cover		6.00
Stamp cards	2.00	14.00

(* The 1st Arnold Machin design was also used for a generic Smilers sheet. The two 1st class designs also appear in The Making of a Masterpiece prestige stamp book.)

Graham Hill (1st)
Stirling Moss (1st)
Jackie Stewart (54p)
Jim Clark (54p)
James Hunt (78p)
Nigel Mansell (78p)

■ 2007, July 3. Grand Prix

Des: True North, from photographs by James Callaghan. Printed in litho by Cartor.

Set	5.50	5.50
Gutter pairs	12.50	
First day cover		7.00
Stamp cards	3.00	15.00

Harry Potter and the Philosopher's Stone (1st)
Harry Potter and the Chamber of Secrets (1st)
Harry Potter and the Prisoner of Azkaban (1st)
Harry Potter and the Goblet of Fire (1st)
Harry Potter and the Order of the Phoenix (1st)
Harry Potter and the Half-blood Prince (1st)
Harry Potter and the Deathly Hallows (1st)

■ 2007, July 17. Harry Potter

Des: from book covers. Printed in litho by Walsall.

Set	5.00	5.00
Gutter pairs	12.50	
Traffic light gutter pairs	11.00	
First day cover		6.50
Stamp cards	6.50	28.00

Symbol of Gryffindor (1st)
Symbol of Hufflepuff (1st)
Crest of Hogwarts (1st)
Symbol of Ravenclaw (1st)
Symbol of Slytherin (1st)

■ 2007, July 17. Harry Potter

Printed in litho by Walsall.

Miniature sheet	2.75	3.00
First day cover		4.00

(* These designs also appear on a generic Smilers sheet.)

Scout looking at the Moon (1st)
Scouts conquering a mountain (46p)
Scout planting a tree (48p)
Scout practicing archery (54p)
Scout piloting an aircraft (69p)
Group of Scouts (78p)

■ 2007, July 26. Scouts. Europa
Des: The Workroom. Printed in litho by Enschedé.

Set	5.50	5.50
Gutter pairs	11.00	
First day cover		7.00
Stamp cards	3.00	11.00

(* These designs were also issued as a set of six stamped postcards, imprinted with either the 1st class or 54p on the address side: priced at £7.50 mint.)

White-tailed Eagle (1st)
Bearded Tit (1st)
Red Kite (1st)
Cirl Bunting (1st)
Marsh Harrier (1st)
Avocet (1st)
Bittern (1st)
Dartford Warbler (1st)
Corncrake (1st)
Peregrine (1st)

■ 2007, September 4. Endangered Species. Birds
Des: Kate Stephens. Printed in litho by De La Rue. Issued in a se-tenant block.

Set (in block)	5.50	5.75
Gutter pairs	12.50	
First day cover		7.00
Stamp cards	4.75	16.00

NCO British Military Police, 1999 (1st)
Tank Commander 5th Royal Tank Regiment, 1944 (1st)
Observer Royal Field Artillery, 1917 (1st)
Rifleman, 95th Rifles (78p)
Grenadier Royal Regiment of Foot of Ireland, 1704 (78p)
Trooper Earl of Oxford's Horse, 1661 (78p)

■ 2007, September 23. British Army Uniforms
Des: Atelier Works and Graham Turner. Printed in litho by Enschedé. Issued in se-tenant strips of three.

Set	5.50	5.75
Gutter pairs	11.00	
Traffic light gutter pairs	14.00	
First day cover		7.50
Stamp cards	3.00	11.00

(*These stamps are also available in a prestige stamp book.)

The Queen and Prince Philip in 2006 (1st)
The Queen and Prince Philip in 1997 (1st)
The Queen and Prince Philip in 1980 (54p)
The Queen and Prince Philip in 1969 (54p)
The Queen and Prince Philip in 1961 (78p)
The Queen and Prince Philip in 1947 (78p)

■ 2007, October 16. Royal Diamond Wedding Anniversary
Des: Pentagram. Printed in gravure by Walsall. Normal gum. Issued in se-tenant pairs.

Set	4.75	5.00
Gutter pairs	11.00	
First day cover		7.00

Photographs of the Royal Family (1st, 1st, 69p, 78p)

■ 2007, October 16. Royal Diamond Wedding Anniversary
Des: Pentagram. Printed in gravure by Walsall. Miniature sheet. Self-adhesive. The reverse of the sheet shows photographs of the Royal couple leading up to their marriage.

Miniature sheet	3.50	3.50
Press sheet	60.00	
First day cover		6.00
Stamp cards	5.00	28.00

Angels playing musical instruments
(2nd, 2nd Large, 1st, 1st Large, 78p, £1.24)

■ **2007, November 6. Christmas**
Des: Rose Design, with illustrations by Marco Ventura. Printed in gravure by De La Rue. Self adhesive.

Set	6.00	6.00
Gutter pairs	12.50	
First day cover		7.50
Miniature sheet (normal gum)	5.00	5.00
Miniature sheet first day cover		7.50
Stamp cards	4.50	17.50

(*The 2nd, 1st and 78p designs also appear as a generic Smilers sheet.)

'Madonna & Child' by William Dyce (2nd)
'The Madonna of Humility' by Lippo di Dalmasio (1st)

■ **2007, November 6. Christmas. Madonna and Child**
Des: Peter Willberg, from paintings. Printed in gravure by De La Rue.

Set	1.25	1.25
Gutter pairs	4.00	
First day cover		2.50

(*These stamps were produced for customers wishing to have 'religious' designs, and will be re-issued in future years.)

Part of poppy (1st)
Country definitives (78p, 78p, 78p, 78p)

■ **2007, November 8. Lest We Forget**
Des: Hat-Trick Design. Printed in gravure by De La Rue.

Miniature sheet	5.50	5.75
First day cover		7.50

(*The 1st design also appeared in a generic Smilers sheet.)

Book cover of Casino Royale (1st)
Book cover of Dr No (1st)
Book cover of Goldfinger (54p)
Book cover of Diamonds Are Forever (54p)
Book cover of For Your Eyes Only (78p)
Book cover of From Russia With Love (78p)

■ **2008, January 8. Centenary of the Birth of Ian Fleming**
Des: A2. Prined in litho by De La Rue.

Set	5.00	5.00
Gutter pairs	12.50	
First day cover		6.50
Miniature sheet	5.00	5.00
Miniature sheet first day cover		12.50
Press sheet	75.00	
Stamp cards (set and miniature sheet)	3.00	20.00

(*The same stamps are also found in the Ian Fleming's James Bond prestige stamp book issued on January 8, 2008.)

Assistance dog with letter (1st)
Mountain rescue dog (46p)
Police dog (48p)
Customs dog (54p)
Sheepdog (69p)
Guide dog (78p)

■ **2008, February 5. Working Dogs**
Des: Redpath Design. Printed in litho by Cartor.

Set	5.00	5.00
Gutter pairs	12.50	
First day cover		6.50
Stamp cards	2.75	14.00

HENRY IV
1399-1413

Henry IV (1st)
Henry V (1st)
Henry VI (54p)
Edward IV (54p)
Edward V (69p)
Richard III (69p)

■ **2008, February 28. Kings and Queens. Houses of Lancaster and York**
Des: Ian Chilvers, Atelier Works. Printed in litho by Walsall.

Set	5.00	5.00
Gutter pairs	12.50	
First day cover		6.50
Stamp cards (set and miniature sheet)	5.00	26.00

THE AGE OF **LANCASTER AND YORK**

Owain Glyndwr (1st)
Battle of Agincourt (1st)
Battle of Tewkesbury (78p)
William Caxton (78p)

■ **2008, February 28. Kings and Queens. Houses of Lancaster and York**
Des: Ian Chilvers. Printed in litho by Walsall.

Miniature sheet	3.50	3.50
First day cover		5.00
Press sheet	90.00	

■ **2008, February 28. Pictorial definitives**
As previous designs of Hello, Gazania splendens and Union flag of October 4, 2005, and New baby, Firework and Champagne, flowers and butterfly of October 17, 2006, but with one elliptical perforation on each vertical side.

Booklet	3.50	3.50
First day cover		5.00

Carrickfergus Castle (1st)
St Patrick (78p)
The Queen's Bridge, Belfast (78p)
The Giant's Causeway (1st)

■ **2008, March 11. Celebrating Northern Ireland**
Des: Silk Pearce (sheet) and David Lyons, Clare Melinsky, Tony Pleavin and Ric Ergenbright (stamps). Printed in litho by De La Rue.

Miniature sheet	3.50	3.50
First day cover		5.00
Stamp cards (stamps and miniature sheet)	2.25	15.00

Lifeboat at Barra (1st)
Lifeboat and dinghy at Appledore (46p)
Helicopter rescue at Portland (48p)
Lifeboat at St Ives (54p)
Rescue helicopter at Lee-on-Solent (69p)
Lifeboat at Dinbych-y-Pysgod, Tenby (78p)

■ **2008, March 13. Rescue at Sea**
Des: Hat Trick Design. Printed in litho by Walsall.

Set	5.00	5.00
Gutter pairs	12.50	
First day cover		6.50
Stamp cards	2.75	13.00

ST PAUL'S CATHEDRAL
BENEATH LIES BURIED THE FOUNDER OF THIS CHURCH AND CITY,
CHRISTOPHER WREN, WHO LIVED MORE THAN 90 YEARS,
NOT FOR HIMSELF BUT FOR THE PUBLIC GOOD.
READER, IF YOU SEEK HIS MONUMENT, LOOK AROUND YOU.

Adonis blue butterfly (1st)
Southern damselfly (1st)
Red-barded ant (1st)
Barberry carpet moth (1st)
Stag beetle (1st)
Hazel pot beetle (1st)
Field cricket (1st)
Silver-spotted skipper (1st)
Purbeck mason wasp (1st)
Noble chafer beetle (1st)

Composite view inside St Paul's Cathedral (1st, 1st, 81p, 81p)

■ 2008, April 15. Insects.
Des: Andrew Ross. Printed in litho by De La Rue. Issued in se-tenant blocks of ten.

Set	5.25	5.25
Gutter pairs	13.00	
First day cover		6.75
Stamp cards	4.50	20.00

■ 2008, May 13. Cathedrals
Des: Howard Broiwn. Printed in litho by Enschedé.

Miniature sheet	3.50	3.50
First day cover		5.00
Press sheet	90.00	

LICHFIELD CATHEDRAL

WILLIAM HARTNELL ★ BOB MONKHOUSE
SHIRLEY EATON ★ ERIC BARKER ★ DORA BRYAN
BILL OWEN ★ KENNETH CONNOR

CARRY ON SERGEANT

CHARLES HAWTREY KENNETH WILLIAMS TERENCE LONGDON NORMAN ROSSINGTON
HATTIE JACQUES GERALD CAMPION

Lichfield Cathedral (1st)
Belfast Cathedral (48p)
Gloucester Cathedral (50p)
St Davids Cathedral (56p)
Westminster Cathedral (72p)
St Magnus Cathedral, Kirkwall, Orkney (81p)

Carry On Sergeant (1st)
Dracula (48p)
Carry on Cleo (50p)
The Curse of Frankenstein (56p)
Carry On Screaming (72p)
The Mummy (81p)

■ 2008, May 13. Cathedrals
Des: Howard Brown. Printed in litho by Enschedé.

Set	5.25	5.25
Gutter pairs	13.00	
First day cover		6.75
Stamp cards (set and miniature sheet)	5.00	26.00

■ 2008, June 10. Classic Carry On and Hammer Films
Des: Elmwood Design Group, from film posters. Printed in litho by Walsall.

Set	5.25	5.25
Gutter pairs	13.00	
First day cover		6.75
Stamp cards	2.75	13.00

(*Also issued was a set of six cards showing the stamp designs against a brick wall background, together with a folder containing three of the 1st class and three of the 56p values: price £6.50.)

Red Arrows (1st)
FAF Falcons parachute display (48p)
Watching the Red Arrows (50p)
Avro Vulcan prototype and Avro 707S (56p)
Robert Wyndham, one-armed parachutist (72p)
WB Moorhouse at Hendon air race (81p)

■ **2008, July 17. Air Displays**
Des: Roundel. Printed in litho by Cartor.

Set	5.25	5.25
Gutter pairs	13.00	
First day cover		6.75
Stamp cards	2.75	13.00

(*The 1st class design also appeared in the Pilot To Plane: RAF Uniforms prestige stamp book of September 18, 2008, and on a Smilers sheet.)

Beijing National Stadium (1st)
The London Eye (1st)
The Tower of London (1st)
Corner Tower the Forbidden City, Beijing (1st)

■ **2008, August 22. Olympics Handover**
Des: Why Not Associates. Printed in litho by Walsall, with the Olympic rings in a silk screen varnish.

Miniature sheet	1.50	1.50
First day cover	2.50	2.50

Drum Major, RAF Central Band (1st)
Helicopter rescue winchman, 1984 (1st)
Hawker Hunter pilot, 1951 (1st)
Lancaster air gunner, 1944 (81p)
WAAF plotter, World War II (81p)
Pilot, 1918 (81p)

■ **2008, September 18. RAF Uniforms**
Des: Quentin Newark of Atelier Works and Graham Turner.
Printed in litho by Walsall. Issued in se-tenant strips of three.

Set	5.50	5.50
Gutter pairs	15.00	
First day cover		7.00
Stamp cards	2.75	15.00

(* The same stamps are also found in the Pilot To Plane: RAF Uniforms prestige stamp book issued on September 18, 2008.)

1958 Northern Ireland 3d design (1st)
1958 Northern Ireland 6d design (1st)
1958 Northern Ireland 1s 3d design (1st)
1958 Scotland 3d design (1st)
1958 Scotland 6d design (1st)
1958 Scotland 1s 3d design (1st)
1958 Wales 3d design (1st)
1958 Wales 6d design (1st)
1958 Wales 1s 3d design (1st)

■ **2008, September 29. 50th anniversary of the Regional definitives**
As the 1958 regional stamps of Northern Ireland, Scotland and Wales, with changed values. Printed in gravure by De La Rue.

Miniature sheet	–	–
First day cover	–	–

(*The same stamps were also issued in a prestige stamp book issued on September 29, 2008.)

Millicent Garrett Fawcett (Votes for Women) (1st)
Elizabeth Garrett Anderson (Women's Health) (48p)
Marie Stopes (Family Planning) (50p)
Eleanor Rathbone (Family Allowance) (56p)
Claudia Jones (Civil Rights) (72p)
Barbara Castle (Equal Pay Act) (81p)

■ 2008, October 14. Women of Distinction
Des: Together Design. Printed in gravure by Walsall.

Set	5.25	5.25
Gutter pairs	13.00	
First day cover		6.75
Stamp cards	2.75	13.00

■ 2008, November 4. Christmas
Des: Steve Haskins, from photographs by Peter Thorpe. Printed in gravure by De La Rue. Self adhesive.

Set	4.50	4.50
Gutter pairs	11.00	
First day cover		6.00
Miniature sheet (normal gum)	4.50	4.50
Miniature sheet first day cover		6.00
Stamp cards	4.50	14.00

■ 2008, November 6. Lest We Forget
Des: Hat-Trick Design. Printed in litho by De La Rue.

Miniature sheet	5.25	5.25
First day cover		6.75

(* The 1st design also appeared in a generic Smilers sheet.)

■ 2008, November 6. Lest We Forget
The Poppy designs from the miniature sheets of 2006, 2007 and 2008, but sold from sheets. Printed in litho by De La Rue.

Set	1.50	1.50
First day cover		3.00
Stamp cards (three stamps and three miniature sheets)	4.00	25.00

OFFICIAL STAMPS

During the reigns of Queen Victoria and King Edward VII stamps were overprinted for use by Government Departments. The prices in this section are quoted in two columns: mint (left) and fine used (right). Dates in brackets refer to the stamps overprinted.

QUEEN VICTORIA

1d 'VR' official

■ Penny Black 'VR'

As the standard stamp but with the stars in the top corners replaced by the letters 'V' and 'R'. Never officially issued.

1d black (with gum)	£28,000	-
1d black (without gum)	£14,000	-
1d black (with trial cancellation)	-	£40,000

10s blue 'IR official'

■ Overprinted 'I.R. OFFICIAL' for use by the Inland Revenue

½d green (1880 issue)	60.00	15.00
½d blue (1884 issue)	45.00	13.00
½d orange (1887 issue)	6.00	1.00
½d green (1900 issue)	8.00	3.50
1d lilac (1881 issue)	2.75	1.40
2½d lilac (1884 issue)	£250	50.00
2½d purple (1887 issue) (blue paper)	80.00	6.00
6d grey (1881 issue)	£280	50.00
6d purple (1887 issue) (red paper)	£250	45.00
1/- green (1884 issue)	£4,000	£1,100
1/- green (1887 issue)	£700	95.00
1/- green, red (1900 issue)	£3,000	£1,100
5/- red (1884 issue)	£4,500	£1,500
10/- blue (1884 issue)	£7,000	£2,500
£1 brown (1884 issue) Wmk: Imperial Crowns	£50,000	£22,000

£1 brown (1888 issue) Wmk: Orbs	£75,000	£30,000
£1 green (1891 issue)	£9,000	£2,000

■ Overprinted 'O.W. OFFICIAL' for use by the Office of Works

½d orange (1887 issue)	£200	£100
½d green (1900 issue)	£300	£150
1d lilac (1881 issue)	£350	£100
5d purple, blue (1887 issue)	£2,700	£900
10d purple, red (1887 issue)	£4,500	£1,500

■ Overprinted 'ARMY OFFICIAL' for use by the Army

½d orange (1887 issue)	2.75	1.25
½d green (1900 issue)	3.00	5.00
1d lilac (1881 issue)	2.50	2.00
2½d purple (1887 issue) (blue paper)	25.00	10.00
6d purple (1887 issue) (red paper)	60.00	30.00

■ Overprinted 'GOVT PARCELS' for use by the Government

1d lilac (1881 issue)	70.00	10.00
1½d lilac (1884 issue)	£300	40.00
1½d purple, green (1887 issue)	£100	4.00
2d green, red (1887 issue)	£150	14.00
4½d green, red (1887 issue)	£260	£110
6d green (1884 issue)	£2,400	£900
6d purple (1887 issue) (red paper)	£200	40.00
9d green (1884 issue)	£2,000	£700
9d purple, blue (1887 issue)	£275	60.00
1/- brown (1881 issue, plate 13 or 14)	£1,200	£200
1/- green (1887 issue)	£500	£110
1/- green, red (1887 issue)	£500	£125

1s green, red 'Board of Education'

■ Overprinted 'BOARD OF EDUCATION'

5d purple, blue (1887 issue)	£3,000	£800
1/- green, red (1887 issue)	£7,500	£4,500

£1 green 'IR official'

KING EDWARD VII

■ Overprinted 'I.R OFFICIAL' for use by the Inland Revenue
Printed by De La Rue

½d blue-green	20.00	2.00
1d red	15.00	1.25
2½d blue	£900	£200
6d purple	-	-
1/- green, red	£3,500	£600
5/- red	£13,000	£8,000
10/- blue	£85,000	£35,000
£1 green	£52,000	£22,000

■ Overprinted 'O.W. OFFICIAL' for use by the Office of Works
Printed by De La Rue

½d blue-green	£400	£110
1d red	£400	£100
2d green, red	£1,500	£400
2½d blue	£2,500	£500
10d purple, red	£27,000	£6,000

■ Overprinted 'ARMY OFFICIAL' for use by the Army
Printed by De La Rue

½d blue-green	4.00	1.25
1d red	4.00	1.25
6d purple	£130	45.00

■ Overprinted 'GOVT PARCELS' for use by the Government
Printed by De La Rue

1d red	30.00	10.00
2d green, red	£150	25.00
6d purple	£240	20.00
9d purple, blue	£550	85.00
1/- green, red	£1,000	£250

■ Overprinted 'BOARD OF EDUCATION'
Printed by De La Rue

½d blue-green	£150	20.00
1d red	£150	20.00
2½d blue	£4,000	£275
5d purple, blue	£20,000	£5,500
1/- green, red	£100,000	-

■ Overprinted 'R.H. HOUSEHOLD' for use by Royal Household
Printed by De La Rue

½d blue-green	£300	£200
1d red	£275	£150

■ Overprinted 'ADMIRALTY OFFICIAL'
Printed by De La Rue

½d blue-green	20.00	10.00
1d red	12.00	4.00
1½d purple, green	£275	70.00
2d green, red	£300	80.00
2½d blue	£425	75.00
3d purple (yellow paper)	£375	70.00

POSTAGE DUE LABELS

Up to 1936, prices are quoted in three columns: unmounted mint (left), mounted mint (centre) and used (right). After 1936, they are quoted for mint (left) and fine used (right).

Except where stated, all these stamps were printed by Harrison in typography and are perf 14 x 15.

½d to 1/-

2/6 to £1

■ 1914-1923

A) Wmk: Crown and script GVR (Royal Cypher), sideways; crown faces to the right when viewed from front of stamp. Printed by Harrison (all values except 1/-) or at Somerset House (½d, 1d, 5d, 1/-).

½d green	1.25	0.40	0.35
1d red	1.25	0.50	0.25
chalky paper	7.50	4.00	4.00
1½d brown	95.00	35.00	13.00
2d black	1.25	0.80	0.30
3d violet	18.00	4.00	0.60
4d green	90.00	20.00	4.50
5d brown	11.00	4.00	2.00
1/- blue	90.00	19.00	3.00
Set	£300	65.00	22.00

B) Wmk: inverted; crown faces to the left.

½d green	1.50	1.00	1.00
1d red	2.00	1.00	1.00
1½d brown	£120	50.00	15.00
2d black	3.00	1.00	1.00
3d violet	20.00	6.50	2.50
4d green	£110	35.00	5.00
5d brown	32.00	12.00	4.00
1/- blue	90.00	20.00	15.00

■ 1924-1931

A) Wmk: Multiple Crown and block GVR, sideways; crown·faces to the left. Printed by Waterlow and (from 1934) Harrison.

½d green	1.25	0.50	0.30

1d red	1.25	0.50	0.10
1½d brown	90.00	27.00	9.00
2d black	6.00	1.25	0.20
3d violet	6.00	1.75	0.20
4d green	40.00	5.00	0.85
5d brown	110.00	35.00	17.00
1/- blue	25.00	4.00	0.25
2/6 purple (yellow paper)	190.00	50.00	0.80
Set	£150	100.00	24.50

B) Wmk: inverted.

½d green	4.50	2.00	1.50
1d red	-	-	8.50
1½d brown	-	-	25.00
2d black	-	-	8.50
3d violet	10.00	5.00	5.00
4d green	80.00	30.00	30.00
1/- blue	-	-	-
2/6 purple (yellow paper)	-	-	-

■ 1936-1937

Wmk: Multiple Crown and E8R (sideways).

½d green	7.00	6.50
1d red	1.00	1.50
2d black	6.00	6.00
3d violet	1.50	1.50
4d green	30.00	22.00
5d brown	25.00	18.00
1/- blue	8.00	6.50
2/6 purple (yellow paper)	£220	10.00
Set	£300	65.00

■ 1937-1938

A) Wmk: Multiple Crown and GVIR (sideways).

½d green	8.50	4.50
1d red	2.00	0.20
2d black	1.25	0.30
3d violet	7.00	0.30
4d green	60.00	7.00
5d brown	7.00	0.80
1/- blue	45.00	0.90
2/6 purple (yellow paper)	50.00	2.00
Set	£160	12.00

B) Wmk: inverted.

1d red	£120	-
2d black	10.00	-
3d violet	25.00	-
4d green	£110	-
5d brown	30.00	-
1/- blue	60.00	-

■ 1951-1952

As before but with changed colours.

½d orange	3.50	3.50
1d blue	1.25	0.50
Wmk inverted	-	-
1½d green	1.25	1.50
Wmk inverted	3.00	-
4d blue	30.00	12.00

1/- brown	22.00	4.00
Wmk inverted	£2,000	-
Set	45.00	18.00

■ 1954-1955
Wmk: Tudor Crown E2R (sideways).

½d orange	8.00	8.50
Wmk inverted	12.00	-
2d black	20.00	16.00
3d violet	35.00	30.00
4d blue	16.00	16.00
5d brown	15.00	10.00
2/6 purple (yellow paper)	75.00	8.00
Set	£130	70.00

■ 1955-1957
A) Wmk: St Edward's Crown E2R (sideways).

½d orange	4.00	4.00
1d blue	3.00	1.25
1½d green	7.00	4.50
2d black	25.00	5.25
3d violet	3.50	1.25
4d blue	16.00	2.00
5d brown	20.00	1.75
1/- brown	40.00	2.00
2/6 purple (yellow paper)	£115	10.00
5/- red (yellow paper)	60.00	18.00
Set	£240	40.00

B) Wmk: inverted.

½d orange	9.00	-
1½d green	12.00	-
3d violet	25.00	-
4d blue	30.00	-
1/- brown	-	-
2/6 purple (yellow paper)	-	-
5/- red (yellow paper)	-	75.00

■ 1959-1963
A) Wmk: Multiple St Edward's Crown (sideways).

½d orange	0.15	0.25
1d blue	0.15	0.10
1½d green	1.50	2.00
2d black	1.00	0.30
3d violet	0.35	0.15
4d blue	0.35	0.15
5d brown	0.35	0.30
6d purple	0.50	0.15
1/- brown	1.00	0.15
2/6 purple (yellow paper)	1.50	0.20
5/- red (yellow paper)	4.00	0.50
10/- blue (yellow paper)	10.00	3.00
£1 black (yellow paper)	30.00	4.50
Set	45.00	9.50

B) Wmk: inverted.

½d orange	1.25	-
1d blue	12.00	-
2d black	40.00	-
3d violet	10.00	-

4d blue	30.00	-
5d brown	4.00	. -
6d purple	40.00	-
1/- brown	7.00	-
2/6 purple (yellow paper)	6.00	-
5/- red (yellow paper)	10.00	-
10/- blue (yellow paper)	20.00	-

■ 1968-1969
No watermark. Chalky paper.
i) With gum Arabic.

2d black	0.50	0.50
4d blue	0.40	0.20

ii) With PVA gum.

2d black	1.50	1.00
3d violet	0.50	0.50
5d brown	5.00	5.00
6d purple	1.00	1.25
1/- brown	3.00	2.00

■ 1968-1969
Printed in photogravure by Harrison. No watermark.
Chalky paper. PVA gum.

4d blue	4.50	5.00
8d red	0.50	1.00

½p to 7p

10p to £5

■ 1970. Decimal Currency
Des: J. Matthews. Printed in photogravure by Harrison. No watermark. Chalky paper. Perf: 14 x 15.
i) PVA gum. Original coated paper.

½p turquoise	0.10	0.25
1p purple	0.50	0.10
2p green	0.25	0.10
3p blue	0.75	0.20
4p sepia	0.25	0.10
5p violet	1.00	0.30
10p carmine	0.80	0.30
20p deep green	1.10	0.50

50p blue	2.25	1.00
£1 black	4.00	0.25

ii) PVA gum. Fluorescent coated paper.

1p purple	0.50	-
3p blue	1.75	-
5p violet	2.25	-
10p carmine	45.00	-
20p deep green	45.00	-
£5 orange, black	20.00	1.00

iii) PVAD (blue-tinged dextrin gum).

1p purple	0.10	-
2p green	0.10	-
3p blue	0.15	-
4p sepia	0.15	-
5p violet	0.15	-
7p red-brown	0.25	0.25
10p carmine	0.25	-
11p green	0.40	0.35
20p deep green	0.50	-
50p blue	1.00	-
£1 black	2.00	-
£5 orange, black	18.00	1.00
Set (one of each value)	17.00	10.00

iv) PVAD gum. Phosphor coated paper (giving a green phosphor reaction).

10p carmine	0.70	0.50
20p deep green	1.00	0.75

1p to 5p

10p to £5

■ 1982, June 9
Des: Sedley Place Design Ltd. Printed in photogravure by Harrisons. No wmk. Perf: 14 x 15.

1p crimson	0.15	0.10
2p bright blue	0.15	0.10
3p purple	0.15	0.15
4p blue	0.15	0.10

5p brown	0.15	0.10
10p light brown	0.20	0.10
20p sage green	0.40	0.30
25p blue-grey	0.60	0.60
50p charcoal	1.00	1.50
£1 red	2.00	0.50
£2 turquoise	4.00	2.50
£5 dull orange	8.50	1,25
Set	14.00	5.00
Gutter Pairs	30.00	-

1p, 2p, 5p, 10p, 20p, 25p, £1, £1.20, £5

■ 1994, February 15
Des: Sedley Place Design Ltd. Printed in lithography by House of Questa. No wmk. Perf: 14 x 15.

Set	27.00	28.00
First day cover		35.00

STOP PRESS: IMPORTANT INFORMATION

PERCENATGE OF INCREASE FOR THE LAST 3 YEARS IN STANLEY GIBBONS CATALOUGE VALUE OF ROYAL MAIL SCARCER PRESENTATION PACKS. COMPARING STANLEY GIBBONS CONCISE CATALOUGES 2005 AND 2008 EDITIONS.

- 1964 FORTH ROAD BRIDGE PRESENTATION PACK. NO INCREASE...0%
- 1964 GEOGRAPHICAL PRESENTATION PACK. NO INCREASE..............0%
- 1964 BOTANICAL PRESENTATION PACK. LESS THAN.............................7%
- 2000 STAMP SHOW 2000 PRESENTATION PACK. LESS THAN.............12%
- 2002 WILDING No1 PRESENTATION PACK. NO INCREASE....................0%
- 2003 FRUIT & VEG PRESENTATION PACK. LESS THAN..........................19%
- 2003 RUGBY PRESENTATION PACK..400%

THE VERY SCARCE 2003 RUGBY PRESENTATION PACK HAS ACHIEVED A MASSIVE INCREASE IN CAT VALUE OF 400% IN THE LAST THREE YEARS.
LAST YEAR ALONE IT INCREASED BY OVER 87% IN CATALOGUE VALUE.

Did you miss the boat or did you take our advice?

In 1973 we recommended and sold the British definitive 1/2p (SG X842) with one phosphor band on side. We told our customers to buy them at 25p each. WE WERE RIGHT!!! Today this stamp is catalogued at £55.00 each. If you had taken our advice, for an outlay of only £50.00 in 1973, the current catalogue value of your investment would be a staggering total of £11,000.00

In 1999 we recommended our customers to buy the Princess Diana Welsh Language Presentation Packs. The catalogue value was only £2.50 each, but we were telling our customers to buy them for up to double catalogue value £5.00 each. Within only 6 years they had increased in catalogue value by 5,900%.

In 2003 we recommended our customers to buy the Coronation £1 Green (SG 2380) it was catalogued by Stanley Gibbons at £1.50 per stamp. Within one year the catalogue value had increased to £55 per stamp, an increase of over 3,500%.

As recently as 2004 we told our customers to buy the Fruit & Veg Presentation Pack - it was catalogued at £4.50. We said ignore the catalogue value, it's cheap even at treble catalogue value - this pack increased in Stanley Gibbons Catalogue to £60.00 within two years. An increase of well over 1,200%.

We hope that you took our advice recently. We recommended you to buy the Locomotives Miniature Sheet (SG.MS.2423). The Stanley Gibbons Catalogue value was £3.75 each. Now the Stanley Gibbons Catalogue value has increased to £30 each. An increase of over 700%!

As everyone knows, investments can go down as well as up and the past is not necessarily a guide to the future. However, being selective and taking sound advice is the best way to make your hobby pay for itself.

Only recently we recommended our customers to buy the Entrente Cordiale (English version) presentation pack. It was then catalogued at £4.25, now the latest Stanley Gibbons catalogue value (CBS) is £35 - an increase of well over 600%!

NOW RECOMMENDED: *The Rugby Mini Sheet MS2416 Catalogue valued in SG 2008 edition of CBS at £6 each. We recommend you buy it at the cheapest price from any dealer willing to sell!*

PLEASE LISTEN TO US NOW!
We most strongly advise our customers to buy the
GB 2003 Rugby World Cup **Presentation Pack** (number M9B)

Catalogue value in the Stanley Gibbons 2008 edition of Collect British Stamps is £16.00.
WE RECOMMEND YOU BUY IT AT THE CHEAPEST PRICE FROM ANY DEALER WILLING TO SELL.

ENGLAND WINNERS!
WORLD CHAMPIONS

BUY IT NOW!

ALSO RECOMMENDED: *The Rugby Mini Sheet MS2416 Catalogue valued in SG 2008 edition of CBS at £6 each. We recommend you buy it at the cheapest price from any dealer willing to sell!*

GUSTAMPS
12 Prince Albert Street, Brighton, Sussex BN1 1HE
Tel: 01273 326994 Fax: 01273 321318

Telephone, Fax or postal orders accepted Payment by Access or Visa credit cards

REGIONAL ISSUES

Prices in this section are quoted in two columns: mint (left) and fine used (right).

The definitive issues for Guernsey, the Isle of Man and Jersey which pre-date their postal independence are listed first, followed by those for the four countries that comprise the United Kingdom.

CHANNEL ISLANDS

Gathering seaweed (1d)
Islanders gathering seaweed (2½d)

■ **1948, May 10. Third Anniversary of Liberation**
Des: J.R.R. Stobie (1d), E. Blampied (2½d). Printed in photogravure by Harrison. Multiple GVIR watermark. Perf: 15 x 14.

Set	0.15	0.20
First day cover		17.50

GUERNSEY

2½d, 3d, 4d

■ **1958-68**
Des: E.A. Piprell. Printed in photogravure by Harrison. Perf: 15 x 14.

A) Wmk: Multiple St Edward's Crown. Non phosphor (except where stated).

2½d red (June 8, 1964)	0.30	0.35
3d lilac (August 18, 1958)	0.30	0.30
one centre phos band (May 24, 1967)	0.10	0.15
4d ultramarine (February 7, 1966)	0.20	0.25
two phos bands (October 24, 1967)	0.10	0.15
First day cover (2½d)		25.00
First day cover (3d)		20.00
First day cover (4d)		10.00

B) No watermark. Chalky paper. Two phosphor bands (except where stated).

4d ultramarine (April 16, 1968)	0.10	0.15
4d sepia (September 4, 1968)		
one centre phosphor band	0.10	0.15
4d red (February 26, 1969)		
one centre phosphor band	0.10	0.20
5d deep blue (September 4, 1968)	0.10	0.20
First day cover (4d sepia, 5d)		2.00
First day cover (4d red)		1.50

JERSEY

2½d, 3d, 4d

■ **1958-69**
Des: E. Blampied (2½d), W.M. Gardner (others). Printed in photogravure by Harrison. Perf: 15 x 14.

A) Wmk: Multiple St. Edward's Crown. Non phosphor (except where stated).

2½d carmine-red (June 8, 1964)	0.20	0.25
3d lilac (August 18, 1958)	0.25	0.25
one centre phos band (June 9, 1967)	0.10	0.15
4d ultramarine (February 7, 1966)	0.20	0.25
two phos bands (September 5, 1967)	0.10	0.15
First day cover (2½d)		25.00
First day cover (3d)		20.00
First day cover (4d)		10.00

B) No watermark. Chalky paper, PVA gum. One centre phosphor band (4d), two phosphor bands (5d).

4d sepia (September 4, 1968)	0.10	0.15
4d red (February 26, 1969)	0.10	0.20
5d deep blue (September 4, 1968)	0.10	0.20
First day cover (4d sepia, 5d)		2.00
First day cover (4d red)		1.50

2½d, 3d, 4d

■ 1958-69
Des: J. Nicholson. Printed in photogravure by Harrison.
Perf: 15 × 14.

A) Wmk: Multiple St Edward's Crown. Non phosphor (except
where stated).

2½d carmine-red (June 8, 1964)	0.20	0.35
3d lilac (August 18, 1958)	0.15	0.20
chalky paper (May 17, 1964)	4.50	4.00
one centre phos band (Jun 27, 1968)	0.10	0.15
4d ultramarine (February 7, 1966)	0.75	0.75
a) two phosphor bands (July 5, 1967)	0.10	0.15
First day cover (2½d)		25.00
First day cover (3d)		30.00
First day cover (4d)		10.00

B) No watermark. Chalky paper. Two phosphor bands
(except where stated).

4d ultramarine (June 24, 1968)	0.10	0.15
4d sepia (September 4, 1968)		
one centre phosphor band	0.10	0.15
4d red (February 26, 1969)		
one centre phosphor band	0.20	0.30
5d deep blue (September 4, 1968)	0.20	0.30
First day cover (4d sepia, 5d)		2.00
First day cover (4d red)		1.50

■ 1971, July 7. Regional Decimal Issue
Des: J. Matthews. Printed in photogravure by Harrison.

2½p magenta	0.20	0.20
3p ultramarine	0.20	0.20
5p violet	0.60	0.60
7½p pale brown	0.75	0.60
First day cover		2.50

(* The 2½p and 3p exist on either ordinary coated paper or
fluorescent coated paper.)

COUNTRY ISSUES

Prices in this section are quoted in two columns: mint (left) and fine used (right).

All stamps are printed in photogravure by Harrisons and perf 15 x 14 unless otherwise stated.

ENGLAND

Three Lions (2nd)
Crowned Lion and shield of St George (1st)
Oak tree (E, 40p, 42p)
Tudor Rose (65p, 68p)

■ **2001, April 23**
Des: Sedley Place, from sculptures by D. Dathan. Printed in gravure by De La Rue. One phosphor band (2nd), two phosphor bands (others).

2nd slate blue and silver	0.50	0.45
1st red-brown and silver	0.65	0.55
E olive-green and silver	0.70	0.65
65p deep lilac and silver	1.40	1.30
68p deep lilac and silver (July 4, 2002)	1.40	1.30
First day cover (2nd to 65p)		3.00
First day cover (68p)		3.00
Stamp cards	3.00	15.00

(* The 2nd and 1st class also appear printed in gravure by Questa in the Across the Universe prestige stamp book of September 24, 2002.)

■ **2003, October 14. Designs with white borders**
Designs as for April 23, 2001 but with a white margin around the stamp design. Printed in gravure by De La Rue (except where stated). One phosphor band (2nd), two phosphor bands (others).

2nd slate blue and silver	0.50	0.45
1st red-brown and silver	0.65	0.60
E olive-green and silver	1.50	1.50
40p olive-green and silver (May 11, 2004)	0.90	0.80
42p olive-green and silver (Apr 5, 2005, printed by Walsall)	0.80	0.80
42p olive-green and silver (May 10, 2005)	0.80	0.75
44p olive-green and silver (May 28, 2006)	1.25	1.25
48p olive-green and silver (March 27, 2007)	0.85	0.80
50p olive green and silver (Apr 1, 2008)	1.00	1.00
68p deep lilac and silver	1.20	1.25
72p deep lilac and silver (Mar 28, 2006)	1.60	1.60
78p deep lilac and silver (Mar 27, 2007)	1.20	1.20
81p deep lilac and silver (Apr 1, 2008)	1.25	1.25
First day cover (2nd, 1st, E, 68p)		3.00
First day cover (40p)		2.50
First day cover (42p)		2.50
First day cover (44p, 72p)		2.50
First day cover (48p, 78p)		3.00
First day cover (50p, 81p)		3.00
Stamp cards	2.00	10.00

(* The 2nd, 1st and 40p also appear in prestige stamp books, printed by Walsall.)

NORTHERN IRELAND

3d lilac

■ **1958-1968**
Des: W.Hollywood (3d, 4d, 5d), L.Philton (6d, 9d), T. Collins (1/3, 1/6)

A) Wmk: Multiple St Edward's Crown. Non phosphor except where stated.

3d lilac (August 18, 1958)	0.15	0.15
one centre band	0.15	0.20
4d blue (February 7, 1966)	0.15	0.15
two phosphor bands	0.15	0.15
6d purple (September 29, 1958)	0.20	0.20
9d green (March 1, 1967)		
two phosphor bands	0.35	0.40
1/3 green (September 29, 1958)	0.35	0.40
1/6 grey-blue (March 1, 1967)		
two phosphor bands	0.40	0.40
First day cover (3d)		25.00
First day cover (6d, 1/3)		30.00
First day cover (4d)		7.50
First day cover (9d, 1/6)		4.00

B) No wmk. Two phosphor bands and PVA gum except where stated.

4d blue (gum Arabic)	0.15	0.15
4d sepia (September 4, 1968)		
one centre band	0.15	0.25
4d red (February 26, 1969)	0.20	0.30
5d blue (September 4, 1968)	0.20	0.20
1/6 grey-blue	1.50	1.40
First day cover (4d sepia, 5d)		2.50
First day cover (4d red)		1.00

(*The 4d blue exists with gum arabic or PVA gum. The latter was not placed on sale in Northern Ireland; priced £8.50 mint.)

3p blue

■ **1971, July 7. Decimal Currency**
Des: J. Matthews.
The symbol on these stamps was re-drawn and moved less close to the top of the design. Where relevant, the original is noted as 'Type I' and the revised version as 'Type II'.

A) Two phosphor bands except where stated.
i) PVA gum. Original coated paper.

2½p pink (one centre band)	0.50	0.30
3p blue	0.30	0.20
5p violet	1.00	1.00
7½p brown	1.30	1.25

ii) PVA gum. Fluorescent coated paper.

2½p pink (one centre band)	5.25	2.00
3p blue	7.50	2.00
3p blue (one centre band)	0.20	0.20

iii) PVAD gum (blue tinged)

3p blue (one centre band)	1.00	0.40

3½p green (January 23, 1974)	0.20	0.20
one centre band	0.20	0.20
4½p grey-blue (November 6, 1974)	0.20	0.20
5½p deep violet (January 23, 1974)	0.20	0.20
one centre band	0.20	0.20
6½p green-blue (January 14, 1976)		
one centre band	0.20	0.20
7p red-brown (January 18, 1978)		
one centre band	0.25	0.20
8p red (January 23, 1974)	0.25	0.20
8½p green (January 14, 1976)	0.25	0.20
9p violet-blue (January 18, 1978)	0.25	0.20
10p orange (October 20, 1976)	0.30	0.25
one centre band	0.35	0.30
10½p grey-blue (January 18, 1978)	0.40	0.30
11p red (October 20, 1976)	0.40	0.30

B) Phosphor coated paper. PVAD gum (blue tinged). Issued on July 23, 1980.

12p yellow-green	0.40	0.40
13½p red-brown	0.50	0.50
15p blue	0.45	0.45

C) Printed in litho by Questa. Perf: 13½ x 14. Phosphor coated paper, except 11½p and 12½p (left side band). PVAD gum (11½p, 14p, 18p, 22p), PVAD gum (others).

11½p mushroom (April 8, 1981)	0.65	0.65
12½p light green (February 24, 1982)	0.40	0.40
14p steel-blue (April 8, 1981)	0.50	0.50
15½p pale violet (February 24, 1982)	0.60	0.60
16p light mushroom (April 27, 1983)	0.70	0.70
18p mauve (April 8, 1981)	0.70	0.70
19½p grey-green (February 24, 1982)	1.30	1.60
20½p bright blue (April 27, 1983)	2.50	2.50
22p deep blue (April 8, 1981)	0.80	0.75
26p red, type I (February 24, 1982)	0.75	0.75
28p blue, type I (April 27, 1983)	0.85	0.85

D) Printed in litho by Questa. Perf: 15 x 14. One side phosphor band (12p, 12½p, 13p); phosphor coated paper (16p, 17p, 31p); advanced coated paper (22p, 26p, 28p), or as indicated. PVAD gum.

12p emerald green (January 7, 1986)	1.00	0.80
12½p light green (February 28, 1984)	4.00	3.50
PVA gum	4.00	-
13p reddish-brown, Type I		
(October 23, 1984)	0.55	0.45
deep brown, Type II	1.00	1.00
deep brown (April 14, 1987)		
printed on paper supplied by Coated		
Papers Ltd. Type II. PVA gum	0.80	0.80
14p deep blue (November 8, 1988)		
one centre band	0.50	0.55
15p bright blue (November 28, 1989)		
one centre band	0.55	0.60
16p light mushroom		
(February 28, 1984)	6.00	5.00
17p steel blue (October 23, 1984)		
type I	0.70	0.70
advanced coated paper, type I	0.70	0.80
advanced coated paper, type II	£100	80.00

18p deep green (Janary 6, 1987)	0.65	0.60
18p bright green (December 3, 1991)		
one centre band	0.50	0.45
18p bright green (December 31, 1992)		
perf: 14	1.40	1.40
18p bright green (August 10 3, 1993)		
left band	2.00	1.80
19p orange-red (November 8, 1988)		
phosphor paper	0.65	0.65
20p brownish-black (November 28, 1989)		
phosphor paper	0.65	0.50
22p yellowish-green (October 23, 1984)	0.70	0.65
22p orange-red (December 4, 1990)		
phosphor paper	0.75	0.80
23p bright green (November 8, 1988)		
phosphor paper	0.80	0.80
24p deep red (November 28, 1989)		
phosphor paper	0.80	0.80
24p chestnut (August 10, 1993)		
two bands	2.50	2.50
26p red, type II (January 27, 1987)	2.60	1.90
26p drab (December 4, 1990)		
phosphor paper	0.80	0.80
28p blue, type II (January 27, 1987)	0.90	0.90
28p bluish grey (December 3, 1991)		
phosphor paper	0.90	0.90
31p purple, type I (October 23, 1984)	1.00	1.00
type II (April 14, 1987)	2.60	1.50
32p greenish blue (November 8, 1988)		
phosphor paper	0.90	0.90
34p bluish grey (November 28, 1989)		
phosphor paper	1.00	1.00
37p rosine (December 4, 1990)		
phosphor paper	1.10	1.10
39p mauve) (December 3, 1991)		
phosphor paper	1.30	1.30

(*The 18p with side phosphor band and 24p chestnut with two phosphor bands come from prestige stamp books.)

E) Stamps with an elliptical perforation along each vertical side, Printed in litho by Questa. One phosphor band (19p and 20p), two phosphor bands (others).

19p bistre (December 7, 1993)	0.60	0.65
19p bistre (band at left)	1.50	1.75
19p bistre (band at right)	1.75	1.50
20p bright green (July 23, 1996)	1.20	1.40
25p red (December 7, 1993)	0.70	0.75
26p red-brown (July 23, 1996)	1.65	1.75
30p olive-grey (December 7, 1993)	1.00	0.85
37p mauve (July 23, 1996)	2.40	2.60
41p grey-brown (December 7, 1993)	1.25	1.00
63p emerald (July 23, 1996)	3.15	2.75

(* Some of these stamps are also found in prestige stamp books, including the 19p with the phosphor band to the left or right.)

F) Stamps with an elliptical perforation along each vertical side. Printed in gravure by Walsall. One phosphor band (19p and 20p), two phosphor bands (others).

19p bistre (June 8, 1999)	1.30	1.30
20p bright green (July 1, 1997)	0.90	0.80

20p bright green (band at right)	1.20	1.10
26p chestnut (July 1, 1997)	1.00	1.00
26p chestnut (perf: 14)	1.75	1.95
26p chestnut (printed by Harrison)	1.60	1.50
37p mauve (July 1, 1887)	1.75	1.60
37p mauve (printed by Harrison)	1.20	1.20
38p ultramarine (June 8, 1999)	5.00	5.25
40p azure (April 25, 2000)	2.00	1.00
63p emerald (July 1, 1997)	3.50	2.65
64p turquoise (June 8, 1999)	4.00	4.00
65p greenish blue (April 25, 2000)	3.00	2.25

(*The 20p with one band at right and 26p with perf: 14 are printed by Harrison. As with the 26p and 37p printed by Harrison, they come from prestige stamp books.)

G) Non value indicator stamp. Printed in gravure by Walsall. One phosphor band.

1st orange-red (February 15, 2000)		
perf: 14	1.50	1.50
1st orange-red (April 25, 2000)		
perf: 15x14	5.00	5.00

(* The perf: 14 stamp also appeared in a prestige stamp book.)

First day cover (2½p, 3p, 5p, 7½p)		2.00
First day cover (3½p, 5½p, 8p)		3.00
First day cover (4½p)		2.00
First day cover (6½p, 8½p)		2.00
First day cover (10p, 11p)		2.00
First day cover (7p, 9p, 10½p)		3.00
First day cover (12p, 13½p, 15p)		3.00
First day cover (11½p, 14p, 18p, 22p)		3.00
First day cover (12½p, 15½p, 19½p, 26p)		3.00
First day cover (16p, 20½p, 28p)		3.00
First day cover (13p, 17p, 22p, 31p)		3.00
First day cover (12p)		1.50
First day cover (18p)		1.50
First day cover (14p, 19p, 23p, 32p)		3.00
First day cover (15p, 20p, 24p, 34p)		3.00
First day cover (17p, 22p, 26p, 37p)		3.00
First day cover (18p, 24p, 28p, 39p)		3.00
First day cover (19p, 25p, 30p, 41p)		5.00
First day cover (20p, 26p, 37p, 63p)		5.00
First day cover (38p, 64p)		4.00
First day cover (1st, 40p, 65p)		7.00

Basalt Columns (2nd)
Patchwork fields (1st)
Linen (E, 40p, 42p)
Pattern on vase (65p, 68p)

■ 2001, March 6
Des: Rodney Miller Associates. Printed in litho by De La Rue (E and 68p), Walsall (2nd, 1st, E, 65p) or Enschedé (2nd, 1st), One phosphor band (2nd), two phosphor bands (others).

2nd multicoloured	0.45	0.50
(Enschedé, Feb 23, 2003)	1.05	1.15
1st multicoloured	0.65	0.55
(Enschedé, Feb 23, 2003)	1.15	1.25
E multicoloured (Walsall)	1.00	1.00
E multicoloured (De La Rue)	1.00	1.00
65p multicoloured	1.60	1.60
68p multicoloured (July 4, 2002)	1.60	1.50
First day cover (2nd to 65p)		3.00
First day cover (68p)		5.00
Stamp cards	3.00	15.00

(* The 2nd and 1st printed by Enschedé come from the £6.99 Microcosmos prestige stamp book.)

■ 2003, October 14. Designs with white borders
Designs as for April 23, 2001 but with a white margin around the stamp design. Printed in gravure by De La Rue (except where stated). One phosphor band (2nd), two phosphor bands (others).

2nd multicoloured	0.50	0.40
1st multicoloured	0.60	0.50
E multicoloured	1.50	1.55
40p multicoloured (May 11, 2004)	0.90	0.75
42p multicoloured (Walsall, Apr 5, 2005)	0.85	0.85
42p multicoloured (July 26, 2005)	0.95	0.90
44p multicoloured (March 25, 2006)	1.25	1.30
48p multicoloured (March 27, 2007)	0.85	0.75
50p multicoloured (April 1, 2008)	1.00	1.00
68p multicoloured	1.20	1.20
72p multicoloured (March 28, 2006)	1.75	1.75
78p multicoloured (March 27, 2007)	1.30	1.10
81p multicoloured (April 1, 2008)	1.25	1.25
First day cover (2nd, 1st, E, 68p)		3.50
First day cover (40p)		2.50
First day cover (42p)		3.00
First day cover (44p, 72p)		2.50
First day cover (48p, 78p)		3.00
First day cover (50p, 81p)		3.00
Stamp cards	2.00	10.00

SCOTLAND

3d lilac

■ 1958-1967
Des: G. F. Huntley (3d, 4d, 5d), J. B. Fleming (6d, 9d), A. B. Imrie (1/3, 1/6).

A) Wmk: Multiple St Edward's Crown. Non phosphor except where stated.

3d lilac (August 18, 1958)	0.15	0.15
two phosphor bands	8.00	2.00
one band at left	0.20	0.35
one band at right	0.20	0.35
Se-tenant pair	0.35	0.70
one centre band	0.20	0.30
4d blue (February 7, 1966)	0.15	0.15
two phosphor bands	0.15	0.15
6d purple (September 29, 1958)	0.15	0.15
two phosphor bands	0.20	0.25
9d green (March 1, 1967)		
two phosphor bands	0.35	0.40
1/3 green (September 29, 1958)	0.35	0.25
two phosphor bands	0.35	0.40
1/6 grey-blue (March 1, 1967)		
two phosphor bands	0.40	0.50
First day cover (3d)		10.00
First day cover (6d, 1/3)		20.00
First day cover (3d, 6d, 1/3 phosphor)		£100
First day cover (4d)		7.50
First day cover (9d, 1/6)		2.75

B) No watermark. Two phosphor bands except where stated.
i) Gum Arabic.

3d lilac (one centre band)	0.15	—
4d blue	0.15	—
ii) PVA gum.		
3d lilac (one centre band)	0.15	0.20
4d blue	0.15	0.20
4d sepia (September 4, 1968)		
one centre band	0.15	0.20
4d red (February 26, 1969)		
one centre band	0.20	0.20
5d blue (September 4, 1968)	0.20	0.25
9d green	3.25	3.25
1/6 grey-blue	1.25	1.00
First day cover (4d sepia, 5d)		2.50
First day cover (4d red)		1.00

3½p green

■ 1971, July 7. Decimal Currency
Des: J. Matthews.
The lion symbol on these stamps was re-drawn. On the original version the eye appears as a circle, while the tongue and claws are thin; on the revised version the eye is solid while the tongue and claws are thicker. These are noted as type I or type II.

A) Two phosphor bands except where stated.
i) Gum Arabic.

2½p pink (one centre band)	0.30	—
3p blue	0.55	—

ii) PVA gum. Original coated paper.

2½p pink (one centre band)	0.30	0.25
3p blue	0.30	0.25
5p violet	0.80	1.00
7½p brown	1.00	0.90

iii) PVA gum. Fluorescent coated paper.

2½p pink (one centre band)	5.00	0.50
3p blue	9.00	0.25
one centre band	0.35	0.25
3½p green	8.50	—
5p violet	20.00	15.00
7½p brown	70.00	40.00

iv) PVAD gum (blue tinged).

3p blue (one centre band)	0.75	—
3½p green (January 23, 1974)	0.25	0.25
one centre band	0.25	0.25
4½p grey-blue (November 6, 1974)	0.30	0.25
5½p deep violet (January 23, 1974)	0.25	0.25
one centre band	0.25	0.25
6½p green-blue (January 14, 1976)		
one centre band	0.25	0.25
7p red-brown (January 18, 1974)		
one centre band	0.25	0.25
8p red (January 23, 1974)	0.30	0.25
8½p green (January 14, 1976)	0.30	0.25
9p violet-blue (January 18, 1978)	0.30	0.25
10p orange (October 20, 1976)	0.35	0.30
one centre band	0.35	0.30
10½p grey-blue (January 18, 1978)	0.40	0.35
11p red (October 20, 1976)	0.40	0.35

B) Phosphor coated paper. PVAD gum (blue tinged). Issued July 23, 1980.

12p yellow-green	0.40	0.40
13½p red-brown	0.50	0.50
15p blue	0.50	0.50

C) Printed in litho by Waddington. Perf 13½ x 14. Phosphor coated paper, except 11½p, 12p, 12½p, 13p, (left side band), 22p (advanced coated paper). PVAD gum (blue tinged) except 11½p and 12½p have PVA gum.

11½p mushroom (April 8, 1981)	0.60	0.50
12p emerald-green (January 7, 1986)	1.50	1.50
12½p light green (February 24, 1982)	0.50	0.50
13p light brown, type I (Oct 23, 1984)	0.55	0.55
type II	5.00	5.00
14p grey-blue (April 8, 1981)	0.60	0.60
15½p pale-violet (February 24, 1982)	0.60	0.60
16p light mushroom (April 27, 1983)	0.60	0.60
printed on Harrison's (November 2, 1983) on advanced coated paper	5.00	3.75
17p steel blue (Oct 23, 1984)		
type I	2.50	2.00
type II	1.10	0.90
type II, PVA gum (June 25, 1985)	0.80	0.80
18p violet (April 8, 1981)	0.80	0.80
19½p grey-green (February 24, 1982)	1.30	1.30
20½p bright blue (April 27, 1983)	2.70	2.50
22p deep blue (April 8, 1981)	2.00	2.00
22p yellowish green (Oct 23, 1984)		
type I	2.00	2.00
type II	25.00	25.00
26p red, type I (February 24, 1982)	0.80	0.80
28p blue, type I (April 27, 1983)	0.90	0.90
31p purple (October 23, 1984)		
type I	1.45	1.45
type II	90.00	60.00

D) Printed in litho by Questa. Perf 15 x 14. One phosphor band (12p, 13p), advanced coated paper (22p, 26p, 28p), or as indicated. PVAD gum. All Type II.

12p emerald-green (April 29, 1986)	1.20	1.20
13p light brown (November 4, 1986)	0.60	0.60
printed on paper supplied by Coated Paper Ltd, PVA gum (April 14, 1987)	0.80	0.60
14p deep blue (November 8, 1988)		
one centre band	0.40	0.40
14p deep blue (March 21, 19898)		
one left band	0.75	0.75
15p bright blue (November 28, 1989)		
one left band	0.50	0.50
17p steel blue (April 29, 1986)	3.00	3.00
18p deep green (January 6, 1987)	0.65	0.65
18p bright green (December 3, 1991)		
one centre band	0.55	0.50
18p bright green (September 26, 1992)		
perf. 14	0.90	0.80
18p bright green (August 10, 1993)		
left band	1.80	1.80
19p orange-red (November 8, 1988)		
phosphor paper	0.80	0.80
19p orange-red (March 21, 1989)		
two bands	1.00	1.00
20p brownish-black (November 28, 1989)		
phosphor paper	0.65	0.50
22p yellowish-green (January 27, 1987)	0.75	0.80
22p orange-red (December 4, 1990)		

phosphor paper	0.75	0.75
23p bright green (November 8, 1988)		
phosphor paper	0.75	0.75
23p bright green (March 21, 1989)		
two bands	7.00	7.00
24p deep red (November 28, 1989)		
phosphor paper	1.00	1.05
24p chestnut (December 3, 1991)		
phosphor paper	1.00	0.65
24p chestnut (October 19, 1992)		
phosphor paper, perf: 14	2.00	1.60
24p chestnut (August 10, 1993)		
two bands	2.00	2.00
26p red (January 27, 1987)	2.00	2.00
26p drab (December 4, 1990)		
phosphor paper	0.75	0.75
28p blue (January 27, 1987)	0.75	0.75
28p bluish grey (December 3, 1991)		
phosphor paper	0.75	0.75
28p bluish grey (February 18, 1993)		
phosphor paper, perf: 14	3.00	3.00
31p purple (April 29, 1986)	1.00	1.00
32p greenish blue (November 8, 1988)		
phosphor paper	1.00	1.00
34p bluish grey (November 28, 1989)		
phosphor paper	1.20	1.25
37p rosine (December 4, 1990)		
phosphor paper	1.25	1.25
39p mauve (December 3, 1991)		
phosphor paper	1.25	1.25
39p mauve (November 1992)		
phosphor paper, perf: 14	2.25	2.25

(* The 19p and 23p with two bands come from a prestige stamp book.)

E) Stamps with an elliptical perforation along each vertical side, Printed in litho by Questa. One phosphor band (19p and 20p), two phosphor bands (others).

19p bistre (December 7, 1993)	0.70	0.75
19p bistre (right band)	1.75	1.75
20p bright green (July 23, 1996)	0.90	0.90
25p red (December 7, 1993)	0.80	0.85
26p red-brown (July 23, 1996)	1.25	1.25
30p olive-grey (December 7, 1993)	1.00	0.90
37p mauve (July 23, 1996)	2.00	2.00
41p grey-brown (December 7, 1993)	1.25	1.30
63p emerald (July 23, 1996)	2.40	2.40

(* The 19p with phosphor band on the right comes from a prestige stamp book.)

F) Stamps with an elliptical perforation along each vertical side. Printed in gravure by Walsall (except where started). One phosphor band (19p and 20p), two phosphor bands (others).

20p bright green (July 1, 1997)	0.80	0.80
20p bright green (right band)	1.50	1.50
26p chestnut (July 1, 1997)	1.00	1.00
26p chestnut (perf: 14)	1.20	1.20
26p chestnut (printed by Harrison)	1.00	1.00
37p mauve (July 1, 1997)	1.50	1.50
37p mauve (printed by Harrison)	1.30	1.30

63p emerald (July 1, 1997)	2.50	2.10

(* The 20p with one band at right and the 26p perf: 14 come from prestige stamp books. The 26p and 37p printed by Harrison also come from a prestige stamp book.)

G) Non value indicator. Printed in gravure by Walsall. One phosphor band. Issued on February 15, 2000, in a prestige stamp book.

1st orange-red	1.50	1.50

First day cover (2½p, 3p, 5p, 7½p)		2.00
First day cover (3½p, 5½p, 8p)		3.00
First day cover (4½p)		1.50
First day cover (6½p, 8½p)		2.00
First day cover (10p, 11p)		2.00
First day cover (7p, 9p, 10½p)		2.50
First day cover (12p, 13½p, 15p)		3.00
First day cover (11½p, 14p, 18p, 22p)		3.00
First day cover (12½p, 15½p, 19½p, 26p)		3.00
First day cover (16p, 20½p, 28p)		3.00
First day cover (13p, 17p, 22p, 31p)		3.00
First day cover (12p)		2.00
First day cover (12p, 17p, 31p, Questa)		3.00
First day cover (13p, Questa)		2.00
First day cover (18p)		2.00
First day cover (22p, 26p, 28p, Questa)		3.00
First day cover (14p, 19p, 23p, 32p)		3.00
First day cover (15p, 20p, 24p, 34p)		3.00
First day cover (17p, 22p, 26p, 37p)		3.00
First day cover (18p, 24p, 28p, 39p)		3.00
First day cover (19p, 25p, 30p, 41p)		4.00
First day cover (20p, 26p, 37p, 63p)		4.00

Scottish flag (*2nd)
Scottish Lion (1st)
Thistle (E, 40p, 42p)
Tartan (64p, 65p, 68p)

■ **1999, June 8**
Des: A. Morris (2nd), F. Pottinger and T. Chalk (1st, E, 40p, 42p), and all adapted by Tayburn. Printed in litho by Walsall (2nd, 1st, E, 64p, 65p), De La Rue (2nd, 1st and 68p) or Questa 2nd, 1st, E and 65p). One phosphor band (2nd), two phosphor bands (others).

2nd multicoloured (Walsall)	0.50	0.45
2nd multicoloured (De La Rue)	0.50	0.45
2nd multicoloured (Questa)	1.10	1.00
1st multicoloured (Walsall)	0.60	0.60
1st multicoloured (De La Rue)	0.60	0.60
1st multicoloured (Questa)	1.10	1.10
E multicoloured (Walsall)	0.85	0.85
E multicoloured (Questa)	1.45	1.45

64p multicoloured	4.75	4.75
65p multicoloured (Walsall, Apr 25, 2000)	1.80	1.80
65p multicoloured (Questa)	2.50	2.50
68p multicoloured (July 4, 2002)	1.50	1.30
First day cover (2nd to 64p)		3.00
First day cover (65p)		3.00
First day cover (68p)		3.00
Stamp cards	3.00	12.50

(* The 2nd, 1st, E and 65p printed by Questa come from prestige stamp books.)

2003, October 14. Designs with white borders

Designs as for April 23, 2001, but with a white margin around the stamp design. Printed in gravure by De La Rue (except where stated). One phosphor band (2nd), two phosphor bands (others).

2nd multicoloured	0.50	0.40
1st multicoloured	0.65	0.50
E multicoloured	1.50	1.50
40p multicoloured (May 11, 2004)	0.80	0.85
42p multicoloured (Walsall, Apr 5, 2005)	0.85	0.85
42p multicoloured (May 10, 2005)	0.80	0.75
44p multicoloured (March 28, 2006)	1.25	1.25
48p multicoloured (March 27, 2007)	0.85	0.85
50p multicoloured (April 1, 2008)	1.00	1.00
68p multicoloured	1.20	1.00
72p multicoloured (March 28, 2006)	1.75	1.75
78p multicoloured (March 27, 2007)	1.20	1.20
81p multicoloured (April 1, 2008)	1.25	1.25
First day cover (2nd, 1st, E, 68p)		3.50
First day cover (40p)		2.50
First day cover (42p)		2.50
First day cover (44p, 72p)		2.50
First day cover (48p, 78p)		3.00
First day cover (50p, 81p)		3.00
Stamp cards	2.00	10.00

WALES

3d lilac

1958-1967

Des: Reynolds Stone.
A) Wmk: Multiple St Edward's Crown. Non phosphor except where stated.

3d lilac (August 18, 1958)	0.15	0.15
one centre band	0.15	0.20
4d blue (February 7, 1966)	0.20	0.15
two phosphor bands	0.15	0.15
6d purple (September 29, 1958)	0.30	0.25
9d green (March 1, 1967)		
two phosphor bands	0.35	0.30
1/3 green (September 29, 1958)	0.45	0.40
1/6 grey-blue (March 1, 1967)		
two phosphor bands	0.40	0.30
First day cover (3d)		10.00
First day cover (6d, 1/3)		20.00
First day cover (4d)		7.50
First day cover (9d, 1/6)		2.75

B) No watermark, Two phosphor bands except where stated.
i) Gum Arabic.

3d lilac (one centre band)	0.20	0.20
ii) PVA gum		
4d blue	0.20	0.30
4d sepia (September 4, 1968)		
one centre band	0.15	0.15
4d red (February 26, 1969)		
one centre band	0.40	0.15
5d blue (September 4, 1968)	0.30	0.25
1/6 grey-blue	2.00	2.00
First day cover (4d sepia, 5d)		2.50
First day cover (4d red)		1.00

3p blue

1971, July 7. Decimal Currency

Des: J. Matthews.
The dragon symbol on these stamps was re-drawn. On the original version the eye is a circle, while the tongue, claws and tail are thin. On the later version, the eye is solid, while the tongue, claws and tail are thick. These are noted as 'type i' and 'type II' where relevant.

A) Two phosphor bands except where stated.

i) **2½p** pink (one centre band)	0.30	-
3p blue	0.50	-
ii) PVA gum. Original coated paper.		

2½p pink (one centre band)	0.30	0.25
3p blue	0.30	0.25
5p violet	1.10	1.10
7½p brown	1.50	1.50
iii) PVA gum. Fluorescent coated paper.		
2½p pink (one centre band)	1.75	0.75
3p blue	8.00	1.75
3p blue (one centre band)	0.35	0.25
5p violet	18.00	3.75
iv) PVAD gum (blue tinged).		
3½p green (January 23, 1974)	0.20	0.20
one centre band	0.20	0.20
4½p grey-blue (November 6, 1974)	0.20	0.20
5½p deep violet (January 23, 1974)	0.20	0.20
one centre band	0.20	0.20
6½p green-blue (January 14, 1976)		
one centre band	0.20	0.25
7p red-brown (January 18, 1978)		
one centre band	0.25	0.20
8p red (January 23, 1974)	0.35	0.30
8½p green (January 14, 1976)	0.25	0.20
9p violet-blue (January 18, 1978)	0.25	0.20
10p orange (October 20, 1976)	0.35	0.25
one centre band	0.35	0.30
10½p grey-blue (January 18, 1978)	0.40	0.30
11p red (October 20, 1976)	0.40	0.30

B) Phosphor coated paper. PVAD gum (blue tinged). Issued on July 23, 1980.

12p yellow-green	0.40	0.40
13½p red-brown	0.50	0.50
15p blue	0.50	0.50

C) Printed in litho by Questa. Perf 13½ x 14. Phosphor coated paper, except 11½p and 12½p (left side band). PVA gum (11½p, 14p, 18p, 22p). PVAD gum (others).

11½p mushroom (April 8, 1981)	0.60	0.65
12½p light green (February 24, 1982)	0.50	0.40
14p steel-blue (April 8, 1981)	0.50	0.50
15½p pale-violet (February 24, 1982)	0.60	0.60
16p light mushroom (April 27, 1983)	1.00	1.00
18p mauve (April 8, 1981)	0.70	0.75
19½p grey-green (February 24, 1982)	1.30	1.60
20½p bright blue (April 27, 1983)	2.50	2.50
22p deep blue (April 8, 1981)	0.80	0.75
26p red, type I (February 24, 1982	0.75	0.75
28p blue, type I (April 27, 1983)	0.80	0.85

D) Printed in litho by Questa. Perf 15 x 14. One side phosphor band (12p, 12½p, 13p), phosphor coated paper (16p, 17p, 31p), advanced coated paper (22p, 26p, 28p) or as indicated. PVAD gum.

12p emerald-green (January 7, 1986)	1.00	1.00
12½p light green (January 10, 1984)	4.00	4.00
13p reddish-brown (Oct 23, 1984)		
type I	0.50	0.50
deep brown, type II	2.25	2.00
deep brown (April 14, 1987),		
on paper supplied by Coated Papers		
Ltd, PVA gum, type II	1.00	1.00
14p deep blue (November 8, 1988)	0.50	0.50

16p light mushroom (January 10, 1984)	1.25	1.25
17p steel-blue (October 23, 1984)		
type I	0.80	0.40
type I, fluorescent brightener omitted	0.80	1.00
type I, advanced coated paper	0.70	0.70
type II	30.00	22.00
18p deep green (January 6, 1987)	0.65	0.60
18p bright green (December 3, 1991)		
one centre band	0.50	0.45
18p bright green (left band)	1.50	1.50
18p bright green (right band)	1.50	1.50
18p bright green (January 12, 1993)		
perf: 14	4.00	4.00
19p orange-red (November 8, 1988)		
phosphor paper	0.75	0.75
20p brownish-black (November 28, 1989)		
phosphor paper	0.65	0.60
22p yellowish-green (Oct 23, 1984)	0.75	0.75
22p orange-red (December 4, 1990)		
phosphor paper	0.70	0.65
23p bright green (November 8, 1988)		
phosphor paper	0.75	0.80
24p deep red (November 28, 1989)		
phosphor paper	0.80	0.80
24p chestnut (December 3, 1991)		
phosphor paper	0.75	0.80
24p chestnut (February 25, 1992)		
two bands	1.00	1.10
24p chestnut (September 14, 1992)		
phosphor paper, perf: 14	2.50	2.50
26p red - Type II (January 27, 1987)	4.50	3.00
26p drab (December 4, 1990)		
phosphor paper	1.00	0.95
28p blue, type II (January 27, 1987)	1.10	1.05
28p bluish grey (December 3, 1991)		
phosphor paper	1.10	0.95
31p purple (October 23, 1984)	1.00	0.95
advanced coated paper (Jan 27, 1987)	1.00	1.00
32p greenish blue (November 8, 1988)		
phosphor paper	1.10	1.10
34p bluish grey (November 28, 1989)		
phosphor paper	1.10	1.10
37p rosine (December 4, 1990)		
phosphor paper	1.30	1.30
39p mauve (December 3, 1991)		
phosphor paper	1.30	1.25

(* The 18p with one band at left or right comes from prestige stamp books. The 18p with a centre band is also found in prestige stamp books.)

E) Stamps with an elliptical perforation along each vertical side. Printed in litho by Questa. One phosphor band (19p and 20p), two phosphor bands (others).

19p bistre (December 7, 1993)	0.60	0.55
19p bistre (right band)	2.00	1.80
20p bright green (July 23, 1996)	1.25	1.30
25p red (December 7, 1993)	0.75	0.75
26p red-brown (July 23, 1996)	1.25	1.25
30p olive-grey (December 7, 1993)	1.00	0.85
37p mauve (July 23, 1996)	2.00	2.00

41p grey-brown (December 7, 1993)   1.25   1.15
63p emerald (July 23, 1996)   3.00   2.75
(* The 19p with phosphor band to right comes from a prestige stamp book.)

F) Stamps with an elliptical perforation along each vertical side. Printed in gravure by Walsall. One phosphor band (19p and 20p), two phosphor bands (others). These stamps do not have the 'p' following the denomination.

20p bright green (July 1, 1997)	0.80	0.60
20p bright green (right band)	1.50	1.50
26p chestnut (July 1, 1997)	1.00	0.70
26p chestnut (perf: 14)	1.40	1.40
26p chestnut (Harrison)	1.25	1.00
37p mauve (July 1, 1997)	1.50	1.40
37p mauve (Harrison)	1.75	1.75
63p emerald (July 1, 1997)	3.00	2.25

(* The 20p with one band at right and the 26p with perf: 14 come from prestige stamp books. The 26p and 37p printed printed by Harrison come from a prestige stamp book.)

G) Non-value indicator stamp. Printed in gravure by Walsall. One phosphor band. Issued on February 15, 2000, in a prestige stamp book.
1st orange-red   1.50   1.50

First day cover (2½p, 3p, 5p, 7½p)	3.00
First day cover (3½p, 5½p, 8p)	2.00
First day cover (4½p)	2.00
First day cover (6½p, 8½p)	2.00
First day cover (10p, 11p)	2.00
First day cover (7p, 9p, 10½p)	2.00
First day cover (12p 13½p, 15p)	3.00
First day cover (11½p, 14p, 18p, 22p)	3.00
First day cover (12½p, 15½p. 19½p, 26p)	3.00
First day cover (16p, 20½p, 28p)	3.00
First day cover (12p, 17p, 22p, 31p)	3.00
First day cover (12p)	1.50
First day cover (18p)	2.00
First day cover (14p, 19p, 23p, 32p)	3.00
First day cover (15p, 20p, 24p, 34p)	3.00
First day cover (17p, 22p, 26p, 37p)	3.00
First day cover (18p, 24p, 28p, 39p)	3.00
First day cover (19p, 25p, 30p, 41p)	5.00
First day cover (20p, 26p, 37p, 63p)	5.00

Leek (2nd)
Welsh Dragon (1st)
Daffodil (E, 40p, 42p)
Prince of Wales' feathers (64p, 65p, 68p)

■ 1999, June 8

Des: D. Petersen (2nd), T. and G. Petersen (1st), I. Rees (E, 40p, 42p), R. Evans (64p, 65p, 68p), and all adapted by Tutssels. Printed in litho by Walsall (2nd, 1st, E, 64p, 65p) or De La Rue (68p). One phosphor band (2nd), two phosphor bands (others).

2nd multicoloured	0.50	0.45
2nd multicoloured (right band)	2.00	2.00
1st multicoloured	0.55	0.55
E multicoloured	1.00	1.00
64p multicoloured	4.00	4.00
65p multicoloured (April 25, 2000)	1.95	1.95
68p multicoloured (July 4, 2002)	1.20	1.30
First day cover (2nd to 64p)		3.00
First day cover (65p)		3.00
First day cover (68p)		3.00

(* The 2nd class with band at right comes from the Treasury of Trees prestige stamp book.)

■ 2003, October 14. Designs with white borders

Designs as for April 23, 2001 but with a white margin around the stamp design. Printed in gravure by De La Rue (except where stated). One phosphor band (2nd), two phosphor bands (others).

2nd multicoloured	0.45	0.50
1st multicoloured	0.65	0.60
E multicoloured	1.60	1.40
40p multicoloured (May 11, 2004)	0.80	0.90
42p multicoloured (Walsall, Apr 5, 2005)	0.90	0.85
42p multicoloured (May 10, 2005)	1.00	0.85
44p multicoloured (March 28, 2006)	1.25	1.30
48p multicoloured (March 27, 2007)	0.85	0.85
50p multicoloured (April 1, 2008)	1.00	1.00
68p multicoloured	1.30	1.20
72p multicoloured (March 28, 2006)	1.75	1.80
78p multicoloured (March 27, 2007)	1.20	1.15
81p multicoloured (April 1, 2008)	1.25	1.25
First day cover (2nd, 1st, E, 68p)		3.00
First day cover (40p)		2.50
First day cover (42p)		2.50
First day cover (44p, 72p)		2.50
First day cover (48p, 78p)		3.00
First day cover (50p, 81p)		3.00
Stamp cards	2.00	10.00

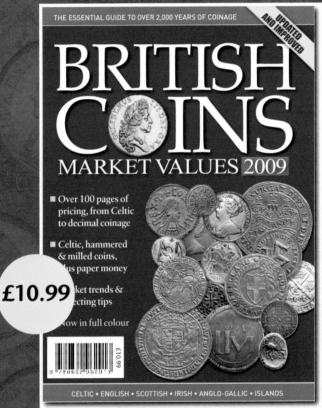

BOOKLETS

In this section, items are priced in mint condition only.

EDWARD VII, 1904-10

■ 2/- booklets
24 at 1d (sold at 2s ½d)	£300
12 at 1d, 23 at ½d	£1,000
18 at 1d, 11 at ½d (printed by De La Rue)	£1,200
18 at 1d, 11 at ½d (printed by Harrison)	£1,400

GEORGE V, 1910-35

■ 2/- booklets
18 × 1d, 12 × ½d. Wmk: Imperial Crown	£800
as above but Wmk: Simple Royal Cypher	£850
as above but stamps of 1911-1913 issue	£600
10 × 1½d, 6 × 1d, 6 × ½d. Wmk: Simple Royal Cypher	£1,200
as above but Wmk: Block GVR, printed by Waterlow	£475
as above but Postal Union Congress issue	£375
as above but Wmk: Block GVR, printed by Harrison	£550
as above but printed in photogravure, intermediate	£1,300
as above but printed in photogravure, small	£350
12 × 1½d, 4 × 1d, 4 × ½d. Silver Jubilee issue	70.00

■ 3/- booklets
12 × 1½d, 12 × 1d, 12 × ½d. Wmk: Simple Royal Cypher	£700
18 × 1½d, 6 × 1d, 6 × ½d. Wmk: Simple Royal Cypher	£700
18 × 2d	£900
24 × 1½d	£1000

18 × 1½d, 6 × 1d, 6 × ½d. Wmk: Block Cypher, Waterlow	£375
as above but Postal Union Congress issue	£325
as above but printed by Harrison	£450
as above but printed in photogravure, intermediate	£1,100
as above but printed in photogravure, small	£325
20 × 1½d, 4 × 1d, 4 × ½d. Silver Jubilee issue	60.00

■ 3/6 booklets
18 × 2d, 6 × 1d	£900
12 × 2d, 6 × 1½d, 6 × 1d, 6 × ½d	£900

■ 5/- booklets
34 × 1½d, 6 × 1d, 6 × ½d. green cover, Waterlow	£3,500
as above but buff cover	£2,500
as above but printed by Harrison	£1,100
as above but printed in photogravure, intermediate	£2,750
as above but printed in photogravure, small	£375

EDWARD VIII, 1936

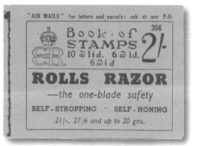

■ 6d booklets
4 × 1½d	30.00

■ 2/- booklets
10 × 1½d, 6 × 1d, 6 × ½d	85.00

■ 3/- booklets
18 × 1½d, 6 × 1d, 6 × ½d	75.00

■ 5/- booklets
34 × 1½d, 6 × 1d, 6 × ½d	£175

GEORGE VI, 1937-52

■ 6d booklets

4 x 1½d	50.00
2 x 1½d, 2 x 1d, 2 x ½d	£190
4 x 1d, 4 x ½d	80.00

■ 1/- booklets

4 x 1½d, 4 x 1d, 4 x ½d. Pale colours, in panes of two	15.00
as above but in panes at four	£5,000
with changed colours, in panes of two	15.00
with changed colours, in panes of four	15.00

■ 2/- booklets

10 x 1½d, 6 x 1d, 6 x ½d, with Royal Cypher on cover	£400
as above but with GPO cypher on cover	£400

■ 2/6 booklets

6 x 2½d, 6 x 2d, 6 x ½d, with red cover	£900
as above but with blue cover	£900
as above but with green cover	£475
as above but stamps in pale colours	£475
as above but no commercial advertising included	70.00
as above but changed colours	40.00
6 x 2½d, 6 x 1½d, 3 x 1d, 6 x ½d	30.00

■ 3/- booklets

18 x 1½d, 6 x 1d, 6 x ½d, with royal cypher on cover	£1,000
as above but with GPO cypher on cover	£800

■ 5/- booklets

34 x 1½d, 6 x 1d, 6 x ½d, with royal cypher on cover	£1,000
as above but with GPO cypher on cover	£1,000
18 x 2½d, 6 x 2d, 6 x ½d	£1,000
as above but pale colours	£1,000
as above but no commercial advertising included	90.00
as above but changed colours	50.00
18 x 2½d, 6 x 1½d, 3 x 1d, 6 x ½d	35.00
12 x 2½d, 6 x 2d, 6 x 1½d, 6 x 1d, 6 x ½d	45.00

ELIZABETH II WILDINGS, 1953-67

■ 1/- booklets

4 x 1½d, 4 x 1d, 4 x ½d. Wmk: Tudor Crown, panes of two	5.00
as above but panes of four	5.00
as above but Wmk: St. Edward's Crown, panes of two	10.00
as above but panes of four	5.00
Wmk: Multiple Crowns, panes of four	5.00

■ 2/- booklets

4 x 3d, 4 x 1½d, 4 x 1d, 4 x ½d,. Wmk: St. Edward's Crown, pink cover	4.00

as above but Wmk: Multiple Crowns (upright)	6.00
as above but yellow cover	6.00
as above but Wmk: sideways	25.00
as above but stamps with phosphor bands	50.00
4 x 4d, 2 x 1d se-tenant with 2 x 3d	3.00
as above but 3d with phos band at left or right)	8.00
as above but 3d with two phos bands	2.00
8 x 2½d, 3 x ½d se-tenant with 1 x 2½d	3.00
8 x ½d, 8 x 2½d in panes of two of each se-tenant	2.00
8 x 3d	1.00

■ 2/6 booklets

6 x 2½d, 6 x 1½d (QE II), 3 x 1d, 6 x ½d (KGVI)	20.00
as above but only 1d of KGVI	£400
as above but QEII stamps only, Wmk: Tudor Crown	35.00
as above but Wmk: St Edward's Crown	25.00
6 x 2½d, 6 x 2d, 6 x ½d, Wmk: St Edward's Crown	22.00

■ 3/- booklets

6 x 3d, 6 x 1½d, 6 x 1d, 6 x ½d, Wmk: St Edward's Crown	16.00
as above but Wmk: Multiple Crowns	22.00
as above but graphite lined stamps	£180
as above phosphor lined stamps	45.00

■ 3/9 booklets

18 x 2½d, Wmk: Tudor Crown	22.00
as above but Wmk: St Edward's Crown	18.00

■ 4/6 booklets

18 x 3d, Wmk: St Edward's Crown	18.00
as above but Wmk: Multiple Crowns	20.00
as above but graphite lined stamps	15.00
as above but phosphor lined stamps	28.00
12 x 4d, 6 x 1d, Wmk: Multiple Crowns	16.00
as above but phosphor lined stamps	7.00

■ 5/- booklets

12 x 2½d (QEII), 6 x 2d (KGVI), 6 x 1½d (QEII), 6 x 1d (KGVI), 6 at ½d (KGVI)	26.00
as above but only 1d and 2d stamps of KGVI	£275
as above but only 2d stamps of KGVI	£150
as above but QEII stamps only, Wmk: Tudor Crown	35.00
as above but 2d deep brown, Wmk: St Edward's Crown	30.00
as above but 2d brown	25.00
12 x 3d, 6 x 2½d, 6 x 1½d, 6 x ½d, Wmk: St Edward's Crown	18.00
as above but Wmk: Multiple Crowns	24.00
as above but graphite lined stamps	£100
as above but phosphor lined stamps, 2½d with two bands	£100
as above but 2½d with one band	90.00

■ 6/- booklets

18 x 4d, Wmk: Multiple Crowns	24.00
as above but with phosphor lined stamps	22.00

■ 10/- booklets

30 x 3d, 6 x 2d, 6 x 1½d, 6 x 1d, 6 x ½d	90.00
30 x 3d, 6 x 2½d, 6 x 1½d, 6 x 1d	90.00
24 x 4d, 6 x 3d, 6 x 1d	20.00
as above but phosphor lined, 3d with side phos band	8.00
as above but 3d with one centre band	5.00

ELIZABETH II PRE-DECIMAL MACHINS, 1968-70

■ 2/- booklets
Yellow cover, 4 x 4d sepia (two bands), plus 2 x 1d se-tenant with 2 x 3d (two bands)	0.80
Grey cover, 4 x 4d sepia (two bands), plus 2 x 4d sepia (centre band) se-tenant with two labels	0.65
Grey cover, 4 x 4d sepia (centre band), plus 2 x 4d sepia (centre band) se-tenant with two labels	1.50
Grey cover, 4 x 4d red (centre band) plus 2 x 4d red (centre band) se-tenant with two labels	2.00

■ 4/6 booklets
Blue plain cover, 6 x 4d sepia, 6 x 4d sepia (two bands), 6 x 1d	6.00
as above but blue cover showing Cutty Sark	1.75
as above but blue cover showing Golden Hind and 4d with one centre band	1.75
as above but blue cover showing Discovery	1.75
Blue cover showing Queen Elizabeth 2, 6 x 4d red, 6 x 4d red (centre band), 6 x 1d	1.75
as above but cover showing Sirius	2.00
as above but cover showing Dreadnought	2.50
as above but cover showing Mauretania	3.50
as above but cover showing Victory	3.00
as above but cover showing Sovereign on the Seas	3.00

■ 5/- booklets
Bistre covers showing Ightham Mote, 6 x 5d, 6 x 5d	2.00
as above but cover showing Little Moreton Hall	1.75
as above but cover showing Long Melford Hall	2.50
as above but cover showing Mompesson House	2.50
as above but cover showing Cumberland Terrace	2.50
as above but cover showing The Vineyard, Saffron Walden	2.50
as above but cover showing Mereworth Castle	3.50
as above but cover showing Philympia 1970 London	1.50

■ 6/- booklets
Purple plain cover, 6 x 4d sepia, 6 x 4d sepia, 6 x 4d sepia (two bands)	£215
Orange cover showing Kingfisher, 6 x 4d sepia, 6 x 4d sepia, 6 x 4d sepia (two bands)	1.80
as above but cover showing Peregrine Falcon	1.50
Orange cover showing Peregrine Falcon, 6 x 4d sepia, 6 x 4d sepia, 6 x 4d sepia (centre band)	2.00
as above but cover showing Pied Woodpecker	2.00
as above but cover showing Great Crested Grebe	2.25
as above but cover showing Barn Owl	2.25

Orange cover showing Barn Owl*, 6 x 4d red, 6 x 4d red, 6 x 4d red (centre band)	2.75
as above but cover showing Jay*	2.75
as above but cover showing Puffin	3.00
as above but cover showing Cormorant	3.00
as above but cover showing Wren	3.00
as above but cover showing Golden Eagle	3.00

■ 10/- booklets
Purple cover showing Livingstone, 6 x 4d sepia, 6 x 4d sepia, 6 x 4d sepia, 6 x 4d sepia (two bands), 6 x 3d, 6 x 1d	5.50
Green cover showing Scott, 6 x 5d, 6 x 5d, 6 x 4d sepia, 6 x 4d sepia (one centre band) plus 4 x 1d se-tenant with 2 x 4d sepia (one band)	4.00
as above but cover showing Kingsley, and 4d red	3.25
as above but cover showing Shackleton, and 4d red	5.00
as above but cover showing Frobisher, and 4d red	6.50
as above but cover showing Cook, and 4d red	6.50

ELIZABETH II DECIMAL MACHINS, STITCHED, 1971-76

■ 10p booklets
Yellow cover, 2 x ½p, 2 x 1p, 2 x 1½p, 2 x 2p
London's first pillar box	2.00
Pillar box of 1856	2.50
Urban pillar box of 1857	3.00
Penfold type of 1866	3.00
Double aperture type of 1899	2.25
Mellor type of 1968	2.25
King Edward VIII type of 1936	2.25
Queen Elizabeth II type of 1952	2.50
Double aperture type of 1973	2.00
Philatelic Posting Box	1.75
General Letter Carrier 1793	1.50
Letter Carrier 1837	1.50
Letter Carrier 1855	1.50

■ 25p booklets
Violet cover, 5 x ½p, 9 x 2½p
Knifeboard Omnibus	3.00
80 Years of British Stamp Books	3.25
B-type Omnibus	3.50
Showman's Engine	6.00
Royal Mail Van 1913	6.00
Motor Wagonette 1901	5.50
London Taxi Cab 1931	6.00

Norwich Electric Tramway	6.50
Help Children, Save the Children	8.00

■ 30p booklets
Purple cover (except where stated), 10 x 3p

Curlew	4.00
80 Years of British Stamp Books	4.50
Lapwing	4.00
Robin	4.00
Pied Wagtail	4.00
Kestrel	4.00
Black Grouse	4.20
Skylark	4.50
Oyster-catcher	4.00
Oyster-catcher (bistre cover)	5.00
Help Children, Save the Children (red cover)	8.00
Canada Life Assurance Group (red cover)	4.50

■ 35p booklets
Blue cover, 10 x 3½p

Cuthred Penny	3.00
Edward I Silver Groat	3.00
Canada Life Assurance Group	2.75

■ 45p booklets
Brown cover, 10 x 4½p

Elizabeth Gold Crown	4.00

■ 50p booklets
Blue-green cover, 5 x ½p, 7 x 2½p, 10 x 3p

Large Bindweed	7.00
Primrose	7.50
Honeysuckle	7.50
Hop	7.00
Common Violet	7.00
Lords-and-Ladies	7.00
Wood Anemone	7.50
Deadly Nightshade	7.50
Canada Life Assurance Group	6.50
Deep green cover, 5 x 3p, 10 x 3½p	
Canada Life Assurance Group	7.50

■ 85p booklets
Purple cover, 5 x 3½p, 15 x 4½p

Canada Life Assurance Group	6.50

ELIZABETH II DECIMAL MACHINS, FOLDED 1976-89

£1
Royal Mail
Stamps
Ten at 10p

■ 10p booklets
2 x ½p, 3 x 1p, 1 x 6p

Cover design of '10p' made up of red dots	1.25

■ 10p booklets
2 x ½p, 2 x 1p, 1x 7p

Kent farm buildings	0.80
Northern Ireland farm buildings	0.80
Yorkshire farm buildings	1.00
Wales farm buildings	0.80
Scotland farm buildings	0.75
Sussex farm buildings	0.80

■ 10p booklets
2 x 1p, 1 x 8p

Post Office stand at London 1980 Stamp Exhibition	0.60

(* This booklet exists with differing postal rates on its inner covers.)

■ 50p booklets
2 x ½p, 2 x 1p, 2 x 6½p, 4 x 8½p

Cover with bold '50p' (6½p with phos band at left)	2.75
Cover with bold '50p' (6½p with phos band at right)	2.75

■ 50p booklets
2 x 1p, 3 x 7p, 3 x 9p

Cover with bold '50p' (7p with phos band at left)	8.00
Cover with bold '50p' (7p with phos band at right)	7.50

■ 50p booklets
2 x 1p, 3 x 7p, 3 x 9p

Clement Talbot Van (7p with phos band on left)	5.00
Clement Talbot Van (7p with phos band on right)	3.00
Austin Cape Taxi (7p with phos band on left)	5.00
Austin Cape Taxi (7p with phos band on right)	3.00
Morris Royal Mail Van (7p with phos band on left)	5.00
Morris Royal Mail Van (7p with phos band on right)	3.50
Guy Electric Dustcart (7p with phos band on left)	5.00
Guy Electric Dustcart (7p with phos band on right)	4.00
Albion Van (7p with phos band on left)	6.50
Albion Van (7p with phos band on right)	5.50
Leyland Fire Engine (7p with phos band on left)	5.00
Leyland Fire Engine (7p with phos band on right)	4.00

■ 50p booklets
2 x 2p, 2 x 8p, 3 x 10p

Leyland Fire Engine (8p with phos band left or right)	2.00

■ 50p booklets
2 x 2p, 2 x 8p, 3 x 10p

Rolls Royce Silver Ghost (8p with phos band left or right)	2.50

■ 50p booklets
3 x 2p, 2 x 10p, 2 x 12p

Grand Prix Austin (10p with phos band left or right)	2.75
1903-1905 Vauxhall car (10p with phos band left or right)	2.25
1900 Daimler (10p with phos band left or right)	2.25

■ 50p booklets
1 x ½p, 1 x 1p, 1 x 14p, 3 x 11½p

BOOKLETS

Lanchester 1896 (11½p with phos band left or right)	2.25
Bullnose Morris 1913 (11½p with phos band left or right)	2.75
Mugdock Castle (11½p with phos band left or right)	3.75

■ **50p booklets**
3 x 2½p, 2 x 4p, 3 x 11½p

Mugdock Castle (11½p with phos band at left)	3.00
Mugdock Castle (11½p with phos band at right)	5.00
Mow Cop Castle (11½p with phos band at left)	3.50
Mow Cop Castle (11½p with phos band at right)	3.50

■ **50p booklets**
1 x ½p, 4 x 3p pink, 3 x 12½p

Paxton's Tower (12½p with phos band left or right)	2.00
Temple of the Winds (12½p with phos band left or right)	2.00
Temple of the Sun (12½p with phos band at left or right)	2.00
Water Garden (12½p with phos band at left or right)	2.00
Bagot Goat (12½p with phos band at left or right)	3.00

■ **50p booklets**
2 x 1p, 3 x 3½p, 3 x 12½p (all with one centre band)

Gloucester Old Spot Pig	3.25
Toulouse Goose	3.25
Orkney Sheep	3.25

■ **50p booklets**
3 x 1p, 2 x 4p, 3 x 13p (all with one centre band)

Orchids, Dendrobium nobile	2.00
Cyripedium calcedolus and ophrys apifera	2.00
Bifienasia and Vandatricolour	2.00
Cymbodium and Arpophyllum	2.00

■ **50p booklets**
3 x 17p (two phosphor bands and 'stars' printed on the gummed side)

Pillar box	2.50
Emperor dragonfly	2.00
Common frog	3.00

■ **50p booklets**
3 x 17p (two phosphor bands without 'stars' on gummed side)

Common frog	2.00

■ **50p booklets**
2 x 1p, 4 x 12p emerald-green (all with one centre band)

Hadrian's Wall	3.70

■ **50p booklets**
1 x 1p (right band), 1 x 13p (left band), 2 x 18p (two bands)

Roman Theatre at St Albans	3.00
Portchester Castle, Hampshire	2.50
Weather Vane at Thomas Lord's original cricket ground	2.20
Ashes Urn	2.25
Current Lord's pavilion	2.25
Lord's New Stand	2.25

■ **50p booklets**
1 x 1p, 2 x 5p, 3 x 13p (all with one centre band)

Moorhen and Dabchicks	4.00
Great Pond Snail	3.75

Bondnant Gardens, Colwyn Bay	3.00
Botanical Gardens, Edinburgh	3.00
Mount Stuart Gardens (side edges imperforate)	3.00
Mount Stewart (corrected spelling)	3.00
Kew Gardens	2.50
Common whelk and jellyfish	2.50

■ **50p booklets**
1 x 1p, 1 x 13p, 2 x 18p

Pigs	2.50
Birds	2.50
Elephants	2.50

■ **50p booklets**
1 x 14p, 2 x 19p

The Yeomen of the Guard	2.00
The Pirates of Penzance	3.00
The Mikado	3.50
Hermit crab, bladder wrack and laver spire shell	3.00

■ **50p booklets**
2 x 15p, 1 x 20p

Armstrong Whitworth Atalanta & De Havilland Dragon	4.25
Vickers Viscount 806 & De Havilland Comet 4	
(contains Penny Black Anniversary definitives)	4.00
BAC 1-11 & VC10	3.00
BAe ATP, BAe 146 & Concorde	3.00

■ **50p booklets**
2 x 1p, 2 x 24p

Sir Arthur Evans at Crete	2.00
Howard Carter of the tomb of Tutankhamun	2.00
Sir Austen Layard in Assyria	1.75
Sir Flinders Petrie at Giza	2.25
Sheriff's Millennium 1992	1.75
Airmail markings	1.75
Ship mail markings	1.75
Registered mail	1.75

■ **50p booklets**
2 x 25p

'Paid' marking	1.75
Swan with Two Necks	1.75
Bull and Mouth	1.75
Golden Cross	1.75
Pheasant Inn	1.75
John O'Groats	1.75
Land's End	1.75
St. David's Head	3.00
Giant's Causeway	3.50

■ **£1 booklets**
6 x 17p (advanced coated paper)

Violin	3.75

■ **£1 booklets**
1 x 13p (right band), 5 x 18p (two bands)

French horn	5.25
Bass Clarinet	4.50
A Study in Scarlet	5.25

The Hound of the Baskervilles	4.75
Adventure of the Speckled Band (side edges imperforate)	5.00
Bears	4.25
Oliver Twist	4.25
Nicholas Nickleby	4.50
David Copperfield	3.50
Great Expectations	4.25
Sea urchin, starfish and crab	3.25

■ £1 booklets
5 x 20p

Wicken Fen	4.25
Wicken Fen (glossy cover)	
(contains Penny Black Anniversary definitives)	10.00
Click Mill (contains Penny Black Anniversary definitives)	3.50
Jack and Jill Mills	3.00
Howell Mill	3.00

■ £1 booklets
2 x 2p, 4 x 24p

Punch illustrations by Richard Doyle and Hoffnung	3.25
Punch illustrations by Sir John Tenniel and Eric Burgin	3.00
Punch illustrations by Sir John Tenniel and Anton	3.25
Punch illustrations by Sir John Tenniel and Hewison	3.00
Sheriff's Millennium 1992	3.00
University of Wales	3.75
St. Hilda's College, Oxford	3.75
Marlborough College	3.75

■ £1 booklets
4 x 25p

Free Church of Scotland College	3.75
Herbert Asquith	3.00
David Lloyd-George	2.75
Winston Churchill	2.75
Clement Attlee	2.75
Violette Szabo	2.75
Dame Vera Lynn	2.75
R. J. Mitchell	2.75
Archibald McIndoe	3.25

■ £1 booklets with red cover and Royal Mail cruciform

4 x 25p	3.25
2 x 1p, 1 x 20p, 3 x 26p (stamps printed in litho)	3.00
2 x 1p, 1 x 20p, 3 x 26p (stamps printed in gravure)	2.75
1 x 1p, 1 x 2p, 1 x 19p, 3 x 26p	2.50
1 x 2nd, 3 x 1st	2.50

Panes with a margin to the left or right. Prices are the same for both varieties, except where stated:

■ 65p booklets
10 x 6½p

Cover with bold '65p', right margin	5.50
Cover with bold '65p', left margin	8.50

■ 70p booklets
10 x 7p

Cover with bold '70p', either margin	4.25
With left margin	4.25

■ 70p booklets
10 x 7p

Horse-shoeing, right margin	4.00
Horse-shoeing, left margin	25.00
Thatching, right margin	4.00
Thatching, left margin	£110
Dry-stone Walling, right margin	4.00
Dry-stone Walling, left margin	£150
Wheel making, right margin	4.50
Wheel making, left margin	5.00
Wattle fence making, right margin	4.50
Wattle fence making, left margin	12.50
Basket making, right margin	4.50
Basket making, left margin	6.50
Keddlestone Hall, either margin	5.50

■ 80p booklets
10 x 8p

1915 Vickers, either margin	3.25

■ 85p booklets
10 x 8½p

Cover with bold '85p', right margin	7.50
Cover with bold '85p', left margin	8.00

■ 90p booklets
10 x 9p

Cover with bold '90p', left margin	4.25
Cover with bold '90p', right margin	5.00

■ 90p booklets
10 x 9p

Grand Union Canal, right margin	4.50
Grand Union Canal, left margin	21.00
Llangollen Canal, left margin	3.75
Llangollen Canal, right margin	£300
Kennet & Avon Canal, right margin	7.00
Kennet & Avon Canal, left margin	17.50
Caledonian Canal, left margin	4.50
Caledonian Canal, right margin	6.50
Regent's Canal, right margin	6.00
Regent's Canal, left margin	9.00
Leeds & Liverpool Canal	5.00
Tramway Museum, Crich	6.50

■ £1 booklets
10 x 10p (all-over phosphor)

Ironbridge, Telford, Shropshire	3.75

■ £1 booklets
10 x 10p (one centre band)

Sopwith Camel and Vickers Vimy	3.50
Hawker Fury and Handley Page Heyford	3.75
Wellington Bomber and Hurricane	3.50

■ £1.15 booklets
10 x 11½p (one centre band)

Spitfire and Lancaster	3.75
Lightning and Vulcan	4.25
Natural History Museum, London	3.75

National Museum of Antiquities of Scotland — 3.75

■ £1.20 booklets
10 x 12p yellow-green

Beetle Mill, Ireland	4.00
Tin mines in Cornwall	4.25
Bottle Kilns, Stoke	4.25

■ £1.20 booklets
10 x 12p emerald-green (one centre band)

Pillar box	3.75
National Gallery	3.75
'Maybe'	3.75

■ £1.25 booklets
10 x 12½p (one centre band)

Ashmolean Museum, Oxford	3.75
National Museum of Wales	3.75
Ulster Museum, Belfast	3.75
Castle Museum, York	3.75
GWR Isambard Kingdom Brunel	4.25
LMS Class 4P Passenger Tank Engine	4.25
LNER Mallard	4.25
SR/BR Clan Line	4.25

■ £1.30 booklets
10 x 13p (one centre band)

Swansea/Mumbles Railway Car	3.50
The Glasgow Tram	4.25
Blackpool car No. 717	3.75
'D' Class London tram	3.50
The Three Bears starting the day	4.00
Keep in Touch	3.50
Garden Scene	3.50
Brighter Writer	3.50
Jolly Postman	3.50
Linnean Society	3.75
Recipes (vegetables)	3.50
Children's Parties (balloons)	3.50

■ £1.30 booklets
6 x 14p (two bands), 2 x 11½p (left band), 2 x 11½p (right band)

Penny Black, right margin	4.50
Penny Black, left margin	4.50
King George V ½d and 1d 'Downey Head', left margin	5.00
King George V ½d and 1d 'Downey Head', right margin	14.00

■ £1.40 booklets
10 x 14p (phosphor coated paper)

Preston Mill in Scotland	3.75
Talyllyn Railway, Tywyn	4.00
Costumes of 1860-1880	4.00
Costumes of 1815-1830	4.00
Legal Charge	4.00
Fox Talbot photographs	4.00

■ £1.43 booklets
6 x 15½p (two bands), 2 x 12½p (left band), 2 x 12½p (right band)

James Chalmers portrait	4.00
Edmund Dulac (KGVI 5/- red)	4.00

■ £1.44 booklets

Forces Postal Service	3.75
£5 orange of 1882	4.00
Postmark Collecting	4.00
Golden Hinde inscribed 'Holiday Postcard Stamp Book'	3.75

■ £1.45 booklets
10 x 16p (phosphor coated paper)

Lyme Regis, Dorset	4.75

(* Sold at a discount of 15p off face value; stamps have a 'D' printed on the gummed side.)

■ £1.46 booklets
6 x 16p (two bands), 2 x 12½p (left band), 2 x 12½p (right band)

Seahorse high values	8.00
Parcel Post	7.00
Regional Stamps	7.00

(* Panes have either the four 12½p followed by one 16p on the bottom row, or one 16p followed by four 12½p; prices are the same either way.)

■ £1.50 booklets
6 x 17p (two bands), 2 x 12p (left band), 2 x 12p (right band)

Pillar box	4.00
National Gallery	4.00
'No'	4.00

(* Panes have either the four 12p followed by one 17p on the bottom row, or one 17p followed by four 12p; prices are the same either way.)

■ £1.54 booklets
6 x 17p (two bands), 2 x 13p (left band), 2 x 13p (right band)

To Pay Labels	3.75
Embossed stamps	3.75
Surface printed stamps	3.75
350th Anniversary of The Post Office	3.75

(* Panes have either the four 13p followed by one 17p on the bottom row, or one 17p followed by four 13p; prices are the same either way.)

■ £1.55 booklets
10 x 15½p (phosphor coated paper)

Costumes of 1830-1850	4.50
Costumes of 1850-1860	4.75
Costumes of 1860-1880	4.00
Costumes of 1880-1900	4.00

■ £1.55 booklets
10 x 17p (phosphor coated paper)

Paper boat and paper plane	5.25

(* Sold at a discount; stamps have a 'D' printed on the gummed side.)

■ £1.60 booklets
10 x 16p (phosphor coated paper)

Birthday Cake	5.25
Weavers Cottages, Bibury	4.25
Write It	4.50

■ £1.70 booklets
10 x 17p (phosphor coated paper)

Love Letters	4.00
Hands exchanging letters	4.00
Pillar box	4.25
National Gallery	4.50
'Yes'	4.25

■ £1.80 booklets
10 x 18p (phosphor coated paper)

Rag, Tag and Bobtail	5.25
Keep in Touch	5.50
Garden Scene	5.50
Brighter Writer	5.25
Jolly Postman	5.00
Linnean Society	5.00
Recipes (fruits)	5.00
Children's Parties (balloons)	5.25

■ £1.90 booklets
10 x 19p

Pocket Planner	5.50
Fox Talbot photographs	5.50

■ £2 booklets
8 x 25p

Motorised cycle	4.00
Motor mail van	3.75
Electric mail van	3.75
Sir Rowland Hill (London and Brighton Railway)	3.75
Sir Rowland Hill (Hazlewood School)	3.75
Sir Rowland Hill (Secretary to the Post Office)	4.75
Sir Rowland Hill (Uniform Penny Postage)	4.75

■ £2 booklets with red cover and Royal Mail cruciform
8 x 25p	4.50
1 x 20p, 7 x 26p (stamps printed in litho)	4.50
1 x 20p, 7 x 26p (stamps printed in gravure)	6.00
1 x 19p, 7 x 26p	4.50
2 x 2nd, 6 x 1st	4.50

RETAIL STAMP BOOKS WITH NON-ELLIPTICAL PERFORATIONS, 1987-93

These booklets were intended to be sold not only over post office counters, but also through alternative retail outlets. A distinguishing feature of all these booklets is a bar code on the outside back cover.

Booklets with a 'window' in the cover, through which one of the stamps can be seen, and with the panes surrounded by a white margin.

■ 4 x 13p
August 4, 1987. Printed by Harrison	2.50

■ 10 x 13p
August 4, 1987. Printed by Harrison	3.75

■ 4 x 14p
August 23, 1988. Printed by Harrison	4.50
October 11, 1988. Stamps by Harrison; cover by Walsall	5.00

■ 10 x 14p
August 23, 1988. Printed by Harrison	6.00
October 11, 1988. Printed by Questa	11.00

■ 4 x 18p
August 4, 1987. Printed by Harrison	2.75

■ 10 x 18p
August 4, 1987. Printed by Harrison	5.00

■ 4 x 19p
August 23, 1988. Printed by Harrison	4.00
October 11, 1988. Stamps by Harrison; cover by Walsall	4.50

■ 10 x 19p
August 23, 1988. Printed by Harrison	9.50
October 11, 1988. Printed by Questa	12.50

■ 4 x 26p
August 4, 1987. Printed by Harrison	14.00

■ 4 x 27p
August 23, 1988. Printed by Harrison	8.50

Booklets with an illustration of the contents on the cover, and panes with no margin, but either the top and bottom or all three edges imperforate.

■ 4 x 14p
October 11, 1988. Printed by Harrison	4.50
January 24, 1989. Stamps by Harrison, cover by Walsall	15.00

■ 10 x 14p
October 11, 1988. Printed by Harrison	8.00
October 11, 1988. Printed by Questa	11.00

■ 4 x 19p
October 11, 1988. Printed by Harrison	5.00
January 24, 1989. Stamps by Harrison, cover by Walsall	17.50

■ 10 x 19p
October 11, 1988. Printed by Harrison	8.00
October 11, 1988. Printed by Questa	11.50

■ 4 x 27p
October 11, 1988. Printed by Harrison	20.00

■ 4 x 29p

October 2, 1989. Printed by Walsall (two phos bands)	8.00
April 17, 1990. Printed by Walsall (phos paper)	7.00

■ 4 x 31p

September 17, 1990. Printed by Walsall	4.00

■ 4 x 33p

September 16, 1991. Printed by Walsall	3.00
September 8, 1992. Printed by Walsall (yellow strip at right is inscribed 'For Worldwide Postcards')	3.00

■ 2 x 39p

July 28, 1992. Printed by Harrison	2.00

■ 4 x 39p

September 16, 1991. Printed by Walsall	2.75

Booklets comprising non-value indicator stamps and with either the top and bottom edges or all three edges imperforate.

■ 4 x 2nd bright blue

August 22, 1989. Printed by Walsall	4.00
November 28, 1989. Stamps by Harrison; cover by Walsall	9.50
August 6, 1991. Printed by Walsall	
Cover features Royal Mail cruciform	3.50
January 21, 1992. Printed by Walsall	
Cover features logos of Olympic and Paralympic Games	3.50

■ 10 x 2nd bright blue

August 22, 1989. Printed by Harrison	6.00
September 19, 1989. Printed by Questa	6.50
August 6, 1991. Printed by Walsall	
Cover features Royal Mail cruciform	4.75
August 6, 1991. Printed by Questa	
Cover features Royal Mail cruciform	4.75
January 21, 1992. Printed by Walsall	
Cover features logos of Olympic and Paralympic Games	4.75
March 31, 1992. Printed by Questa	
Cover features logos of Olympic and Paralympic Games	5.00
September 22, 1992. Printed by Harrison	
Cover features Royal Mail cruciform	4.75

■ 4 x 2nd deep blue

August 7, 1990. Printed by Walsall	3.00

■ 10 x 2nd deep blue

August 7, 1990. Printed by Harrison	4.75
August 7, 1990. Printed by Questa	6.00
August 7, 1990. Printed by Walsall	4.75

■ 4 x 1st brownish-black

August 22, 1989. Printed by Walsall	4.50
December 5, 1989. Stamps by Harrison; cover by Walsall	11.00

■ 10 x 1st brownish-black

August 22, 1989. Printed by Harrison	7.50
September 19, 1989. Printed by Questa	9.75

■ 4 x 1st orange-red

August 7, 1990. Printed by Walsall	4.00
August 7, 1990. Printed by Walsall. Perf: 13	7.00
January 21, 1992. Printed by Walsall	
Cover features logos of Olympic and Paralympic Games	4.00

■ 10 x 1st orange-red

August 7, 1990. Printed by Harrison	6.00
August 7, 1990. Printed by Questa	6.00
August 7, 1990. Printed by Walsall	6.00
January 21, 1992. Printed by Harrison	6.00
Cover features logos of Olympic and Paralympic Games	
January 21, 1992. Printed by Walsall	6.00
Cover features logos of Olympic and Paralympic Games	
February 9, 1993. Printed by Walsall	
Cover features Royal Mail cruciform; back cover has advertisement for Greetings stamps	6.00

RETAIL STAMP BOOKS WITH ELLIPTICAL PERFORATIONS, 1993-2000

Booklets with panes with all four edges perforated.

■ 4 x 30p

May 5, 1998. Printed by Walsall	3.00
August 3, 1998. Printed by Walsall	
Cover inscribed 'Make their post memorable'	3.00

■ 4 x 35p

November 1, 1993. Printed by Walsall	
Cover illustrates a single stamp	3.50
May 16, 1995. Printed by Walsall	
Cover shows a block of stamps	3.50
March 19, 1996. Printed by Walsall	
Back cover features Olympic symbols	6.50

■ 4 x 37p

July 8, 1996. Printed by Walsall.	
Back cover features Olympic symbols	4.00
February 4, 1997. Printed by Walsall.	
No Olympic symbols	4.00
August 26, 1997. Printed by Walsall.	
Cover shows street names in London	3.00

August 3, 1998. Printed by Walsall
Cover inscribed 'Make their post memorable'   3.25

■ **4 x 38p**
April 26, 1999. Printed by Walsall   3.00

■ **4 x 40p**
April 27, 2000. Printed by Walsall   3.00

■ **4 x 41p**
November 1, 1993. Printed by Walsall
Cover illustrates a single stamp   3.75
May 16, 1995. Printed by Walsall
Cover shows a block of stamps   3.75
March 19, 1996. Printed by Walsall
Back cover features Olympic symbols   7.00

■ **4 x 60p**
August 9, 1994. Printed by Walsall
Cover illustrates a single stamp   5.50
October 4, 1994. Printed by Walsall
As above but 'Worldwide Airmail Stamps' in a scroll design 5.50
May 16, 1995. Printed by Walsall
Cover shows a block of stamps   4.75
March 19, 1996. Printed by Walsall
Back cover features Olympic symbols   7.50

■ **4 x 63p**
July 8, 1996. Printed by Walsall
Back cover features Olympic symbols   5.00
February 4, 1997. Printed by Walsall
No Olympic symbols. Stamps printed in litho   5.00
August 26, 1997. Printed by Walsall
Stamps printed in gravure   4.00
May 5, 1998. Printed by Walsall
Cover air mail label below block of stamps   4.00

■ **4 x 64p**
April 26, 1999. Printed by Walsall   4.00

■ **4 x 65p**
April 27, 2000. Printed by Walsall   4.00

**Booklets of non-value indicator stamps in panes with all
four edges perforated.**

■ **4 x 2nd bright blue**
April 6, 1993. Printed by Walsall   3.50
September 7, 1993. Printed by Harrison   3.50
January 10, 1995. Printed by Harrison.
Cover has white lines through block of stamps   3.50
December 12, 1995. Printed by Walsall.
Cover shows block of stamps   3.50
February 6, 1996. Printed by Walsall.
Back cover features Olympic symbols   3.50
February 4, 1997. Printed by Walsall.
Cover has no line through block of stamps   3.50
August 26, 1997. Printed by Walsall.
Stamps printed in gravure   3.50

■ **10 x 2nd bright blue**
April 6, 1993. Printed by Questa   4.75
November 1, 1993. Printed by Walsall   4.75
January 10, 1995. Printed by Questa   4.75
Cover has white lines through block of stamps   4.75
December 12, 1995. Printed by Harrison
Cover shows block of stamps   4.75
February 6, 1996. Printed by Harrison.
Back cover features Olympic symbols   4.75
February 6, 1996. Printed by Questa
Back cover features Olympic symbols   4.75
August 6, 1996. Printed by Harrison
Cover has no white line through block of stamps
Back cover features Olympic symbols   4.75
August 6, 1996. Printed by Questa
Cover has no white line through block of stamps
Back cover features Olympic symbols   4.75
February 4, 1997. Printed by Harrison
Cover has no white line through block of stamps   4.75
February 4, 1997. Printed by Questa
Cover has no white line through block of stamps   4.75
May 5, 1998. Printed by De La Rue
Cover has no white line through block of stamps   4.75
December 1, 1998. Printed by Questa
Stamps printed in gravure   4.75

■ **4 x 1st orange-red**
April 6, 1993. Printed by Harrison   4.00
August 17, 1993. Printed by Walsall   4.00
January 10, 1995. Printed by Walsall
Cover has white lines through block of stamps   4.00
February 6, 1996. Printed by Walsall
Back cover features Olympic symbols   4.00
February 4, 1997. Printed by Walsall
Cover has no white line through block of stamps   4.25
August 26, 1997. Printed by Walsall
Stamps printed in gravure   4.00

■ **4 x 1st orange-red with commemorative label**
July 27, 1994. Printed by Questa.
Label marks 300th anniversary of Bank of England   4.00
May 16, 1995. Printed by Walsall
Label marks the centenary of birth of R. J. Mitchell   4.00
April 16, 1996. Printed by Walsall
Label marks 70th birthday of Queen Elizabeth II   4.00
February 12, 1997. Printed by Walsall
Label marks Hong Kong '97 stamp exhibition   4.00
October 21, 1997. Printed by Walsall
Label marks Commonwealth Heads of Govt Meeting   4.00
November 14, 1998. Printed by Walsall
Label marks 50th birthday of the Prince of Wales   4.00
May 12, 1999. Printed by Walsall
Label marks 50th anniversary of the Berlin Airlift   4.00
October 1, 1999. Printed by Walsall.
Label marks the Rugby World Cup   4.00
(* Panes with commemorative labels, Millennium definitives or
the self-adhesive definitives are listed in the relevant sections.)

■ **8 x 1st class orange-red, 2 x Millennium definitives**
May 12, 1999. Printed by Walsall

Containing the Settlers' Tale 26p stamp	6.00
September 21, 1999. Printed by Walsall	
Containing the Farmers' Tale 26p stamp	6.50
May 26, 2000. Printed by Walsall	
Containing the Above & Beyond 26p stamp	6.50
September 5, 2000. Printed by Walsall	
Containing the Stone & Soil 26p stamp	6.50

■ 10 x 1st orange-red

April 6, 1993. Printed by Harrison	6.00
April 6, 1993. Printed by Walsall	6.00
November 1, 1993. Printed by Questa	6.00
November 1, 1993. Printed by Walsall	
Back cover has advertisement for Greetings stamps	6.00
February 22, 1994. Printed by Walsall	
With 'FREE POSTCARDS' on yellow edge at right	6.00
July 1, 1994. Printed by Walsall	
With 'OPEN NOW Chance to win a kite' on yellow strip,	
and 'Better luck next time' on inside back cover	6.00
July 1, 1994. Printed by Walsall	
With 'OPEN NOW Chance to win a kite' on yellow strip, and	
'You've won' on inside back cover	6.00
September 20, 1994. Printed by Walsall	
With 'STAMPERS' and 'DO NOT OPEN UNTIL' on cover	6.00
September 20, 1994. Printed by Walsall	
With 'STAMPERS' and 'KEEP IN TOUCH' on cover	6.00
September 20, 1994. Printed by Walsall	
With 'STAMPERS' and 'HAPPY BIRTHDAY' on cover	6.00
September 20, 1994. Printed by Walsall	
With 'STAMPERS' and 'What's happenin'' on cover	6.00
January 10, 1995. Printed by Harrison	
Cover has white lines through block of stamps	6.00
January 10, 1995. Printed by Questa	
Cover has white lines through block of stamps	6.00
January 10, 1995. Printed by Walsall	
Cover has white lines through block of stamps	5.50
February 14, 1995. Printed by Walsall.	
Cover shows Thornton's chocolates	6.00
April 4, 1995. Printed by Harrison	
Stamps have two phosphor bands	5.50
April 24, 1995. Printed by Walsall	
With 'W.H. Smith Special Offer' on yellow strip	6.00
June 26, 1995. Printed by Questa	
With 'Sainsbury's Promotion' on yellow strip	9.00
September 4, 1995. Printed by Harrison	
Cover shows Benjy Bear and Harry Hedgehog	6.00
February 6, 1996. Printed by Walsall	
Back cover features Olympic symbols	5.25
February 19, 1996. Printed by Harrison	
Cover showing Walt Disney World	6.00
March 19, 1996. Printed by Harrison	
Back cover features Olympic symbols	6.00
May 13, 1996. Printed by Harrison	
Cover shows lighting the Olympic flame	
Back cover shows Shot Put	6.00
May 13, 1996. Printed by Harrison	
Cover showing lighting the Olympic flame,	
Back cover shows Hurdles	6.00
May 13, 1996. Printed by Harrison	
Cover showing lighting the Olympic flame	

Back cover shows Archery	6.00
July 15, 1996. Printed by Walsall	
With 'W. H. Smith Offer Inside' on yellow strip	6.00
August 16, 1996. Printed by Harrison	
Cover has no white line through block of stamps	
Back cover features Olympic symbols	6.00
August 16, 1996. Printed by Walsall	
Cover has no white line through block of stamps	
Back cover features Olympic symbols	6.00
September 9, 1996. Printed by Walsall	
Cover shows iced cakes	6.00
October 7, 1996. Printed by Walsall.	
With 'Offer Inside' on yellow strip	6.00
February 4, 1997. Printed by Harrison	
Cover has no white line through block of stamps	6.50
February 4, 1997. Printed by Walsall	
Cover has no white line through block of stamps	6.00
November 8, 1997. Printed by Walsall	
Stamps printed in gravure	6.00
February 2, 1998. Printed by De La Rue	
With 'Win an Adventure holiday to Disney Animal Kingdom'	6.00
April 27, 1998. Printed by De La Rue	
Cover shows Peugeot 106. 'Stick one of these on your drive'	6.00
May 5, 1998. Printed by De La Rue	6.00
July 1, 1998. Printed by De La Rue	
Cover shows JVC Camcorder	6.00
August 3, 1998. Printed by De La Rue	
Cover inscribed 'Make their post memorable'	6.00
September 7, 1998. Printed by Questa	
Stamps printed in litho	6.00
December 1, 1998. Printed by Questa	
Stamps printed in gravure	6.00

■ 10 x 1st gold

April 21, 1997. Printed by Harrison	6.00
April 21, 1997. Printed by Walsall	6.00
September 15, 1997. Printed by Harrison	
Cover shows beach, inscribed 'FIRST CLASS TRAVEL'	6.00

■ 4 x E dark blue

January 19, 1999. Printed by Walsall	
Cover shows block of stamps and 'By Air Mail' label	3.25

RETAIL STAMP BOOKS WITH SELF ADHESIVE STAMPS, 1993-date

Experimental booklet with a horizontal format.

■ **20 x 1st orange-red**
October 19, 1993. Printed by Walsall   9.00

Booklets with a mainly red cover, and an illustration of the contents.

■ **6 x 2nd bright blue**
January 29, 2001. Printed by Walsall   3.50

■ **10 x 2nd bright blue**
January 29, 2001. Printed by Questa   3.50

■ **12 x 2nd bright blue**
January 29, 2001. Printed by Questa   4.00

■ **4 x 1st orange-red and a commemorative label**
January 29, 2001. Printed by Walsall
Label marks centenary of the death of Queen Victoria   4.50

■ **6 x 1st orange-red**
January 29, 2001. Printed by Walsall   4.00
July 4, 2002. Printed by Questa   4.50

■ **10 x 1st orange-red**
January 29, 2001. Printed by Questa   5.00

■ **12 x 1st orange-red**
January 29, 2001. Printed by Questa   6.50
January 29, 2001. Printed by Walsall   6.50

Booklets in the colour of the stamps, and with one (1st class), two (2nd class) or no notches (other values) along the right hand edge.

■ **12 x 2nd bright blue**
July 4, 2002. Printed by Questa   5.00
March 27, 2003. Printed by Walsall
Inscription 'The Real Network' under Royal Mail cruciform   5.00
June 15, 2004. Printed by Walsall

No 'The Real Network' inscription   5.00
June 5, 2007. Printed by Walsall
Includes PiP information   4.00

■ **6 x 1st gold**
June 5, 2002. Printed by Questa   3.75
June 5, 2002. Printed by Walsall   3.75
March 27, 2003. Printed by Walsall
Inscription 'The Real Network' under Royal Mail cruciform   3.00
June 15, 2004. Printed by Walsall
Inscription 'Supporting London 2012'   3.75
March 22, 2005. Printed by Walsall
Advertisement for Smilers on inside front cover   3.75
June 5, 2007. Printed by Walsall
Includes PiP information   3.75
June 5, 2007. Printed by Walsall
Includes facsimile of Arnold Machin's signature   4.00
August 28, 2007. Printed by Walsall
Advertisement for Harry Potter stamps   4.00
September 29, 2007. Printed by Walsall
Improved postcode information   3.50
June 10, 2008. Printed by Walsall
Advertisement for Classic Carry On & Hammer stamps   3.50

■ **12 x 1st gold**
June 5, 2002. Printed by Walsall   6.50
March 27, 2003. Printed by Walsall
Inscription 'The Real Network' under Royal Mail cruciform   6.50
June 5, 2007. Printed by Walsall
Includes PiP information   6.50

■ **6 x E**
July 4, 2002. Printed by Walsall   5.00
May 28, 2003. Printed by Walsall
Inscription 'The Real Network' under Royal Mail cruciform   5.50

■ **6 x 42p**
July 4, 2002. Printed by Walsall   5.00
May 28, 2003. Printed by Walsall
Inscription 'The Real Network' under Royal Mail cruciform   6.50

■ **6 x 68p**
July 4, 2002. Printed by Walsall   8.50
May 28, 2003. Printed by Walsall
Inscription 'The Real Network' under Royal Mail cruciform   8.00

■ **4 x Europe**
March 27, 2003. Printed by Walsall
Inscription 'The Real Network' under Royal Mail cruciform   3.50
June 15, 2004. Printed by Walsall
No 'The Real Network' inscription   4.50

■ **4 x Worldwide**
March 27, 2003. Printed by Walsall
Inscription 'The Real Network' under Royal Mail cruciform   7.00
June 15, 2004. Printed by Walsall
No 'The Real Network' inscription   5.00

■ **4 x Worldwide Postcard**
April 1, 2004. Printed by Walsall   3.75

2003 Extreme Endeavours booklet

Booklets containing a mixture of 1st class definitives and special issues, with the cover matching the colour of the definitives (except where stated), and illustrating the special stamps inside (except Cats & Dogs); the 1st class gold booklets have one notch along the right hand edge.

■ **2 x 1st orange-red, 10 x Cats & Dogs**
February 13, 2001. Printed by Walsall   18.00

■ **4 x 1st orange-red, 2 x 1st class Submarines**
April 17, 2001. Printed by Questa   65.00

■ **4 x 1st orange-red, 2 x 1st class Punch & Judy**
September 4, 2001. Printed by Questa   14.00

■ **4 x 1st orange-red, 2 x 1st class Flags & Ensigns**
October 22, 2001. Printed by Questa   14.00

■ **4 x 1st orange-red, 2 x 1st class Airliners**
May 2, 2002. Printed by Questa   5.50

■ **4 x 1st orange-red, 2 x 1st class World Cup**
May 21, 2002. Printed by Questa   4.00

■ **4 x 1st gold, 2 x 1st class Bridges of London**
September 10, 2002. Printed by Questa   5.50

■ **4 x 1st gold, 2 x 1st class Hello!**
March 4, 2003. Printed by Questa   8.00

■ **4 x 1st gold, 2 x 1st class Extreme Endeavours**
April 29, 2003. Printed by De La Rue   5.00

■ **4 x 1st gold, 2 x 1st class British Journey: Scotland**
July 15, 2003. Printed by De La Rue   3.50

■ **4 x 1st gold, 2 x 1st class Toys**
September 18, 2003. Printed by De La Rue   8.00

■ **4 x 1st gold, 2 x 1st class British Journey: N Ireland**
March 16, 2004. Printed by De La Rue   3.50

■ **4 x 1st gold, 2 x 1st class Ocean Liners**
April 13, 2004. Printed by De La Rue   4.50

■ **4 x 1st gold, 2 x 1st class British Journey: Wales**
June 15, 2004. Printed by De La Rue   5.00

■ **4 x 1st gold, 2 x 1st class Beside The Seaside**
March 13, 2008. Printed by Walsall, red cover   3.50

CHRISTMAS STAMP BOOKLETS, 1978-date

1978 Christmas booklet

■ **1978**
£1.60 (10 x 7p, 10 x 9p definitives).
Decoration of holly, 'Greetings Christmas 1978'   3.50

■ **1979**
£1.80 (10 x 8p, 10 x 10p definitives).
Christmas cracker, 'Greetings Christmas 1979'   3.75

■ **1980**
£2.20 (10 x 10p, 10 x 12p definitives).
Nativity scene, 'Greetings Christmas 1980'   4.75

■ **1981**
£2.55 (10 x 14p, 10 x 11½p definitives).
Skating scene, 'Christmas Greetings 1981'   6.25

■ **1982**
£2.50 (10 x 15½p, 10 x 12½p definitives).
Christmas mummers   6.50
(* Sold at a discount of 30p off face value; stamps
have a blue star printed on the gummed side)

■ **1983**
£2.20 (20 x 12½p definitives).
Pantomime scene   6.50
(* Sold at a discount of 30p off face value; stamps
have a blue star printed on the gummed side.)

■ **1984, November 20**
£2.30 (20 x 13p Christmas stamps)
Cover shows a Manger Scene   6.00
(* Stamps have a five-pointed star on the gummed side)

■ **1985, November 19**
£2.40 (20 x 12p Christmas stamps).
Cover shows Cinderella's slipper on a cushion   6.00

■ **1986**
£1.20 (10 x 13p definitives).
Cooking Shetland yule cakes   5.00

(* Sold at a discount of 10p off the total **face** value; stamps have a blue star printed **on** the gummed side.)

■ **1990, November 13**
20 x 17p Christmas stamps 7.00

■ **1991, November 12**
20 x 18p Christmas stamps 7.00

■ **1992, November 10**
20 x 18p Christmas stamps 6.00

■ **1993, November 9**
20 x 19p Christmas stamps 7.00

■ **1993, November 9**
10 x 25p Christmas stamps 5.75

■ **1994, November 1**
20 x 19p Christmas stamps 6.75

■ **1994, November 1**
10 x 25p Christmas stamps 5.00

■ **1995, October 30**
20 x 19p Christmas stamps 7.00

■ **1995, October 30**
10 x 25p Christmas stamps 4.50

■ **1995, October 30**
4 x 60p Christmas stamps 4.50

■ **1996, October 28**
20 x 2nd Christmas stamps 7.00

■ **1996, October 28**
10 x 1st Christmas stamps 6.50

■ **1997, October 27**
20 x 2nd Christmas stamps 7.00

■ **1997, October 27**
10 x 1st Christmas stamps 6.50

■ **1998, November 2**
20 x 20p Christmas stamps 6.50

■ **1998, November 2**
10 x 26p Christmas stamps 6.50

■ **1999, November 2**
20 x 19p Christmas stamps 6.50

■ **1999, November 2**
10 x 26p Christmas stamps 4.75

■ **2000, November 7**
20 x 2nd Christmas stamps 6.00

■ **2000, November 7**
10 x 1st Christmas stamps 6.50

■ **2001, November 6**
24 x 2nd Christmas stamps 7.00

■ **2001, November 6**
12 x 1st Christmas stamps 5.00

■ **2002, November 5**
24 x 2nd Christmas stamps 6.50

■ **2002, November 5**
12 x 1st Christmas stamps 5.00

■ **2003, November 4**
24 x 2nd Christmas stamps 7.00

■ **2003, November 4**
12 x 1st Christmas stamps 5.00

■ **2004, November 2**
24 x 2nd Christmas stamps 7.00

■ **2004, November 2**
12 x 1st Christmas stamps 5.00

■ **2005, November 1**
24 x 2nd Christmas stamps 7.00

■ **2005, November 1**
12 x 1st Christmas stamps 5.00

■ **2006, November 7**
12 x 2nd Christmas stamps 5.50
12 x 1st Christmas stamps 7.00

■ **2007, November 6**
12 x 2nd Christmas stamps 5.50
12 x 1st Christmas stamps 7.00

ROYAL MAIL COMMEMORATIVE BOOKLETS, 1985

■ **1985, July 30. 350th Anniversary of Royal Mail Service to the Public**
£1.53 (10 x 17p 350th Anniversary stamp, with an all-over 'D' pattern printed on the back).
Cover shows a Datapost van, plane, Concorde 4.50

PENNY BLACK COMMEMORATIVE BOOKLETS, 1990

■ 4 x 15p
January 30, 1990. Printed by Walsall — 3.75

■ 10 x 15p
January 30, 1990. Printed by Harrison — 6.00
April 17, 1990. Printed by Questa — 11.50
June 12, 1990. Printed by Walsall — 6.00

■ 4 x 20p
January 30, 1990. Printed by Walsall — 4.25
April 17, 1990. Stamps by Harrison; cover by Walsall — 5.00

■ 5 x 20p
January 30, 1990.
Cover showing Wicken Fen, printed on glossy card — 10.00
Cover showing Click Mill — 3.50

■ 10 x 20p
January 30, 1990. Printed by Harrison — 6.00
April 17, 1990. Printed by Questa — 11.00
June 12, 1990. Printed by Walsall — 7.50

■ 2 x 15p, 1 x 20p se-tenant
January 30, 1990.
Cover showing Vickers Viscount and De Havilland Comet — 3.50

MILLENNIUM DEFINITIVE BOOKLETS, 2000

■ 4 x 1st with a commemorative label
March 21, 2000. Printed by Walsall
Label showing Postman Pat — 4.25

April 4, 2000. Printed by Walsall
Label for the National Botanic Garden of Wales — 4.50

■ 10 x 1st
January 6, 2000. Printed by Questa — 6.00
January 6, 2000. Printed by Walsall — 6.25

RETAIL STAMP BOOKS WITH PICTORIAL DEFINITIVES, 2005-date

■ 6 x pictorial stamps issued on October 4, 2005
October 4, 2005. Printed by Walsall — 7.00
July 17, 2006. Printed by Walsall. With PiP information. — 4.00

■ 6 x pictorial stamps issued on October 17, 2006
October 17, 2006. Printed by Walsall — 3.50

■ 1x 'Love' stamp, 5 x 1st class definitive
January 16, 2007. Printed by Walsall — 4.00

■ 6 x pictorial stamps issued in 2005 and 2006
February 2, 2008. Printed by Walsall — 3.50

■ 2 x 'Love' stamp, 5 x 1st class definitive
January 15, 2008. Printed by Walsall — 3.50

RETAIL STAMP BOOKS WITH PRICING IN PROPORTION STAMPS, 2006-date

■ 4 x 2nd Large
August 15, 2006 — 7.00

■ 4 x 1st Large
August 15, 2006 — 7.00

■ 6 x 1st gold
September 12, 2006 — 3.50

■ 6 x 1st gold
February 1, 2007
With postcode advertisement inside front cover — 3.50

■ 12 x 2nd bright blue
September 12, 2006 — 5.00

■ 12 x 1st gold
September 12, 2006 — 5.50

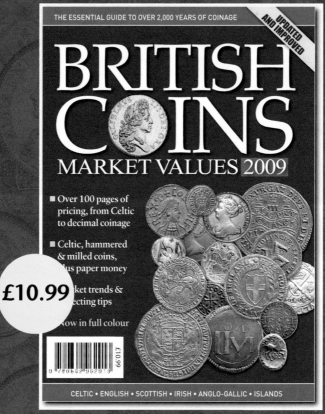

GREETINGS BOOKS

In this section, prices are quoted for mint condition only.

These booklets contain the GB Greetings stamps, which are listed individually in the Decimal QEII section. Normally the panes comprise one of each of the designs, often with additional greetings labels.

Greetings book, 1989

■ **1989, January 31. Various designs**
Cover shows elements from the stamp designs. Pane comprises two of each of the five designs
The stamps are all of 19p 30.00

■ **1990, February 6. Smiles**
Cover shows the stamps within smiling lips.
The stamps are all of 20p 17.50

■ **1991, February 5. Good luck**
Cover shows good luck charms
The stamps are all 1st class NVIs 7.00

■ **1991, March 26. Smiles**
Cover shows a happy pillar box. Designs as for
February 6, 1990, but inscribed 1st 8.00

■ **1992, January 28. Memories**
Cover shows a label inscribed Memories
and pressed flowers 7.00

■ **1993, February 12. Gift Giving**
Cover shows Rupert the Bear 6.50

■ **1994, February 1. Messages**
Cover shows Rupert the Bear 7.00

■ **1995, March 21. Art**
Cover shows a clown (the yellow strip has either
the inscription 'Pull Open' or no inscription) ... 6.50

■ **1996, February 26. Cartoons**
Cover shows asking for more, with bowl marked
'Love'. Stamps are on phosphor paper 7.00

■ **1996, November 11. Cartoons**
As booklet of February 26, 1996, but stamps
have two phosphor bands 24.00

■ **1997, January 6. Flower Paintings**
Cover shows a flower 7.00

■ **1997, February 3. Flower Paintings**
Cover as for January 6, 1997, but with the
additional inscription 'WIN A BEAUTIFUL
BOUQUET INSTANTLY' 7.50

■ **1998, January 5. Flower Paintings**
Cover shows a box of chocolates. 7.50

■ **1998, August 3. Flower Paintings**
Cover inscribed 'Make their post memorable' ... 8.00

'Art' greetings book, 1995

'Cartoons' greetings book, 1996

'Flower Paintings' greetings book, 1996

PRESTIGE STAMP BOOKS

In this section, prices are quoted for mint condition only.

Stamps for Cooks, 1969

■ 1969, December 1. £1 Stamps for Cooks

Pane of six 1d, three 4d, three 4d, three 5d (recipe label)	10.00
Pane of fifteen 4d (label 'Stuffed Cucumber')	3.00
Pane of fifteen 4d (label 'Method')	3.00
Pane of fifteen 5d (recipe label)	3.00
Complete book	10.00

(* A stapled version of this stitched book exists that is much more rare. It retails at around £400.)

The Story of Wedgwood book, 1972

■ 1972, May 24.
£1 The Story of Wedgwood

Pane of twelve 3p	4.00
Pane of six 2½p, six 3p	6.00
Pane of nine 2½p, one ½p	7.50
Pane of four ½p, two 2½p	45.00
Complete book	45.00

The Story of Wedgwood book, 1980

■ 1980, April 16.
£3 The Story of Wedgwood

Pane of six 2p	1.00
Pane of nine 10p	2.50
Pane of nine 12p	2.75
Pane of one 2p, four 10p, four 12p	2.75
Complete book	6.00

■ 1982, May 19. £4 Story of Stanley Gibbons

Pane of six 12½p	2.25
Pane of six 15½p	3.50
Pane of nine 15½p	2.50
Pane of one 2p, one 3p, seven 12½p	4.00
Complete book	7.50

■ 1983, September 14.
£4 Story of the Royal Mint

Pane of six 12½p (label 'The Royal Mint & America')	2.25
Pane of six 12½p (label 'Maundy Money')	2.25
Pane of nine 16p	2.50
Pane of one 3p, two 3½p, six 16p	4.00
Complete book	7.50

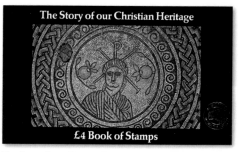

The Story of our Christian Heritage book, 1984

■ 1984, September 4. £4 The Story of Our Christian Heritage

Pane of six 17p	2.75
Pane of six 13p (label 'William Wilberforce')	2.50
Pane of six 13p (label 'Lillian Bayliss')	2.50
Pane of one 10p, one 13p, seven 17p	15.00
Complete book	20.00

■ 1985, January 8.
£5 The Story of The Times

Pane of six 17p	2.75
Pane of nine 13p	3.25
Pane of nine 17p	3.50
Pane of two 4p, four 13p, two 17p, one 34p	7.50
Complete book	11.00

■ 1986, March 18. £5 The Story of British Rail

Pane of six 17p	3.00
Pane of nine 12p	3.50
Pane of nine 17p	3.50
Pane of six 12p, two 17p, one 31p	11.00
Complete book	15.00

■ 1987, March 3. £5 The Story of P&O

Pane of six 13p	2.75
Pane of nine 13p	3.25
Pane of nine 18p	3.50
Pane of one 1p, two 13p, five 18p, one 26p	8.50
Complete book	12.00

■ 1998, March 3. £5 FT100 (Financial Times)

Pane of nine 18p	2.50
Pane of six 13p	2.00
Pane of six 13p, one 18p, one 22p, one 34p	12.00
Pane of six 18p	1.75
Complete book	17.00

■ 1989, March 21. £5 The Scots Connection

Pane of nine 19p Scotland	2.75
Pane of six 14p Scotland	1.50
Pane of five 14p, two 19p, one 23p, all Scotland	11.00
Pane of six 19p Scotland	2.00
Complete book	13.00

■ 1990, March 20. £5 London Life

Pane of four 20p Alexandra Palace	1.50
Pane of six 20p Penny Black Anniversary (label 'Eros')	1.75
Pane of six 20p Penny Black Anniversary (label 'Street Signs')	1.75
Pane of one 15p, one 20p, one 29p all Penny Black Anniversary, plus one 2nd, one 1st, one 15p, one 20p, one 50p	11.00
Complete book	15.00

■ 1991, March 19. £6 Alias Agatha Christie

Pane of six 17p (label 'Styles')	1.50
Pane of six 17p (label "mousetrap")	1.50
Pane of nine 22p	3.00
Pane of six 22p, two 33p	6.50
Complete book	11.00

■ 1992, February 25. £6 Cymru Wales

Pane of four 39p Wintertime	2.50
Pane of six 18p Wales	1.50
Pane of two 18p, two 24p, all Wales, plus one 2nd, one 1st, two 33p	8.00
Pane of six 24p Wales	2.25
Complete book	11.00

■ 1992, October 27. £6 Tolkien

Pane of six 24p (label 'Runes')	2.00
Pane of six 24p (label 'Hobbit')	2.00
Pane of six 18p	1.75
Pane of one 2nd, one 1st, two 18p, two 24p, two 39p	7.50
Complete book	11.00

■ 1993, August 10. £5.64 The Story of Beatrix Potter

Pane of four 1st Beatrix Potter	1.50
Pane of one 24p of each of Scotland, Wales and Northern Ireland, one 18p of each of Scotland, Wales and Northern Ireland	6.00
Pane of three 1st, three 2nd	4.00
Pane of two 2nd, two 18p, two 33p, two 39p	6.50
Complete book	12.00

■ 1994, July 26. £6.04 Northern Ireland

Pane of four 30p Prince of Wales Paintings	1.75
Pane of one 6p, one 19p, four 25p	7.50
Pane of two 19p, four 25p, one 30p, one 41p, all Northern Ireland	5.00
Pane of one 19p, one 25p, one 30p, one 41p, all Northern Ireland	3.25
Complete book	14.00

■ 1995, April 25. £6 The National Trust

Pane of six 25p National Trust	2.75
Pane of two 19p, two 25p, one 10p, one 30p, one 35p, one 41p	10.00
Pane of one 19p of each of Scotland, Wales and Northern Ireland, plus one 25p of each of Scotland, Wales and Northern Ireland	5.00
Pane of six 19p	5.50
Complete book	14.00

■ 1996, May 14. £6.48 European Football Championships

Pane of four 19p Football Legends	1.60
Pane of four 25p Football Legends	1.75
Pane of two 35p, two 41p, two 60p Football Legends	5.00
Pane of two 25p, two 25p Scotland, two 25p Wales, two 25p Northern Ireland	3.50
Complete book	11.00

■ 1997, September 23. £6.15 75 Years of the BBC

Pane of one 26p, one 37p Scotland, one 26p, one 37p Wales, one 26p, one 37p Northern Ireland	5.50
Pane of four 26p gold, four 1st gold	4.00
Pane of three 20p, three 26p	3.50
Pane of four 20p Children's Television	4.50
Complete book	12.00

■ 1998, March 10. £7.49 The Wilding Definitives

Pane of nine 26p Wilding	4.00
Pane of six 20p Wilding	2.75
Pane of four 20p, two 26p, two 37p Wilding	5.00
Pane of three 26p, three 37p Wilding	5.00
Complete book	15.00

Tolkien book, 1992

Breaking Barriers

A Century of Great British Speed Records

Breaking Barriers book, 1998

■ **1998, October 13. £6.16 Breaking Barriers**

Pane of four 20p Land Speed Records	4.00
Pane of one 20p Scotland, one 20p Wales, one 20p Northern Ireland, three 43p	5.50
Pane of three 2nd, one 26p Scotland, one 26p Wales, one 26p Northern Ireland	4.50
Pane of three 43p, two 10p, three 2nd	8.00
Complete book	17.50

Profile on Print book, 1999

■ **1999, February 16. £7.54 Profile on Print**

Pane of eight 1st orange-red	3.25
Pane of four 1st Machin large format embossed	6.00
Pane of four Machin large format intaglio	6.00
Pane of four Machin large format typographed	6.00
Pane of nine 1st orange-red	3.25
Complete book	20.00

■ **1999, September 21. £6.99 World Changers**

Pane of four 20p Millennium Jenner's vaccination	1.50
Pane of four 44p Millennium Faraday's electricity	7.00
Pane of four 26p Darwin's theory	6.00
Pane of four 63p Computers in brain	7.50
Pane of four 1p, three 19p, one 26p	2.50
Complete book	19.00

■ **2000, February 15. £7.50 Special by Design**

Pane of eight 1st Millennium definitive	4.50
Pane of three 1st Scotland, three 1st Wales, three 1st Northern Ireland	11.00
Pane of four 19p, olive-green, two 38p	8.00

Pane of six 1st Penny Black Anniversary	5.50
Complete book	25.00

■ **2000, August 4. £7.03 HM Queen Elizabeth The Queen Mother**

Pane of six 2nd Scotland, two 65p Scotland	5.00
Pane of nine 1st Millennium definitives	4.50
Queen Mother's Century miniature sheet	6.00
Pane of four 27p Queen Mother	5.50
Complete book	18.00

■ **2000, September 18. £7 A Treasury of Trees**

Pane of two 65p Millennium Doire Dach, Forest for Scotland	2.50
Pane of four 45p Millennium Sycamore Seeds, Seed Bank, Ardingly	4.00
Pane of two 65p Millennium Bluebell Wood Groundwork's Changing Places	2.50
Pane of four 1st Millennium definitives, four 2nd Northern Ireland	10.00
Pane of four 2nd Millennium Yews	2.00
Complete book	18.00

■ **2001, October 21. £6.76 Unseen and Unheard**

Pane of two 1st, two 65p Submarines	7.00
Pane of two 2nd, two 45p Submarines	7.00
Pane of four Flags and Ensigns	3.50
Pane of four 1st Scotland, four E Scotland	5.00
Complete book	18.00

■ **2002, February 6. £7.29 A Gracious Accession**

Pane of four 2nd, four E	5.00
Pane of one 2nd, one 1st, one E, one 45p Golden Jubilee	6.00
Pane of one 1st, one E, one 45p, one 65p Golden Jubilee	5.50
Pane of four 1st Wilding, five 2nd Wilding (one of the 2nd is tilted)	6.00
Complete book	18.00

■ **2002, September 24. £6.83 Across the Universe**

Pane of four 1st England, four 2nd England, one 1st Scotland	4.00
Pane of four 1st Millennium National Space Centre	10.00
Pane of four 1st gold, four E	5.00
Astonomy miniature sheet	4.00
Complete book	18.00

■ **2003, February 25. £6.99 Microcosmos**

Pane of four 1st Northern Ireland, five 2nd Northern Ireland	3.25
Pane of four 1st gold, four E	4.00
Pane of two 1st and two 2nd Discovery of DNA	2.00
Pane of four E Discovery of DNA	2.50
Complete book	12.00

■ **2003, June 2. £7.46 A Perfect Coronation**

Pane of four 1st gold, four 2nd	4.25
Pane of four 1st 50th Anniversary of Coronation	3.25
Pane of four (different) 1st Anniversary of Coronation	3.25
Pane of two 47p Wilding, two 68p Wilding, one £1 1953 Coronation	32.50

Complete book   40.00

(* This book is rare as over half its print run was bought by a publisher to mail out a Coronation book. It also contains a £1 'remake' of the 1953 1/3 Coronation stamp that is unavailable elsewhere.)

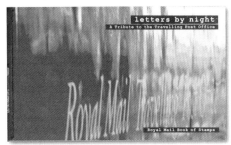

Letters by Night book, 2004

■ **2004, March 16. £7.44 Letters by Night**
Pane of three 2nd Scotland, three 68p Scotland	4.75
Pane of one 28p, one E, one 42p Classic Locomotives	2.00
Pane of four 1st Pub Signs	2.00
Pane of four 1st gold, four 37p	4.25
Complete book	14.00

■ **2004, May 25. £7.23 The Glory of the Garden**
Pane of four 1st gold, two 42p, two 47p	7.50
Pane of one 2nd, one E, one 68p, one 42p RHS	5.00
Pane of one 1st Iris latifolia, two 1st Tulipa, one 1st Gentiana acaulis	6.00
Pane of two 1st, two 47p RHS	4.00
Complete book	20.00

■ **2005, February 24. £7.43 The Brontë Sisters**
Pane of four 2nd, two 39p, two 42p	4.50
Pane of two 2nd England, two 40p England	2.50
Pane of two 1st Brontë, two 1st Bronté	2.00
Pane of one 40p, one 57p, one 68p, one £1.12 Bronté	4.50
Complete book	14.00

■ **2005, October 4. £7.26 Battle of Trafalgar**
Pane of four 1st, two 50p, two 68p	6.00
Pane of two 1st White Ensign	3.50
Pane of one 1st, one 42p, one 68p first Trafalgar	3.00
Pane of one 1st, one 42p, one 68p second Trafalgar	3.00
Complete book	13.00

■ **2006, February 23. £7.40 Brunel**
Pane of one 40p, one 60p, one 47p all Brunel	3.50
Pane of one 1st, one 42p, one 68p all Brunel	3.50
Pane of four 1st, two 35p, two 40p	5.00
Pane of two 68p Ocean Liners, one 47p Brunel	5.50
Complete book	13.00

■ **2006, September 21. £7.41 Victoria Cross**
Pane of first 1st, 64p and 72p Victoria Cross	3.50
Pane of second 1st, 64p and 72p Victoria Cross	3.50
Pane of four 20p Gallantry Awards	6.00

Pane of four 1st, four 50p	5.50
Complete book	13.00

■ **2007, March 1. £7.68 World of Invention**
Pane of three 2nd Scotland and three 44p Wales	4.00
Pane of four 1st revised style and four 5p definitives	3.00
Pane of two 1st and two 64p World of Invention	3.50
Pane of two 1st and two 72p World of Invention	4.00
Complete book	15.00

■ **2007, June 5. £7.66 40th Anniversary of the Machin**
Pane of four 2p, two 46p, two 48p definitives	3.50
Pane of two £1 ruby definitives	4.00
Pane of two 1st Arnold Machin and two 1st 4d deep olive-sepia designs	4.00
Pane of one 2nd and one 1st revised style, and two 2nd and two 1st Large definitives	3.50
Complete book	16.00

■ **2007, September 20. £7.49 British Army Uniforms**
Pane of one each of 1st definitives of England, Northern Ireland, Scotland and Wales	3.50
Pane of three 1st British Army Uniforms	4.00
Pane of three 78p British Army Uniforms	6.00
Pane of two 1p, four 46p and two 54p definitives	5.50
Complete book	16.00

■ **2008, January 8. £7.40 Ian Fleming's James Bond**
Pane of one 1st (Casino Royale), one 54p (Goldfinger), one 78p (For Your Eyes Only)	3.00
Pane of one 1st (Dr No), one 54p (Diamonds are Forever), one 78p (From Russia With Love)	3.00
Pane of eight 1st class gold	4.50
Pane of two 1st White Ensign and two 1st Union Jack, as of October 22, 2001	2.50
Complete book	11.00

■ **2008, September 18. £7.15 Pilot to Plane: RAF Uniforms**
Pane of three 1st RAF Uniforms designs	2.25
Pane of three 81p RAF Uniforms designs	4.00
Pane of four 1st gold and four 2nd definitives	4.00
Pane of two 1st Air Displays design of July 17, 2008, and two 20p Spitfire design of June 10, 1997	3.50
Complete book	10.50

■ **2008, September 29. £9.72 The Regional Definitives: Heraldry and Symbol**
Pane of the 1958 3d, 6d and 1s 3d designs of Northern Ireland, Scotland and Wales re-denominated as 1st	5.00
Pane of the 1958 3d, 6d and 1s 3d designs of Northern Ireland, re-denominated as 1st and three 1st class Northern Ireland of October 14, 2003	3.50
Pane of the 1958 3d, 6d and 1s 3d designs of Scotland, re-denominated as 1st and three 1st class Scotland of October 14, 2003	3.50
Pane of the 1958 3d, 6d and 1s 3d designs of Wales, re-denominated as 1st and three 1st class Wales of October 14, 2003	3.50
Complete book	15.00

SMILERS GENERIC SHEETS

In 2000 Royal Mail introduced customised stamps by which a personal photograph could be printed on a label alongside a conventional stamp (known as Smilers), and sheets of stamps on which decorative labels replace the photographs (known as Generic sheets).

2000 The Stamp Show

■ **2000, May 22. The Stamp Show 2000.**
Sheet of ten Smiles   27.50

■ **2000, October 3. Christmas.**
Sheet of 20 Robin looking through slit in pillar box.
Copyright 'Post Office 2000'   £150
Sheet of 10 Father Christmas with Cracker.
Copyright 'Post Office 2000'   £150

■ **2001, June 5. Occasions: Hallmarks**
Sheets of 20 comprising four of each designs   £150

■ **2001, July 3. Smiles**
Sheet of ten Smiles stamps as May 22, 2000,
but with revised labels and border   £200

■ **2001, October 9. Christmas**
Sheet of 20 Robin looking through slit in pillar box.
Copyright 'Consignia 2001'   £700
Sheet of 10 Father Christmas with Cracker.
Copyright 'Consignia 2001'   £700

■ **2001, December 18. Cartoons.**
Sheet of 10 with labels of humorous quotes   35.00

■ **2002, April 23. Occasions: Pictorial messages**
Sheet of 20 comprising four of each of the five designs 50.00

■ **2002, May 21. Football World Cup**
Sheet of 20 of the lower right hand corner flag design 25.00

■ **2002, October 1. Smiles**
Sheet of 10 of the Teddy Bear design and ten of the
Dennis the Menace design   25.00

■ **2002, October 1. Christmas**
Sheet of 20 of the Father Christmas with Cracker design 25.00

■ **2003, January 21. Flower paintings**
Sheet of 20 comprising two of each of the ten designs 25.00

■ **2003, February 4. Occasions**
Sheet of 20 comprising a multiple of the six designs 20.00

■ **2003, July 29. Cartoons Crossword**
Sheet of 20 comprising two of each of the ten designs,
with the labels forming a crossword   16.00

■ **2003, September 30. Christmas: Winter Robins**
Sheet of 20 of the 1st class Winter Robins design.
Self-adhesive   16.00

■ **2003, November 4. Christmas: Ice Sculptures**
Sheet of 20 of the 2nd class Ice Sculptures design.
Self-adhesive   20.00
Sheet of 20 of the 1st class Ice Sculptures design.
Self-adhesive   20.00

■ **2004, January 30. Hong Kong stamp exhibition**
Sheet of 20 of the Hello greetings stamp design   15.00

■ **2004, February 3. Occasions: Envelopes**
Sheet of 20 comprising four of each of the five designs 15.00

■ **2004, May 25. Royal Horticultural Society**
Sheet of 20 of the 1st class design   15.00

■ **2004, July 27. Rule Britannia**
Sheet of 20 of the 1st class Union Flag design   15.00

■ **2004, November 2. Christmas: Father Christmas**
Sheet of 20 comprising 10 2nd and ten 1st designs   15.00

■ **2005, January 11. Farm Animals**
Sheet of 20 comprising two of each of the ten designs 20.00

■ **2005, March 1. Magic**
Sheet of 20 of the 1st class design   15.00

■ **2005, April 21. Pacific Explorer stamp exhibition**
Sheet of 20 of the 1st class Hello design   15.00

■ **2005, June 21. White Ensign**
Sheet of 20 of the 1st class White Ensign design   15.00

■ **2005, September 15. ITV**
Sheet of 20 of the 1st class Emmerdale design   15.00

■ **2005, November 1. Christmas**
Sheet of 20 comprising 10 of the 1st class and
ten of the 2nd class Winter Robins designs   12.50

A Bear called Paddington

2006 A Bear Called Paddington

■ **2006, January 10. A Bear Called Paddington**
Sheet of 20 of the Paddington Bear stamp
from the Animal Tales set   15.00

■ **2006, March 7. Fun Fruit and Veg**
Sheet of 20 of the Fruit and Veg stamps   20.00

■ **2006, May 25. Washington Stamp Exhibition 2006**
Sheet of 20 of the large size 'Hello' stamp   15.00

■ **2006, June 6. World Cup Winners**
Sheets of 20 of the 1st World Cup Winners stamp   17.50

■ **2006, July 4. For Life's Special Moments**
Sheet of 20 of the small size pictorial definitives   15.00

■ **2006, November 7. Christmas**
Sheet of ten 1st and ten 2nd of the Christmas designs 15.00

■ **2006, October 17. For Life's Extra Special Moments**
Sheet of 20 of the pictorial definitives of October 2006 15.00

■ **2006, November 9. We Will Remember Them**
Sheet of 20 of the 1st Poppies design   15.00

■ **2006, November 14. Belgica stamp exhibition**
Sheet of 20 of the 1st large size Hello design   15.00

■ **2007, March 1. Glorious Wales**
Sheet of 20 of the 1st Wales design, self-adhesive   12.50

■ **2007, April 23. Glorious England**
Sheet of 20 of the 1st England design, self-adhesive   12.50

■ **2007, May 17. Wembley Stadium**
Sheet of 20 of the 1st Lion & Shield of St George design 12.50

■ **2007, June 5. 40th Anniversary of the Machin Definitive**
Sheet of 20 of the 1st Arnold Machin design   12.50

■ **2007, July 17. Harry Potter**
Sheet of 20 of the 1st Crest designs   12.50

■ **2007, November 6. Christmas**
Sheet of 20 of the 2nd, 1st and 78p designs   12.50

■ **2007, November 8. We Will Remember Them**
Sheet of 20 of the 1st Lest We Forget design   15.00

■ **2007, November 30. Glorious Scotland**
Sheet of 20 of the 1st Scotland design, self-adhesive   12.00

■ **2008, January 15. I Wrote To Say …**
Sheet of 20, comprising six Hello, eight Love, six Union flag
small pictorial definitive designs, self-adhesive,
with circular labels   12.00

■ **2008, March 11. Glorious Northern Ireland**
Sheet of 20 of the 1st Northern Ireland design,
self-adhesive   12.00

■ **2008, July 17. 100 Years of Aviation**
Sheet of 20 of the 1st Air Displays design   12.00

■ **2008, August 5. Beijing 2008 Olympic Expo**
Sheet of 20 of the large 1st Hello design,   12.00

■ **2008, September 29. Glorious United Kingdom**
Sheet of five each of 1st England, Northern Ireland,
Scotland and Wales designs, self-adhesive   12.00

COMMEMORATIVE SHEETS

2008 Centenary of the Territorial Army

■ **2008, April 1. Centenary of the Territorial Army**
Sheet of 20 of the 1st Union Jack (large) design with
commemorative labels   20.00

■ **2008, July 24. London 1908 Olympic Games**
Sheet of 20 of the 1st Union Jack (large) design with
commemorative labels   20.00

PRESENTATION PACKS

In this section, prices are quoted for packs in mint condition only.

Many collectors regard the first GB presentation packs (the 'forerunners') as the pre-packaged definitives sold in 1960 to mark the international stamp exhibition in London (with a sales tour undertaken by the Post Office in the USA). Low value Wildings, Castle high values, phosphor/graphite definitives and the regional stamps were each made available in these packs, which can be found priced in sterling or in US dollars.

In 1964 the Post Office introduced the presentation pack to accompany the Shakespeare Festival special issue, and since then they have regularly been issued for GB special stamps, as well as for new definitives.

Some have been issued in foreign language and other special versions.

'FORERUNNERS'

Wilding Definitives 'forerunner' pack, 1960

■ 1960

Wilding definitives (priced in Sterling)	£175
Wilding definitives (priced in Dollars)	£275
Phosphor-graphite definitives (priced in Sterling)	£175
Phosphor-graphite definitives (priced in Dollars)	£275
Regional definitives (priced in Sterling)	£175
Regional definitives (priced in Dollars)	£275
Castle high values (priced in Sterling)	£1,100
Castle high values (priced in Dollars)	£1,600

SPECIAL ISSUES

Shakespeare Festival pack, 1964

■ 1964

Shakespeare Festival	16.00
Geographical Congress	£100
Botanical Congress	£100
Forth Road Bridge	£450

■ 1965

Churchill	50.00
Parliament	65.00
Battle of Britain	50.00
Post Office Tower	5.00

■ 1966

Robert Burns	50.00
Westminster Abbey	45.00
World Cup	11.00
Birds	9.00
Technology	9.00
Battle of Hastings	4.00
Christmas	4.00

■ 1967

EFTA	3.00
British Flowers	4.00
British Paintings	4.00
Discoveries	2.50

■ 1968

British Bridges	2.50
Anniversaries	2.00
Paintings	2.00
Paintings (German version)	10.00
Christmas	2.00
Christmas (German version)	7.00

Anniversaries (German language version), 1969

■ 1969

British Ships	3.00
British Ships (German version)	20.00
British Ships (Cunard version)	30.00
Concorde	7.50
Concorde (German version)	30.00
Anniversaries	3.00
Anniversaries (German version)	50.00
Cathedrals	3.00

Cathedrals (German version)	18.00
Prince of Wales Investiture	2.25
Prince of Wales (German version)	18.00
Prince of Wales (Welsh version)	25.00
Post Office Technology	2.00
Christmas	2.00

■ 1970
Cottages	3.00
Anniversaries	2.00
Literary Anniversaries	3.50
Commonwealth Games	2.00
Philympia	2.00
Christmas	2.00

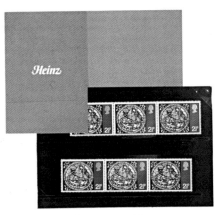

Heinz promotional Christmas pack, 1971

■ 1971
Ulster Paintings	3.50
Literary Anniversaries	3.50
Anniversaries	3.50
Universities	4.50
Christmas	3.25
Christmas (Heinz version*)	25.00

(* A Heinz soup promotion allowed the labels from eight
different Heinz soups to be exchanged for six 2½d Christmas
stamps that were sent in a presentation pack format.)

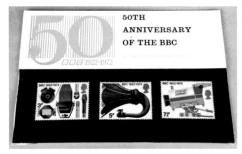

BBC presentation pack (staff version), 1972

■ 1972
Explorers	4.00
Anniversaries	3.00
Churches	5.00
Churches (Belgica pack)	5.00
BBC	2.50
BBC (staff version)	15.00
Christmas	2.50
Royal Silver Wedding	2.00
Royal Silver Wedding (Japanese version)	5.00

(* To mark the 50th anniversary of the BBC a special
version of the BBC pack was sent to all staff.)

■ 1973
EEC	1.75
Oak	1.50
Explorers	2.25
Cricket	5.00
Paintings	1.85
Inigo Jones	1.85
Parliament	1.85
Royal Wedding	1.50
Christmas	2.00

British Post Office Mint Stamps

British trees:
The Horse Chestnut

ERRATUM
THIS PACK IS WRONGLY
SHOWN AS No. 58 ON THE
REVERSE OF THE COVER
IT SHOULD CORRECTLY
BE NUMBERED 59 IN THE
SERIES. NUMBER 56 BEING
THE COLLECTORS PACK
ISSUED ON 28-11-73

Horse Chestnut pack, 1974

■ 1974
Horse Chestnut	2.00
Fire Service	2.00
UPU	2.00
Great Britons	2.00
Churchill	2.00
Christmas	2.00

■ 1975
Turner	2.00
Architecture	2.00
Sailing	1.50
Railways	4.00
Parliament	1.25
Jane Austen	2.00
Christmas	2.50

■ 1976
Telephones	3.00
Social Pioneers	2.00
USA Bicentennial	1.00

Cultural Traditions	2.50
Roses	2.00
Caxton	2.00
Christmas	2.50

■ 1977

Racket Sports	2.00
Chemistry	3.00
Silver Jubilee	1.25
Heads of Government	0.75
Wildlife	1.00
Christmas	2.00

Energy pack, 1978

■ 1978

Energy	1.75
Buildings	2.00
25th anniversary of Coronation	1.25
Horses	1.25
Cycling	1.25
Christmas	1.25

■ 1979

Dogs	1.25
Spring Flowers	1.25
Elections	1.25
Derby	1.25
Year of the Child	2.00
Rowland Hill	1.25
Police	1.25
Christmas	1.25

■ 1980

Birds	1.25
Liverpool & Manchester Railway	1.25
London 1980	1.25
Landmarks	1.30
Authors	1.75
Conductors	1.25
Sport	1.25
Christmas	1.25

■ 1981

Folklore	2.25
Year of the Disabled	1.35

Butterflies	1.35
National Trust	1.50
Royal Wedding	1.50
Royal Wedding (Japanese version)	4.50
Duke of Edinburgh Award	1.50
Fishing	1.50
Christmas	1.50

Charles Darwin pack, 1982

■ 1982

Darwin	1.50
Youth Organisations	1.85
Theatre	3.00
Maritime	2.50
Textiles	1.50
Information Technology	1.00
Cars	1.60
Christmas	1.60

(* The Charles Darwin issue was the first of a new style of presentation pack. The essential style has changed little since.)

■ 1983

Fish	1.50
Commonwealth Day	1.50
Engineering Achievements	2.25
British Army	2.00
Gardens	1.60
Fairs	1.60
Christmas	1.75

■ 1984

Heraldry	1.75
Cattle	2.00
Urban Renewal	1.60
Europa	2.75
Greenwich Meridian	1.75
Mail Coaches	1.75
British Council	1.75
Christmas	1.75

■ 1985

Famous Trains	3.75
Insects	2.25
Composers	3.00
Safety at Sea	1.75
Royal Mail	1.75

Arthurian Legends	1.75
British Film Year	2.75
Christmas	2.00

Christmas folder, 1986

1986

Industry	2.00
Halley's Comet	2.00
The Queen's 60th birthday	2.75
Conservation	2.50
Medieval	2.00
Sport	2.50
Royal Wedding	1.25
RAF	2.50
Christmas	2.25
Christmas folder	8.50

(*The Christmas stamps were also made available in a special folder that contained 36 of the 13p Glastonbury Thorn design.)

1987

Flowers	2.25
Newton	2.25
Architects	2.75
St John Ambulance	2.25
Heraldry	2.25
Victorian Life	2.25
Pottery	2.25
Christmas	2.25

1988

Linnean Society	2.25
Welsh Bible	2.25
Sport	2.25
Transport	2.75
Australian Bicentennial	2.25
Spanish Armada	2.25
Edward Lear	2.25
Christmas	2.25

1989

Birds	2.25
Food and Farming	2.25
Anniversaries	2.75

Toys	2.75
Industry	2.25
Microscopes	2.25
Lord Mayor's Show	2.25
Christmas	2.00

1990

Penny Black	5.00
RSPCA	2.50
Buildings	3.25
Queen's Awards	2.50
Kew Gardens	2.25
Thomas Hardy	1.25
Queen Mother	3.50
Gallantry	2.25
Astronomy	2.50
Christmas	2.40

1991

Dogs	2.50
Science	2.40
Europe in Space	2.75
Sport	2.40
Roses	2.40
Dinosaurs	3.00
Ordnance Survey	2.40
Christmas	2.40

1992

Wintertime	2.40
Happy and Glorious	3.50
Tennyson	2.50
International	3.25
Civil War	2.40
Gilbert and Sullivan	2.50
Greener Environment	2.40
Europe	1.25
Christmas	2.25

1993

Abbotsbury Swannery	4.00
Harrison Timekeepers	3.00
Orchids	2.50
Art	3.25
Roman Britain	2.40
Waterways	2.40
Autumn	2.40
Sherlock Holmes	2.50
Christmas	2.75

1994

Steam Locomotives	3.25
Prince of Wales Paintings	2.50
Picture Postcards	2.50
Channel Tunnel	2.50
D-Day	3.50
Golf	2.60
Summertime	2.50
Medical	2.75
Christmas	2.50

■ 1995

Cats	3.25
Springtime	2.50
National Trust	2.50
Peace and Freedom	3.00
Science Fiction	2.60
Shakespeare	2.60
Communications	2.60
Rugby	3.00
Christmas	3.00

■ 1996

Robert Burns	2.50
Wildfowl Trust	2.50
Cinema	2.50
Football	3.50
Olympics	2.40
Women	2.75
Children's Television	3.00
Classic Cars	3.50
Christmas	3.00

■ 1997

King Henry VIII	5.00
Missions of Faith	2.75
Legends	2.50
Architects of the Air	4.25
The Queen's Horses	3.00
Sub Post Offices	3.00
Enid Blyton	3.00
Christmas	3.00
Royal Golden Wedding Anniversary	5.00

DIANA
TYWYSOGES CYMRU
1961-1997

Princess of Wales Memorial pack, 1998 (Welsh version)

■ 1998

Endangered Species	3.50
Princess of Wales Memorial	4.50
Princess of Wales (Welsh version)	55.00
The Queen's Beasts	2.50
Lighthouses	3.25
Comedians	3.25
National Health Service	3.00
Fantasy Novels	3.25
Carnival	3.00
Speed	3.50
Christmas	3.25

(* The Princess of Wales pack's limited edition Welsh language version was made available only at post office counters in Wales.)

Inventors' Tale pack, 1999

■ 1999

Inventors' Tale	3.75
Travellers' Tale	3.75
Patients' Tale	3.75
Settlers' Tale	3.75
Workers' Tale	3.75
Entertainers' Tale	3.75
Royal Wedding	2.00
Citizens' Tale	3.75
Scientists' Tale	3.75
Farmers' Tale	3.75
Soldiers' Tale	3.75
Christians' Tale	3.75
Artists' Tale	3.75
Millennium Timekeeper	16.00

Her Majesty's Stamps pack, 2000

■ 2000

Above and Beyond	3.75
Fire and Light	3.75
Water and Coast	3.75
Life and Earth	3.75
Art and Craft	3.75
Her Majesty's Stamps	40.00
Penny Black	35.00

People and Places	3.75
Stone and Soil	3.75
Tree and Leaf	3.75
Queen Mother's 100th birthday	10.00
Mind and Matter	3.75
Body and Bone	3.75
Spirit and Faith	3.75
Sound and Vision	3.75

(* The Her Majesty's Stamps and Penny Black packs were produced specifically for Stamp Show 2000.)

■ 2001

Hopes for the Future	3.75
Occasions	5.00
Cats and Dogs	11.00
Weather	6.50
Submarines	5.50
Double deck buses	5.50
Hats	4.00
Pond Life	4.50
Punch and Judy	3.25
Nobel Prizes	11.00
Flags and Ensigns	10.00
Christmas	3.75

■ 2002

Just So Stories	9.00
Golden Jubilee	4.00
Occasions	2.75
Coastlines	4.50
Queen Mother Memorial	3.25
Circus	3.50
Aircraft	3.50
Football World Cup	4.50
Commonwealth Games	3.50
Peter Pan	3.50
London Bridges	20.00
Astronomy	4.50
Pillar Boxes	4.50
Wildings I, 50th anniversary	47.50
Christmas	3.50

(* A Wildings I pack was issued on December 5, 2002 to mark the 50th anniversary of the Wildings designs, but most of the print run was destroyed by Royal Mail as the packs contained printing errors. Only 8,500 were ever in circulation.)

Rugby World Cup pack, 2003

■ 2003

Birds of Prey	4.75
Occasions	3.25
The Secret of Life DNA	3.50
Fruit and Veg	25.00
Extreme Endeavours	4.25
Wildings II, 50th anniversary	4.25
Coronation Anniversary	15.00
Prince William	17.50
British Journey: Scotland	4.25
Pub Signs	6.50
Toys	4.00
British Museum	6.50
Christmas	5.50
Rugby World Cup	35.00

(* The Fruit and Veg pack was a self-adhesive issue brought out with accompanying stickers to add facial features to the stamps. Many packs are thought to have been used rather than being collected in mint condition.)

Classic Locomotives pack, 2004

■ 2004

Classic Locomotives	25.00
Occasions	3.25
Lord of the Rings	11.00
British Journey: Northern Ireland	4.25
Entente Cordiale	17.50
Ocean Liners	5.00
Royal Horticultural Society	4.75
British Journey: Wales	4.75
Royal Society of Arts	5.00
Woodland Animals	5.00
Crimean War	5.75
Christmas	5.75

(* The Classic Locomotives pack was meant to herald a redesign of GB presentation packs to make the stamp 'mounts' integral to the whole pack. A few early prints of this were produced before the redesign was scrapped due to 'technical problems', but none has yet come onto the market.)

■ 2005

Farm Animals	5.00
British Journey: South-West England	4.50
Jane Eyre	5.75
Magic!	5.25
Royal Wedding	4.50
World Heritage Sites	6.00
Trooping the Colour	7.00

Motorcycles	6.50	World of Invention	6.00
London 2012	6.50	Abolition of Slavery	5.50
Changing Tastes	5.50	Celebrating England	4.50
Classic ITV	5.50	Beside the Seaside	5.75
The Ashes (miniature sheet)	6.00	Machin Anniversary	4.50
Battle of Trafalgar	6.75	Grand Prix	6.00
Christmas	5.50	Harry Potter	7.50
		Scouts	5.50
■ 2006		Birds	6.00
Animal Tales	5.75	Army Uniforms	5.75
British Journey: England	5.25	Golden Wedding	9.00
Brunel	6.00	Christmas	6.50
Ice Age Animals	6.00	Lest We Forget	5.75
The Queen's 80th birthday	6.00		
World Cup Winners	6.00	**■ 2008**	
Building Modern Britain	6.00	Ian Fleming	5.50
National Portrait Gallery	5.75	Working Dogs	5.50
Victoria Cross	6.50	Houses of Lancaster and York	9.00
Sounds of Britain	5.75	Celebrating Northern Ireland	4.25
Smilers	6.50	Rescue at Sea	5.50
Christmas	6.50	Insects	6.00
Lest We Forget	7.50	Cathedrals	9.50
Celebrating Scotland	4.25	Classic Carry On & Hammer Films	5.50
		Air Displays	5.50
■ 2007		Olympic Handover	3.00
The Beatles	8.00	RAF Uniforms	6.00
Sea Life	5.75	50th Anniversary of Regional Stamps	5.50
Sky at Night	5.50	Women of Distinction	5.50

Beside The Seaside pack, 2007

Classic Carry On & Hammer Films pack, 2008

DEFINITIVES

Scandinavia Tour pack, 1971

■ Low value Machins

1967	½d to 1/9	2.50
1967	(German version)	80.00
1971	½p to 9p	2.25
1971	Scandinavia Tour	12.50
1971	NABA stamp exhibition	85.00
1971	½p to 10p	12.00
1977	To 50p	2.75
1981	To 75p (pack no. 129a)	12.50
1983	To 75p (pack no. 1)	26.00
1984	½p to 75p	21.00
1987	1p to 75p	27.00
1988	14p to 35p	6.00
1989	15p to 37p	5.00
1990	Penny Black Anniversary	4.50
1990	10p to 33p	5.00
1991	1p to 75p	27.00
1991	6p to 39p	5.00
1993	Self-adhesive booklet	9.50
1993	19p to 41p	4.50
1995	1p to £1	30.00
1996	20p to 63p	6.00
1997	2nd and 1st	4.50
1997	26p and 1st	4.50
1998	2nd, 1st, 1p to £1	11.00
1999	7p to 64p	5.25
2000	Millennium 1st	3.00
2000	Jeffery Matthews Palette	80.00
2000	8p to 65p	5.50
2002	2nd, 1st, 1p to £1	7.50
2002	37p to 68p	3.75
2002	Wildings (part 1)	35.00
2003	Worldwide and Europe	3.25
2003	Wildings (part 2)	10.00
2004	1st, Worldwide Postcard, 7p to 43p	8.00
2005	Re-issued Wilding Castle definitives	5.00
2005	9p, 35p, 46p	1.50
2005	1p, 2p, 5p, 9p, 10p, 20p, 35p, 40p, 42p, 46p, 47p, 50p, 68p, £1, plus self-adhesive 2nd, 1st, Europe, Worldwide and postcard	10.00

2005	Definitive Collection folder, containing the low value definitive pack (2005), high values pack (2003), Country stamps packs (2003), Country 42p stamps pack (2005)	32.00
2006	37p to 72p	3.50
2006	Pricing in Proportion	3.25
2007	16p to 78p	4.50
2007	1d to £1 ruby	14.00
2008	15p to 81p	3.00

£10 definitive pack, 1993

■ High value Machins

1969	2/6 to £1	6.50
1969	2/6 to £1 (German version)	50.00
1970	10p to 50p	5.50
1971	20p to £1	9.50
1977	£1 to £5 (pack no. 91)	13.50
1987	£1 to £5 (pack no. 13)	£145
1987	£1.60	20.00
1988	Castles £1 to £5	16.00
1992	Castles £1 to £5	20.00
1993	£10	30.00
1995	£3	14.00
1997	Castles £1.50 to £5	75.00
1999	£1.50 to £5 (Enschedé)	35.00
1999	£1.50 to £5 (De La Rue)	27.50
1999	£1.50 to £5 (gravure)	17.50

POSTAGE DUES

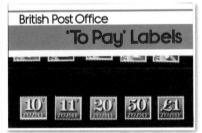

Postage Dues pack, 1971

1971	½p to 5p, 10p, 20p, 50p, £1	17.00
1977	½p to £1	8.50
1982	1p to £5	27.00
1994	1p to £5	35.00

GREETINGS STAMPS

Greetings stamps pack, 1993

1992	Memories	7.50
1993	Gift giving	9.50
1994	Messages	9.50
1995	Art	9.50
1996	Cartoons	10.00
1997	Flowers	10.50

COUNTRY DEFINITIVES

■ England
2001	2nd, 1st, E, 65p	4.00
2003	2nd, 1st, E, 68p	2.75

■ Northern Ireland
1970	3d, 4d sepia, 4d red, 5d, 9d, 1/3, 1/6	2.00
1971	2½p, 3p, 5p, 7½p	1.75
1974	3p, 3½p, 5½p, 8p	1.40
1974	3p, 3½p, 4½p, 5½p, 8p	1.65
1976	6½p, 8½p, 10p, 11p	1.40
1981	7p, 9p, 10½p, 11½p, 12p, 13½p, 14p, 15p, 18p, 22p	4.50
1983	10p, 12½p, 16p, 20½p, 26p, 28p	12.50
1984	10p, 13p, 16p, 17p, 22p, 26p, 28p, 31p	10.00
1987	12p, 13p, 17p, 18p, 22p, 26p, 28p, 31p	13.00
1999	19p, 25p, 30p, 41p	7.50
2000	1st, 40p, 65p	12.50
2001	2nd, 1st, E, 65p	4.50
2003	2nd, 1st, E, 68p	4.00

Scotland pre-decimal definitives pack, 1970

■ Scotland
1970	3d, 4d sepia, 4d red, 5d, 6d, 9d, 1/3, 1/6	4.00
1971	2½p, 3p, 5p, 7½p	1.75
1974	3p, 3½p, 5½p, 8p	1.40
1974	3p, 3½p, 4½p, 5½p, 8p	1.65
1976	6½p, 8½p, 10p, 11p	1.40
1981	7p, 9p, 10½p, 11½p, 12p, 13½p, 14p, 15p, 18p, 22p	4.50
1983	10p, 12½p, 16p, 20½p, 26p, 28p	12.50
1984	10p, 13p, 16p, 17p, 22p, 26p, 28p, 31p	10.00
1987	12p, 13p, 17p, 18p, 22p, 26p, 28p, 31p	13.00
1999	2nd, 1st, E, 64p	7.50
2000	65p	8.00
2002	2nd, 1st, E, 65p	13.00
2003	2nd, 1st, E, 68p	4.00

■ Wales
1970	3d, 4d sepia, 4d red, 5d, 9d, 1/6	3.00
1971	2½p, 3p, 5p, 7½p	1.75
1974	3p, 3½p, 5½p, 8p	1.40
1974	3p, 3½p, 4½p, 5½p, 8p	1.65
1976	6½p, 8½p, 10p, 11p	1.40
1981	7p, 9p, 10½p, 11½p, 12p, 13½p, 14p, 15p, 18p, 22p	4.50
1983	10p, 12½p, 16p, 20½p, 26p, 28p	12.50
1984	10p, 13p, 16p, 17p, 22p, 26p, 28p, 31p	10.00
1987	12p, 13p, 17p, 18p, 22p, 26p, 28p, 31p	13.00
1997	20p, 26p, 37p, 63p	10.50
1999	2nd, 1st, E, 64p	7.50
2000	65p	8.50
2002	2nd, 1st, E, 65p	13.00
2003	2nd, 1st, E, 68p	4.00

■ All Countries
These packs contain the stamps of Northern Ireland, Scotland and Wales up to 1998, and additionally England from 2002.

1988	14p, 19p, 23p, 32p (x 3 countries)	9.50
1989	15p, 20p, 24p, 34p (x 3 countries)	9.50
1990	17p, 22p, 26p, 37p (x 3 countries)	9.50
1991	18p, 24p, 28p, 39p (x 3 countries)	9.50
1993	19p, 25p, 30p, 41p (x 3 countries)	9.50
1996	20p, 26p, 37p, 63p (x 3 countries)	15.00
1998	20p (centre band), 26p, 37p, 63p (x 3 countries)	10.50
2002	68p (x 4 countries)	5.00
2004	40p (x 4 countries)	3.50
2005	42p (x 4 countries)	3.00
2006	44p, 72p (x 4 countries)	7.50
2007	48p, 78p (x 4 countries)	8.00
2008	50p, 81p (x 4 countries)	8.25
2008	2nd, 1st, 50p, 81p (x 4 countries)	12.50

SOUVENIR PACKS

1972	Royal Silver Wedding	1.00
1973	Cricket	3.50
1973	Parliament	4.50
1974	Churchill	2.00
1975	Railways	2.25
1977	Silver Jubilee	1.25
1978	25th Anniversary of Coronation	1.50
1981	Royal Wedding	2.00

Royal Wedding souvenir pack, 1981

1984	Mail coaches	3.75
1985	British Film Year	5.75
1986	The Queen's birthday	4.00
1988	Australian Bicentennial	8.50
1990	Penny Black Anniversary	10.50
1997	Golden Wedding	25.00

Penny Black Reproduction special pack, 2000

SPECIAL PACKS

1971	Decimal low values from ½p to 9p (plus an additional 2p and 2½p)	5.00
1994	Channel Tunnel	37.00
1995	National Trust	12.50
2000	Penny Black reproduction	35.00
2000	Stamp Show 2000 pack of three prestige stamp books	90.00
2001	Occasions: Hallmarks (five packs each containing a block of ten of one of the stamps)	£100
2003	Across the Universe and Microcosmos prestige stamp books	40.00

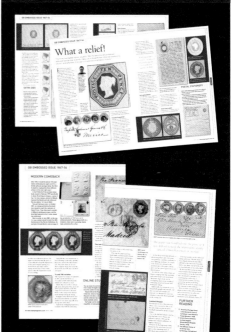

YEAR BOOKS & YEAR PACKS

In this section, prices are quoted for packs in mint condition only.

YEAR PACKS

Year Pack, 1998

1967	1.50
1968 (blue cover)	3.50
1968 (red cover)	2.25
1968 (German version)	25.00
1969	10.00
1970	20.00
1971	26.00
1972	17.50
1973	12.50
1974	5.00
1975	4.50
1976	5.50
1977	4.00
1978	4.00
1979	5.00
1980	5.50
1981	7.50
1982	12.50
1983	12.50
1984	15.00
1985	15.00
1986	15.00
1987	15.00
1988	15.00
1989	15.00
1990	17.00
1991	17.00
1992	17.00
1993	17.00
1994	22.00
1995	22.00
1996	27.00
1997	30.00
1998	42.00
1999	55.00
2000	55.00
2001	55.00
2002	42.00
2003	43.00
2004	43.00
2005	45.00
2006	60.00
2007	75.00

YEAR BOOKS

Year Book, 2000

1984	45.00
1985	40.00
1986	40.00
1987	17.50
1988	17.50
1989	18.50
1990	20.00
1991	20.00
1992	22.00
1993	27.00
1994	22.00
1995	22.00
1996	25.00
1997	30.00
1998	42.00
1999	55.00
2000	55.00
2001	55.00
2002	47.00
2003	55.00
2004	55.00
2005	55.00
2006	60.00
2007	80.00

KEY CONTACTS

To help you find your way around the hobby, here are contact details for the major players in the world of British stamps

ROYAL MAIL
Philatelic Bureau
Tallents House, 21 South Gyle Crescent,
Edinburgh EH12 9PB.
Tel: 08457 641641 (orders)
www.royalmail.com/stamps
London Special Handstamp Centre
Mount Pleasant, Farringdon Road,
London EC1A 1BB.
Midland Special Handstamp Centre
Birmingham Mail Centre, St Stephen's Street,
Birmingham B6 4AA.
**Northern England Special
Handstamp Centre**
South Shields DO, Keppell Street,
South Shields, Tyne & Wear NE33 1AA.
**Scotland & Northern Ireland Special
Handstamp Centre**
Rutherglen DO, Duchess Place,
Rutherglen, Glasgow G73 1BT.
**Wales & The West Special
Handstamp Centre**
220-228 Penarth Road,
Cardiff CF11 8TA.

FAMOUS COLLECTIONS
British Library
96 Euston Road, London
NW1 2DB.
Tel: 020 7412 7635
www.collectbritain.co.uk
British Postal Museum & Archive
Freeling House, Phoenix Place,
London WC1X 0DL.
Tel: 020 7239 2570
www.postalheritage.org.uk
Royal Philatelic Collection
www.royal.gov.uk

SOCIETIES
Royal Philatelic Society London
41 Devonshire Place, London W1N 1PE.
Tel: 020 7486 1044
www.rpsl.org.uk
National Philatelic Society
www.ukphilately.org.uk/nps
British Philatelic Trust
Suite 101, Business Design Centre,
52 Upper Street, London N1 0QH.
Tel: 020 7688 8423
www.ukphilately.org.uk/bpt
**Association of British
Philatelic Societies**
www.ukphilately.org.uk/abps
Modern British Philatelic Circle
www.mbp-circle.co.uk
**Association of Great Britain
First Day Cover Collectors**
www.gbfdc.co.uk
Machin Collectors Club
www.machins.org
British Thematic Association
www.stampdomain.com/thematic
Philatelic Traders Society
PO Box 371, Fleet, Hampshire GU52 6ZX.
Tel: 01252 628006
www.philatelic-traders-society.co.uk

STAMP SHOWS
Stampex
www.stampex.ltd.uk
Philatex
www.stampshows.net

STAMP MAGAZINE
www.stampmagazine.co.uk

Advertisers Index